McGRAW - HILL

SPELLING

AUTHORS

Dr. Gillian E. Cook

Dr. Marisa Farnum

Terry R. Gabrielson

Dr. Charles Temple

CONSULTANT

Dr. Judy Wallis

**McGraw-Hill
School Division**

New York   Farmington

McGraw-Hill School Division

*A Division of The **McGraw·Hill** Companies*

McGraw-Hill School Division
1221 Avenue of the Americas
New York, New York 10020

Printed in the United States of America
ISBN 0-02-2442235 / 5
6 7 8 9 VHJ 02 01

To the Student,

Spelling is part of everything you do in school. It helps you in your writing, in your reading, and in your other subjects. Spelling is also important outside of school. Knowing how to spell helps you share information with friends, family, and other people you need to communicate with.

This book will help you learn to spell the words in each lesson. It will also give you important tools, hints, and tips that you can use with any words at any time.

Spelling words that are pointed out have unusual spellings of a sound. Pay special attention to these words so that you will remember how to spell them.

In the back of the book, you will find resources to help you as a speller and a writer. Take a look at the contents on page 158 to see what's there.

You can help yourself by creating your own **Spelling Journal**. All you need is a lined notebook. Start by making different sections. Here are some ideas.

■ **A Personal Dictionary** Label each right hand page with a letter of the alphabet. If you fill the page, use the back of the page. Add words throughout the year that are important for you to remember how to spell and to use in your writing.

■ **Difficult Words** Keep track of words that give you trouble. Write the word and circle the part that is hard for you. Refer to this section as you write.

■ **Related Words** List words that are related in meaning and spelling. For example, the long vowel sound you hear in *please* can help you to remember how to spell *pleasure*. Add to this section whenever you see words that will help you to spell other words.

■ **Memory Helpers** Collect sayings that you make up that help you remember certain words. A saying such as *You are a youth* can help you remember that the word *youth* contains *y-o-u*.

Remember, this is your journal! You may want to add a section all your own.

Contents

© McGraw-Hill School Division

Word Study Steps

1. **Look** at the word and **say** it carefully.

2. **Picture** the word in your mind.

3. **Study** each letter in the word.

4. **Write** the word carefully.

5. **Check** the word carefully.

Did you spell the word correctly? If you made a mistake, repeat each step.

1

WORDS WITH Short Vowels

PHONICS PATTERNS

1. cash
2. trim
3. lock
4. damp
5. led
6. rod
7. rent
8. silk
9. pump
10. twin
11. dull
12. drag
13. pants
14. bet
15. grip
16. fond
17. lend
18. grant
19. shut
20. club

Learn Spelling Patterns

LOOK & SAY Listen for the sounds in each word.

PICTURE Close your eyes. See each word in your mind.

STUDY The letters *a, e, i, o, u,* and sometimes *y* are vowels. All other letters are consonants. The symbols for short vowel sounds are /a/, /e/, /i/, /o/, and /u/.

WRITE Sort the words. Which words have the short vowel sounds below?

/a/ 1. _____   /i/ 10. _____

2. _____   11. _____

3. _____   12. _____

4. _____   13. _____

5. _____   /o/ 14. _____

/e/ 6. _____   15. _____

7. _____   16. _____

8. _____   /u/ 17. _____

9. _____   18. _____

19. _____

20. _____

CHECK Did you spell each word correctly? Circle the letter or letters that stand for each short vowel sound.

Pattern Power

What letter can spell /a/? 21. _____ /e/? 22. _____

/i/? 23. _____ /o/? 24. _____ /u/? 25. _____

Other Words

Write words you would like to add to this week's list.

_____

_____

Practice Word Meanings

Words in Context

Complete the paragraph below with spelling words that contain the vowel sound below each line.

We earned 1. _____*cash*_____ by holding a walking tour last

           /a/

winter. My sister agreed to 2. _____ me her warm

                                  /e/

3. _____ to wear. You can 4. _____

   /a/   /e/

that the day was not 5. _____! I kept such a tight

                           /u/

6. _____ on my guidebook, I thought my fingers

    /i/

would 7. _____ from the cold. 8. I _____

          /o/   /e/

our group in songs as we walked. By the time the tour

9. _____ down, I was tired, but we had enough

     /u/

money to buy 10. _____ shorts for all!

               /i/

Challenge Words • *Physical Education*

Write the challenge word that matches each clue below. Use the **Spelling Dictionary** on page 214 to help you. Circle the letter that stands for the short vowel sound (/a/, /e/, /i/, /o/, or /u/) in the first syllable of each word.

11. a runner _____

12. the amount of space between two objects _____

13. body tissue _____

14. a person who has ability in sports _____

15. physical activity _____

athlete
jogger
exercise
muscle
distance

Spelling Tip

✦ At the end of most one-syllable words with a short vowel sound, /k/ is spelled *ck*.

✦ The letter *k* almost never appears at the end of a word unless it follows another consonant.

Find two words on your spelling list that follow these rules.

List Words

cash
trim
lock
damp
led
rod
rent
silk
pump
twin
dull
drag
pants
bet
grip
fond
lend
grant
shut
club

Challenge Words

athlete
jogger
exercise
muscle
distance

Review Words

past
yet
fist
love
trust

Build Vocabulary

Word Endings

■ The endings *-ed* and *-ing* can be added to many one-syllable words without changing the spelling of the base word.

dust + ***ing*** = dusting; rest + ***ed*** = rested

■ Add *-ed* and *-ing* to each base word below.

	-ed	-ing
1. grant	_____	_____
2. rent	_____	_____
3. lock	_____	_____

■ When adding *-ed* or *-ing* to a one-syllable word that has one vowel followed by one consonant, double the final consonant.

snap + ***ped*** = snapped; win + ***ning*** = winning

■ Add *-ed* and *-ing* to each base word below.

	-ed	-ing
4. drag	_____	_____
5. grip	_____	_____

■ Use words you made to complete these sentences.

6. The teacher _____ the gym door with her key.

7. She was _____ the key very tightly.

Review Words

Write the review word that has each short vowel sound below.

/i/ 8. _____   /u/ 11. _____

/e/ 9. _____   12. _____

/a/ 10. _____

Write the review word that rhymes with *bet*.

13. _____

Write the review word that does not follow the pattern.

14. _____

past
yet
fist
love
trust

T A K E   H O M E

Write your spelling words in three lists: words with three letters, four letters, and five letters. Circle the letters that spell the short vowel sounds. Use your lists to practice at home.

4

© McGraw-Hill School Division

Apply Spelling Skills

Dictionary Skills

Write the following list words in alphabetical order:

twin fond rent pants grip shut cash dull

1. _____   5. _____

2. _____   6. _____

3. _____   7. _____

4. _____   8. _____

Pattern Power

Look at the list words you just wrote.

• Circle the letter that spells each short vowel sound.

Proofreading

Proofread the paragraph. Use editing marks. Check spelling, capital letters, and punctuation. Then rewrite the paragraph. There are six mistakes.

> The running klub meets on saturdays. We do exercises to pump ourselves up and to keep trimm. The streets are often dampe from rain when we run I am very phond of running.

EDITING MARKS

⬭ check spelling

≡ capital letter

/ lowercase letter

⊙ add a period

∧ add

⌇ take out

⌗ indent the paragraph

↻ move

For more help, see page 171.

Writing • *About Physical Education*

PREWRITE: What is your favorite physical activity or sport? List reasons why you enjoy it.

DRAFT: Create an advertisement for your favorite sport. Write a paragraph that will interest people in the activity.

REVISE: Ask a classmate to comment on your paragraph. Use the **Spelling Thesaurus** on page 182 as you revise.

EDIT/PROOFREAD: Use the editing marks. Then rewrite your paragraph.

PUBLISH: Post your paragraph on the bulletin board, or read it aloud as a TV or radio ad.

WORDS WITH Short Vowels

PHONICS PATTERNS

1. insect
2. lantern
3. expect
4. ugly
5. invent
6. perhaps
7. shocking
8. project
9. upset
10. imagine
11. attach
12. subject
13. itself
14. dishonest
15. active
16. content
17. delicious
18. bubble
19. collar
20. luggage

Learn Spelling Patterns

LOOK & SAY Listen for the sounds in each word. These words have two or more word parts, or **syllables**. In four of the words *(project, upset, subject, content)*, either the first or second syllable can be accented. For this exercise, accent the first syllable.

PICTURE Close your eyes. See each word in your mind.

STUDY Each word below has a short vowel sound in the accented syllable.

WRITE Sort the words. Which words have these vowel sounds in the accented syllables?

/o/ 1. _____   /i/ 11. _____

2. _____   12. _____

3. _____   /e/ 13. _____

4. _____   14. _____

5. _____   15. _____

/a/ 6. _____   /u/ 16. _____

7. _____   17. _____

8. _____   18. _____

9. _____   19. _____

10. _____   20. _____

CHECK Did you spell each word correctly? Circle the letter that stands for the short vowel sound in the accented syllable.

Pattern Power

In words with more than one syllable, a short vowel sound is usually spelled with one vowel letter. Does a syllable with a short vowel sound usually end with a vowel or a consonant? 21. _____

Other Words

Write words you would like to add to this week's list.

_____

Practice Word Meanings

Prefixes

A **prefix** is a word part added to the beginning of a base word or root to change its meaning. Example: *dis* means "not."

dis + honest = dishonest, or not honest

Use spelling words to complete the following paragraphs.

The prefix *sub-* means "a small part of a large group." One

person out of a whole kingdom is called a **1.** _____.

One small topic to be studied is also called a

2. _____. The prefix *pro-* can mean "out front."

To **3.** _____ your voice is to make it go forward.

Also, a job that is before you is called a **4.** _____.

Write a sentence for each of the words you used above.

5. _____

6. _____

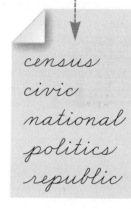

Challenge Words • *Social Studies* ------

Write the challenge word that is a match for each definition listed below. Use the **Spelling Dictionary** on page 214 to help you. Circle the letter that stands for the short vowel sound (/a/, /e/, /i/, /o/, or /u/) in the accented syllable of each word.

7. a form of government _____

8. relating to a city _____

9. an official count _____

10. relating to a nation _____

11. the activities of a government _____

census
civic
national
politics
republic

⑤pelling Tip

Sometimes you can hear a small word that you know in a longer word. You can use the small word to help you spell the longer word. For example:

✦ Listen to the word *content*. You can hear the small word *tent*.

✦ Add *con*. **con + tent = content**

Find other small words in the new words on your spelling list.

List Words

insect

lantern

expect

ugly

invent

perhaps

shocking

project

upset

imagine

attach

subject

itself

dishonest

active

content

delicious

bubble

collar

luggage

Challenge Words

census

civic

national

politics

republic

Review Words

package

nothing

pumpkin

attic

lettuce

Build Vocabulary

Suffixes

■ A **suffix** is a word part added to the end of a base word to change its meaning. The suffix *-able* means "can be."

depend + ***able*** = dependable, can be depended on

■ Add *-able* to each base word below. If a word ends in *e*, drop the final *e* before adding the suffix.

1. imagine _____   2. attach _____

■ The suffixes *-ion* and *-ation* mean "state or process of."

admire + ***ation*** = admiration, state of admiring

■ Add *-ion* or *-ation* to each base word below. If a word ends in *e*, drop the final *e* before adding the suffix. Use the **Spelling Dictionary** on page 214 to help you.

3. project _____

4. invent _____

5. imagine _____

6. expect _____

■ Write words you made to complete these sentences:

7. The sprinkler had an extra hose that was _____.

8. The typewriter is a fairly old _____.

Review Words

Write the review words in which the accented syllables have the short vowel sounds below.

/a/ 9. _____

10. _____

/e/ 11. _____

/u/ 12. _____

13. _____

package
nothing
pumpkin
attic
lettuce

T A K E   H O M E

Write your spelling words in two lists: two-syllable words and three-syllable words. Circle the letter that spells the short vowel sound in the accented syllable. Use your lists to practice at home.

Apply Spelling Skills

Dictionary Skills

Write the following list words in alphabetical order:

expect lantern insect ugly bubble
luggage collar itself delicious active

1. _____   6. _____

2. _____   7. _____

3. _____   8. _____

4. _____   9. _____

5. _____   10. _____

Proofreading

Check spelling, capital letters, and punctuation. Then rewrite the paragraph. There are five mistakes.

Are you kontent or upset with the way people drive. I think purhaps we should expect more from drivers It is shokking that there are so many bad drivers on the road.

EDITING MARKS

⬭ check spelling

≡ capital letter

/ lowercase letter

⊙ add a period

∧ add

⤴ take out

¶ indent the paragraph

↻ move

For more help, see page 171.

Writing • *About Social Studies*

PREWRITE: List ways our highways can be made safer.

DRAFT: Write a new law for highway drivers. Write a paragraph that explains how your new law works.

REVISE: Ask a classmate to comment on your paragraph. Use the **Spelling Thesaurus** on page 182 as you revise.

EDIT/PROOFREAD: Use the editing marks. Then rewrite your paragraph.

PUBLISH: Send your new law to your school or local newspaper.

3

WORDS WITH /ā/ and /ē/

PHONICS PATTERNS

1. bacon
2. explain
3. repeat
4. scale
5. duty
6. delay
7. sweep
8. raise
9. leader
10. paste
11. decorate
12. heel
13. greet
14. gravy
15. pace
16. aim
17. create
18. drain
19. heal
20. receive

Learn Spelling Patterns

LOOK & SAY Listen for the sounds in each word.

PICTURE Close your eyes. See each word in your mind.

STUDY These spelling words have /ā/ or /ē/.

WRITE Sort the words. Which words have /ā/ spelled with the letters below?

a-e 1. _____   **ai** 7. _____

2. _____   8. _____

3. _____   9. _____

4. _____   10. _____

5. _____   **a** 11. _____

ay 6. _____   12. _____

Which words have /ē/ spelled with the letters below?

ea 13. _____   **ee** 18. _____

14. _____   19. _____

15. _____   20. _____

y 16. _____   **e** 21. _____

17. _____   **ei** 22. _____

CHECK Did you spell each word correctly? Circle the letters that stand for /ā/ and /ē/.

Pattern Power

How can /ā/ be spelled? 23. _____ or 24. _____, or 25. _____ or 26. _____ How can /ē/ be spelled? 27. _____ or 28. _____ or 29. _____ or 30. _____ or 31. _____

Other Words

Write words you would like to add to this week's list.

_____

_____

Practice Word Meanings

Word Groups

Write the spelling word in each group that does not relate in meaning to the other words.

1. gravy   bacon   sweep   egg   _____

2. drain   tub   faucet   repeat   _____

3. pace   rhythm   receive   beat   _____

4. flower   grass   bacon   tree   _____

5. bird   greet   robin   nest   _____

6. gravy   song   tune   music   _____

Challenge Words • *Math* -

Write the challenge word that matches each clue. Use the **Spelling Dictionary** on page 214 to help you. Circle the letter or letters that stand for /ā/ or /ē/ in each word. Two words have both /ā/ and /ē/.

7. This is something that is left behind. _____

8. This is a comparison between two things. _____

9. This is the top number in a fraction. _____

10. This is a unit of measurement for temperature. _____

11. This is the middle number in a set. _____

degree
median
ratio
numerator
remainder

Spelling Tip

How can you figure out the spelling of a long word? Long words are easier to spell when you sound them out one syllable at a time. Each syllable must have a vowel sound.

✦ Listen for the first syllable in *decorate*. What vowel sound do you hear?

✦ Listen for the next syllable. What vowel sound do you hear?

✦ Listen for the last syllable. What vowel sound do you hear?

✦ Write the word one syllable at a time.

dec + o + rate = decorate

List Words

bacon
explain
repeat
scale
duty
delay
sweep
raise
leader
paste
decorate
heel
greet
gravy
pace
aim
create
drain
heal
receive

Challenge Words

degree
median
ratio
numerator
remainder

Review Words

behave
agree
fail
believe
dream

Build Vocabulary

Plurals and Word Endings

■ The plural of most nouns is formed by adding *-s*.

Write the plural forms of these nouns.

1. heel _____   4. scale _____

2. delay _____   5. drain _____

3. leader _____   6. pace _____

■ Add *-ed* and *-ing* to each base word. Drop the final *e* before adding the endings.

	-ed	*-ing*
7. decorate	_____	_____
8. paste	_____	_____
9. explain	_____	_____
10. receive	_____	_____

■ Use words you made to complete these sentences.

11. Inventors are the _____ of modern technology.

12. The inventor _____ how her new machine worked.

Review Words

Write the review words with /ā/ spelled with these letters:

ai 13. _____

a-e 14. _____

Write the review words with /ē/ spelled with these letters:

ie 15. _____

ee 16. _____

ea 17. _____

Which review word rhymes with sleeve?

18. _____

behave
agree
fail
believe
dream

T A K E   H O M E

Write your spelling words in alphabetical order. Circle the spelling of /ā/ and /ē/ in the words. Use your lists to practice at home.

Apply Spelling Skills

Dictionary Skills

Read the following dictionary **entry word** and its meanings.

raise 1. To lift. 2. To increase in pay, price, or rent. 3. To bring up. 4. To collect donations.
raise (rāz) *verb*

Write the definition number that matches each usage below.

1. The telephone company decided to *raise* its rates. _____

2. A pulley managed to *raise* the elephant off the ground. _____

3. The show was held to *raise* money for school computers. _____

4. The parents hope to *raise* their child to be an inventor. _____

Pattern Power

Say the word *raise*.

- Write the vowel sound you hear.
  _____

- Write the letter or letters that spell the vowel sound. _____

Proofreading

Check spelling, capital letters, and punctuation. Then rewrite the paragraph. There are six mistakes.

    we should creeate higher standards in math
    It is our dootie to teach our children well.
    Our ame should be to heel the schools.

EDITING MARKS

⬭ check spelling
≡ capital letter
/ lowercase letter
⊙ add a period
∧ add
⤲ take out
⌗ indent the paragraph
⟳ move

For more help, see page 171.

Writing • *About Math*

PREWRITE: Make a list of the ways you use math in your daily life.

DRAFT: Write a paragraph that explains how math helps you in your life.

REVISE: Read your paragraph. Did you use examples? Use the **Spelling Thesaurus** on page 182 to help you.

EDIT/PROOFREAD: Use the editing marks. Then rewrite your paragraph.

PUBLISH: Publish your paragraph by sending it to a friend in a letter.

WORDS WITH /ī/ and /ō/

PHONICS PATTERNS

1. climate
2. obey
3. hose
4. loaf
5. rise
6. crime
7. excite
8. follow
9. coast
10. lotion
11. fold
12. code
13. grind
14. spy
15. rely
16. identify
17. type
18. goal
19. guide
20. height

Learn Spelling Patterns

LOOK & SAY   Listen for the sounds in each word.

PICTURE   Close your eyes. See each word in your mind.

STUDY   These spelling words have /ī/ or /ō/.

WRITE   Sort the words. Which words have /ī/ spelled with the following letters?

i-e   1. _____   **y-e**   7. _____

      2. _____   **i**   8. _____

      3. _____   9. _____

y   4. _____   10. _____

      5. _____   **eigh**   11. _____

      6. _____   **ui-e**   12. _____

Which words have /ō/ spelled with the following letters?

o-e   13. _____   **ow**   18. _____

      14. _____   **o**   19. _____

oa   15. _____   20. _____

      16. _____   21. _____

      17. _____

CHECK   Did you spell each word correctly? Circle the letters that stand for each long vowel sound.

Pattern Power

How can /ī/ be spelled? 22. _____ or 23. _____ or 24. _____ or 25. _____ or 26. _____ or 27. _____

How can /ō/ be spelled? 28. _____ or 29. _____ or 30. _____ or 31. _____

Other Words

Write words you would like to add to this week's list.

_____

Practice Word Meanings

Puns

A **pun** is a joke made with a word having more than one meaning. Write the spelling word that answers each riddle with a pun.

1. What can bread do if it's not busy? _____

2. What kind of socks can water a garden? _____

3. What's the best way to get to the ocean? _____

4. What do hockey players work toward? _____

5. What set of secret rules do spies like to break?

_____

6. What does polite dough do when you open a door?

_____

7. What kind of sheep pen can double over? _____

8. What did one letter say to another? "You're not my

_____."

Challenge Words • *Science*

Write the challenge words to complete the sentences. Use the **Spelling Dictionary** on page 214 to help you. Circle the letters that stand for the long vowel sounds (/ī/ or /ō/) in each word.

9. The _____ of the seasons was interrupted by a warm winter.

10. There was a _____ eclipse this year.

11. A bad _____ infected many people in my class.

12. We use fish heads to _____ the garden.

13. The _____ of the shoreline was caused by the tides.

erosion
solar
cycle
fertilize
virus

Spelling Tip

✦ There are many ways to spell the sound that you hear at the end of *lotion*. These rules will help you when you need to spell a word with that sound.

✦ This sound is never spelled *shun.*

✦ Most of the time this sound is spelled *tion.*

List Words

climate

obey

hose

loaf

rise

crime

excite

follow

coast

lotion

fold

code

grind

spy

rely

identify

type

goal

guide

height

Challenge Words

erosion

solar

cycle

fertilize

virus

Review Words

oak

reply

pine

tomorrow

supply

Build Vocabulary

Word Endings

■ When a word ends in a consonant and *y*, change *y* to *i* before adding *ed*, but not before adding *-ing*.

cry + **ed** = cried   cry + **ing** = crying

■ When a word ends in a vowel and *y*, do not change *y* before adding *-ed* or *-ing*.

play + **ed** = played   play + **ing** = playing

■ When a word ends in *e*, drop the *e* before adding *-ed* or *-ing*.

Add *-ed* or *-ing* to each base word below.

1. rely + ing   _____

2. obey + ing   _____

3. identify + ed   _____

4. spy + ing   _____

5. excite + ing   _____

6. follow + ed   _____

■ Use words you made to complete these sentences.

7. I was _____ on the weather report to know how to dress.

8. I _____ my luggage at the airport.

Review Words

Write the review words with /ī/ spelled with these letters:

i-e 9. _____

y 10. _____

11. _____

Write the review words with /ō/ spelled with these letters:

ow 12. _____

oa 13. _____

oak
reply
pine
tomorrow
supply

T A K E   H O M E

Write your spelling words in alphabetical order. Circle the spelling of /ī/ and /ō/ in the words. Use your list to practice at home.

Apply Spelling Skills

Dictionary Skills

Guide words in a dictionary show the first and last entry words for that page. Which words on the list would you find between these guide words? Write them on the lines below.

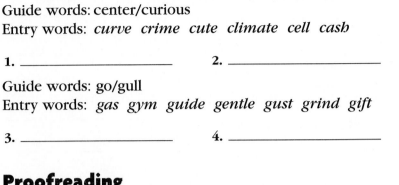

Guide words: center/curious
Entry words: *curve crime cute climate cell cash*

1. _____   2. _____

Guide words: go/gull
Entry words: *gas gym guide gentle gust grind gift*

3. _____   4. _____

Proofreading

Check spelling, capital letters, and punctuation. Then rewrite the paragraph. There are six mistakes.

> Every place has a different climet. People in florida relie on sunny weather The heigt of the tourist season is winter. That's when people use the most suntan loishun.

Writing • *About Science*

PREWRITE: Choose your favorite season of the year. Jot down some words that come to mind when you think about that season.

DRAFT: Write a paragraph that describes your favorite season. Explain why you like the weather.

REVISE: Read your paragraph aloud to a classmate. Revise your paragraph using your classmate's comments. Use the **Spelling Thesaurus** on pages 182 as you revise.

EDIT/PROOFREAD: Use the editing marks. Then rewrite your paragraph.

PUBLISH: Use art or photos from magazines to illustrate your paragraph. Then post your paragraph on the bulletin board.

EDITING MARKS

◯ check spelling
≡ capital letter
∕ lowercase letter
⊙ add a period
∧ add
✗ take out
⌗ indent the paragraph
↷ move

For more help, see page 171.

WORDS WITH /ü/ and /ū/

1. rooster
2. truly
3. prove
4. suitcase
5. include
6. spoon
7. useful
8. lose
9. fool
10. remove
11. boost
12. cruel
13. disapprove
14. reunion
15. mood
16. bruise
17. nephew
18. jewel
19. dispute
20. canoe

Learn Spelling Patterns

LOOK & SAY Listen for the sounds in each word.

PICTURE Close your eyes. See each word in your mind.

STUDY These spelling words have /ü/ and /ū/.

WRITE Sort the words. Which words have /ü/ spelled with the letters below?

oo 1. _____   o-e 9. _____

2. _____   10. _____

3. _____   11. _____

4. _____   12. _____

5. _____   u-e 13. _____

u 6. _____   ui 14. _____

7. _____   15. _____

ew 8. _____   oe 16. _____

Which words have /ū/ spelled with the letters below?

u-e 17. _____   u 19. _____

18. _____   ew 20. _____

CHECK Did you spell each word correctly? Circle the letters that spell /ü/ and /ū/.

Pattern Power

How can /ū/ be spelled with two letters?

21. _____ or 22. _____ How can /ü/ be spelled with two letters? 23. _____ or 24. _____ or

25. _____ or 26. _____ or 27. _____ or 28. _____

Other Words

Write words you would like to add to this week's list.

_____

_____

Practice Word Meanings

Definitions

Write the spelling word that matches each definition below.

1. a class get-together _____

2. to take away _____

3. to show something is true _____

4. really _____

5. a travel bag _____

6. an adult male chicken _____

7. a long narrow boat _____

8. to have as part of the whole _____

9. to have a strong feeling against _____

Challenge Words • *Health*

Write the challenge word that best completes each sentence. Use the **Spelling Dictionary** on page 214 to help you. Circle the letter or letters that stand for /ü/ or /ū/) in each word.

10. This shot will make you _____ to measles.

11. A _____ is a substance found in food.

12. Muscle is a special type of _____ in the body.

13. My grandmother says honey will _____ a sore throat.

14. You should make sure you _____ enough protein at every meal.

nutrient

immune

consume

tissue

soothe

Spelling Tip

✦ When you hear /ü/ in a word and you're not sure how to spell it, there are two spellings you can try first.
  • /ü/ spelled *u*
  • /ü/ spelled *oo*
✦ The fact is that one of these two spellings will be right 75 percent of the time!

rooster
truly
prove
suitcase
include
spoon
useful
lose
fool
remove
boost
cruel
disapprove
reunion
mood
bruise
nephew
jewel
dispute
canoe

Challenge Words

nutrient
immune
consume
tissue
soothe

Review Words

broom
pupil
roof
few
due

Build Vocabulary

Suffixes

■ The suffix -ish means "like."

The suffix -er can mean "one who does."

Add a suffix to each base word in dark print to make a word that matches the given meaning.

1. like a **fool** _____

2. one who **loses** _____

■ Write the plural form of these nouns by adding -s.

3. bruise _____   6. canoe _____

4. spoon _____   7. dispute _____

5. boost _____   8. nephew _____

■ Use words you made to complete these sentences.

9. It is _____ to swim right after you eat.

10. My mother has two nieces and three _____.

Review Words

Write the review words with /ū/ spelled with these letters:

ew 11. _____

u   12. _____

Write the review words with /ü/ spelled with these letters:

oo 13. _____

14. _____

ue 15. _____

broom
pupil
roof
few
due

TAKE HOME

Write your spelling words in alphabetical order. Circle the spelling of /ü/ and /ū/ in the words. Use your lists to practice at home.

Apply Spelling Skills

Dictionary Skills

Write the spelling word from the list that you would find on a page with each set of guide words below.

cruel fool spoon useful jewel bruise dispute mood

1. disk/east   *dispute*

2. shy/spy   _____

3. cow/cute   _____

4. flat/for   _____

5. ivy/joke   _____

6. up/usher   _____

7. boy/bus   _____

8. mole/mow   _____

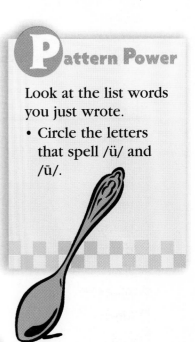

Pattern Power

Look at the list words you just wrote.

• Circle the letters that spell /ü/ and /ū/.

Proofreading

Check spelling, capital letters, and punctuation. Then rewrite the paragraph. There are seven mistakes.

> Proove that You are a wonderful cook. booste the flavor of your food with cinnamon. It is the most usefull spice in the kitchen You may find that you truely enjoy it.

EDITING MARKS

⬭ check spelling

≡ capital letter

/ lowercase letter

⊙ add a period

∧ add

⌒ take out

¶ indent the paragraph

⟲ move

For more help, see page 171.

Writing • *About Health*

PREWRITE: List your favorite healthy foods.

DRAFT: Write a paragraph that describes your favorite dish using healthy foods.

REVISE: Share your paragraph with a classmate. Use your classmate's comments to revise your paragraph. Use the **Spelling Thesaurus** on page 182 as you revise.

EDIT/PROOFREAD: Use the editing marks. Then rewrite your paragraph.

PUBLISH: Include your paragraph in a book about your class's favorite healthy foods.

6

REVIEW Spelling Patterns

Sort the words in each list. Write each word. Circle the spelling pattern.

---

cash
trim
lock
rent
pump
pants
grip
fond
lend
club

Lesson 1
Words with the short vowel sound

/a/ 1. _____   6. _____

     2. _____   /o/ 7. _____

/e/ 3. _____   8. _____

     4. _____   /u/ 9. _____

/i/ 5. _____   10. _____

---

insect
expect
ugly
invent
shocking
attach
active
delicious
bubble
collar

Lesson 2
Words in which the stressed syllable has the short vowel sound

/a/ 11. _____   16. _____

     12. _____   /o/ 17. _____

/e/ 13. _____   18. _____

     14. _____   /u/ 19. _____

/i/ 15. _____   20. _____

---

bacon
scale
duty
delay
sweep
decorate
heel
drain
heal
receive

Lesson 3
Words with /ā/ spelled   Words with /ē/ spelled

a-e 21. _____   ea 26. _____

     22. _____   ee 27. _____

ay 23. _____   28. _____

ai 24. _____   y 29. _____

a 25. _____   ei 30. _____

climate
hose
crime
excite
follow
fold
rely
goal
guide
height

Lesson 4
Words with /ī/ spelled

i-e 31. _____

32. _____

y 33. _____

i 34. _____

eigh 35. _____

ui-e 36. _____

Words with /ō/ spelled

o-e 37. _____

oa 38. _____

ow 39. _____

o 40. _____

---

truly
suitcase
include
spoon
lose
cruel
disapprove
mood
nephew
dispute

Lesson 5
Words with /ü/ spelled

oo 41. _____

42. _____

o-e 43. _____

44. _____

u-e 45. _____

u 46. _____

47. _____

ui 48. _____

Words with /ū/ spelled

u-e 49. _____

ew 50. _____

Spelling Tip

When you hear /ü/ in a word and you're not sure how to spell it, there are two spellings you can try first.

✦ /ü/ spelled *u*

✦ /ü/ spelled *oo*

It's a fact that one of these two spellings will be right 75% of the time! Practice by spelling the words respelled below:

1. trü′ lē _____

2. spün _____

3. krü′ əl _____

4. müd _____

cruel
spoon
mood
truly

Word Meaning Mixed Lesson Review

Synonyms

Write the spelling word that is a synonym for each word below.

cash
climate
delicious
cruel
fold
insect
lend
lose
receive
truly

1. misplace _____

2. weather _____

3. loan _____

4. mean _____

5. really _____

6. bug _____

7. tasty _____

8. bend _____

9. get _____

10. money _____

Context Sentences

Write a spelling word to complete each sentence below.

active
club
crime
heal
nephew

11. Sarah plans to join the chess _____ at school.

12. I never get tired even though I'm very _____.

13. The doctor wanted to _____ the sick.

14. The police help to prevent _____.

15. The son of your brother or sister is your _____.

Analogies

Write the spelling word that completes each analogy.

heel
height
invent
pants
spoon

16. *Arms* are to *shirt* as *legs* are to _____.

17. *Actor* is to *act* as *inventor* is to _____.

18. *Hand* is to *palm* as *foot* is to _____.

19. *Heavy* is to *weight* as *tall* is to _____.

20. *Dirt* is to *shovel* as *food* is to _____.

Vocabulary Mixed Lesson Review

Add Word Endings

Add *-ed* and *-ing* to each base word below. You will need to change the spelling of some base words before adding the endings.

	-ed	*-ing*
1. lock	_____	_____
2. trim	_____	_____
3. attach	_____	_____
4. expect	_____	_____
5. scale	_____	_____
6. decorate	_____	_____
7. follow	_____	_____
8. guide	_____	_____
9. include	_____	_____
10. dispute	_____	_____

Dictionary Skills

Read the words in the box. The two words in dark type are **guide words**. Write the words from the box that would appear on the same page as the guide words. Write your answers in alphabetical order.

> bubble   suitcase   cruel   disapprove   mood   pump
> rent   grip   fond   collar   shocking   ugly   sweep   drain
> bacon   hose   excite   delay   rely   goal

baby/during

1. _____   4. _____   6. _____

2. _____   5. _____   7. _____

3. _____

Spelling and Writing

A story can be historical fiction. The writer tells a fictional tale based on an actual person or event.

FICTIONAL CHARACTER

TIME AND PLACE

REAL PERSON

The year was 1776. Young **Sarah Miller** stood quietly outside the room. Inside, **Thomas Jefferson** read the Declaration of Independence. He had finished writing it days earlier. He hoped it would receive the approval of Congress. But several men continued to disapprove.

Sarah listened to the dispute. Jefferson said, "I'm going outside while you debate this." Suddenly, Sarah saw the great leader standing next to her!

"Why are those men arguing?" she asked. "Isn't their goal to have freedom?"

Jefferson smiled. **"Sometimes, young lady, people fear change. Even when it's needed. But I expect they'll soon follow me."**

IMAGINARY CONVERSATION

WRITING TIPS!!

Historical Fiction
- Mention the time and place of the story.
- Include a real person or event.
- Add fictional characters to the story.
- Create imaginary conversation for the characters.

Now write your own story based on a real person or event.

PREWRITE: What person or event in history interests you? List details about your subject.

DRAFT: Write a story based on your real person or event. Include a conversation between characters.

REVISE: Share your story with a classmate. Use your classmate's comments and the Writing Tips as you revise.

EDIT/PROOFREAD: Use editing marks to correct your capitalization, spelling, and punctuation. Rewrite the story neatly.

PUBLISH: Read your story aloud to the class, or have a classmate perform the story with you.

© McGraw-Hill School Division

SPELLING FUN
CUMULATIVE REVIEW

WORD POEMS

- Choose a spelling word from Lessons 1–5.
- Write a poem based on the word. Start each line with a different letter in the word.
- Be creative. Your poem doesn't have to rhyme.
- Write more poems. Start a class poetry corner.

Bubbles are fun to make.
Use a wand to dip in the soap.
Begin to blow slowly.
Blow a little harder.
Let it get big, bigger...
Explosion!!

SPELL IT OUT

- Choose one word from any list in Lessons 1–5.
- Say the first letter of your word aloud.
- See if your partner can guess your word.
- If the guess is wrong, say the next letter aloud.
- Continue until your partner guesses your word.
- Now switch roles. You guess your partner's word!

SPELLING BEE

You and your classmates write the spelling words from Lessons 1–5 on individual cards.

- Divide into two teams. Give each team half the cards. Each team should have 25 cards.
- The first player on Team A calls out a word.
- The first player on Team B writes the word on the chalkboard.

- If the word is spelled correctly, the card is taken out of the pile. If not, correct the word and return the card to the pile.
- Then, the next Team B player calls out the word for the next Team A player. Continue.
- The first team to finish the other team's pile wins!

WORDS WITH Long Vowels

PHONICS PATTERNS

1. indicate
2. creep
3. pony
4. daisy
5. indeed
6. roast
7. nighttime
8. evening
9. faith
10. awhile
11. fable
12. despite
13. bolt
14. theme
15. site
16. narrow
17. flea
18. decay
19. foam
20. gigantic

Learn Spelling Patterns

LOOK & SAY Listen for the sounds in each word.

PICTURE Close your eyes. See each word in your mind.

STUDY These spelling words have /ā/, /ē/, /ī/, and /ō/.

WRITE Sort the words. Which words have the long vowel sounds below?

/ā/ 1. _____   /ī/ 13. _____
2. _____   14. _____
3. _____   15. _____
4. _____   16. _____
5. _____   17. _____

/ē/ 6. _____   /ō/ 18. _____
7. _____   19. _____
8. _____   20. _____
9. _____   21. _____
10. _____   22. _____
11. _____
12. _____

CHECK Did you spell each word correctly? Circle the letter or letters that stand for each long vowel sound.

Pattern Power

How can these following sounds be spelled? /ā/ 23. ____ or 24. ____ or 25. ____ or 26. ____ /ē/ 27. ____ or 28. ____ or 29. ____ or 30. ____ /ī/ 31. ____ or 32. ____ 33. ____ /ō/ 34. ____ or 35. ____ or 36. ____

Other Words

Write words you would like to add to this week's list.

_____

_____

Practice Word Meanings

Words in Context

Write the spelling words that complete the paragraph.

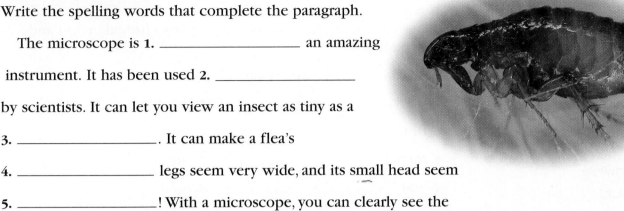

The microscope is **1.** _____ an amazing

instrument. It has been used **2.** _____

by scientists. It can let you view an insect as tiny as a

3. _____. It can make a flea's

4. _____ legs seem very wide, and its small head seem

5. _____! With a microscope, you can clearly see the

thin stem of a **6.** _____, or the **7.** _____

on a rotting log, **8.** _____ its small size. You can even

see germs on the **9.** _____ in soapy water!

Challenge Words • *Science*

Write the challenge word that matches each clue below. Use the
Spelling Dictionary on page 214 to help you. Circle the letters that
stand for the long vowel sounds /ā/, /ē/, /ī/, or /ō/.

sonar
radar
echo
cyclone
frequency

10. a windy storm _____

11. a device for finding objects underwater _____

12. the number of cycles of a radio wave _____

13. the repeating of a sound _____

14. a device for tracking cars and planes _____

Ⓢpelling Tip

How can you figure out the spelling of a long word? Long words
are easier to spell when you sound them out one syllable at a time.

+ Listen for the first syllable in *gigantic*. What vowel sound do you
  hear?
+ Listen for the next syllable. What vowel sound do you hear?
+ Listen for the last syllable. What vowel sound do you hear?
+ Remember, each syllable must have a vowel sound.
+ Write the word one syllable at a time.

gi + gan + tic = gigantic

indicate
creep
pony
daisy
indeed
roast
nighttime
evening
faith
awhile
fable
despite
bolt
theme
site
narrow
flea
decay
foam
gigantic

sonar
radar
echo
cyclone
frequency

tray
chose
secret
tiger
became

Build Vocabulary

Plurals and Suffixes

■ The plural of most nouns is formed by adding -s. The plural of nouns ending in consonant-y is formed by changing y to i and then adding -es.

Write the plural of each noun below.

1. pony ___ponies___   5. daisy _____

2. flea _____   6. fable _____

3. theme _____   7. site _____

4. bolt _____   8. roast _____

■ The suffixes -ful and -less may be added to base words to form new words.

-ful means "full of"   **-less** means "without"

Add **-ful** and **-less** to each base word below.

	-ful	-less
9. faith	_____	_____
10. hope	_____	_____
11. fear	_____	_____
12. mind	_____	_____

■ Use words you made to complete these sentences.

13. Colorful _____ grew in the garden.

14. The _____ soldier was not afraid of battle.

Review Words

Write the review words that have the sounds below.

/ā/15. _____   /ī/ 18. _____

16. _____   /ō/19. _____

/ē/17. _____

Look at the review words you wrote. Circle the letters that spell the long vowel sounds.

tray
chose
secret
tiger
became

TAKE HOME

Write your spelling words in three lists: words with one syllable, two syllables, and three syllables. Circle the long vowel spelling in each word. Use your lists to practice at home.

Apply Spelling Skills

Dictionary Skills

Write each word below in syllables. Put a hyphen (-) between syllables. Use the **Spelling Dictionary** on page 214 to help you.

1. gigantic *gi-gan-tic*
2. evening ____________
3. indicate ____________
4. nighttime ____________
5. narrow ____________
6. despite ____________

Pattern Power

Look at the list words you just wrote.

- Circle the letters that spell the long vowel sounds.

Proofreading

Proofread the paragraph. Use editing marks. Check spelling, capital letters, and punctuation. Then rewrite the paragraph. There are six mistakes.

Did you ever see a sea horse creap along in the ocean. It is a tiny fish that floats in the water and fome. It gets its name because it's head looks like that of a ponie. It is inded unusual.

____

____

____

____

Editing Marks

- check spelling
- capital letter
- lowercase letter
- add a period
- add
- take out
- indent the paragraph
- move

For more help, see page 171.

Writing • *About Science*

PREWRITE: List animals that live in the ocean. Imagine that you are one of the animals on your list.

DRAFT: Write a poem about the life of your animal. It does not have to rhyme.

REVISE: Reread your poem. Could you use more exact or more exciting words? Use the **Spelling Thesaurus** on page 182 as you revise.

EDIT/PROOFREAD: Use editing marks to correct your mistakes. Make a clean copy.

PUBLISH: Create a classroom poetry book. Design a cover. Put all your poems together in the book.

WORDS WITH /ô/ and /ôr/

PHONICS PATTERNS

1. port
2. crawl
3. fault
4. explore
5. sort
6. coffee
7. saucer
8. border
9. aboard
10. lawn
11. worn
12. false
13. source
14. fawn
15. chore
16. hoarse
17. forward
18. astronaut
19. coarse
20. broad

Learn Spelling Patterns

LOOK & SAY Listen for the sounds in each word.

PICTURE Close your eyes. See each word in your mind.

STUDY These spelling words have /ô/and /ôr/.

WRITE Sort the words. Which words have /ô/ spelled with the letters below?

aw 1. _____   **au** 6. _____

2. _____   7. _____

3. _____   8. _____

a 4. _____   **oa** 9. _____

o 5. _____

Which words have /ôr/ spelled with the letters below?

or 10. _____   **oar** 16. _____

11. _____   17. _____

12. _____   18. _____

13. _____   **ore** 19. _____

14. _____   20. _____

our 15. _____

CHECK Did you spell each word correctly? Circle the letter or letters that stand for these sounds.

Pattern Power

How can /ô/ be spelled? 21. _____ or

22. _____ or 23. _____ or 24. _____

or 25. _____ How can /ôr/ be spelled?

26. _____ or 27. _____ or 28. _____ or 29. _____

Other Words

Write words you would like to add to this week's list.

_____

_____

Practice Word Meanings

Synonyms and Antonyms

A **synonym** is a word meaning the same as another word. (*big/large*)
An **antonym** means the opposite of another word. (*big/small*). Write
the spelling word that is the synonym or antonym of each word below.

Synonym	Antonym
1. edge _____	7. true _____
2. job _____	8. smooth _____
3. mistake _____	9. new _____
4. creep _____	10. backward _____
5. travel _____	11. narrow _____
6. harbor _____	12. mix _____

Challenge Words • *Science*

Write the challenge word that best completes each sentence. Use the
Spelling Dictionary on page 214 to help you. Circle the letters that
stand for the sounds /ô/ and /ôr/.

13. The scientists planned to send a rocket into _____.

14. They had to decide when to _____ the rocket from
the ground.

15. A computer helped them work out a complex math

_____.

16. The scientists watched the takeoff from their _____.

17. Clouds of smoke came out of the rocket's _____
system.

launch
formula
observatory
orbit
exhaust

Spelling Tip

Sometimes knowing the history of the parts of a word can help
you remember how to spell the word.

✦ The word *astronaut* is made up of two Greek words.
✦ The word *astro* means "star."
✦ The word *naut* means "sailor."
✦ The word *astronaut* means "sailor among the stars."

Knowing how to spell these word parts will help you to spell
many words.

List Words

port

crawl

fault

explore

sort

coffee

saucer

border

aboard

lawn

worn

false

source

fawn

chore

hoarse

forward

astronaut

coarse

broad

Challenge Words

launch

formula

observatory

orbit

exhaust

Review Words

hawk

daughter

form

toward

office

Build Vocabulary

Suffixes

■ The suffix *-en* means "to make." Add *-en* to each word below. If the word ends in *e*, drop the final *e* before adding *-en*. Write the new word.

1. broad   _____

2. damp   _____

3. loose   _____

4. soft   _____

■ The suffix *-ness* means "state of." Add *-ness* to each word below. Write the new word.

5. coarse   _____

6. hoarse   _____

7. broad   _____

8. forward   _____

■ Use words you made to complete these sentences.

9. The astronaut could barely speak due to _____.

10. They had to _____ the tunnel so trucks could go through.

Review Words

Write the review words that have /ô/ spelled as follows:

aw   11. _____

augh 12. _____

o   13. _____

Write the review words that have /ôr/ spelled as follows:

or   14. _____

ar   15. _____

hawk

daughter

form

toward

office

T A K E   H O M E

Write your spelling words in alphabetical order. Circle the spelling of /ô/ or /ôr/ in each word. Use your list to practice at home.

34

Apply Spelling Skills

Dictionary Skills

Write each spelling word below. Insert a hyphen between syllables to show where the word can be divided at the end of a writing line. Use your **Spelling Dictionary** on page 214 for help.

1. saucer   _____
2. coffee   _____
3. border   _____
4. explore   _____
5. forward   _____
6. astronaut   _____

Proofreading

Check spelling, capital letters, and punctuation. Then rewrite the paragraph. There are six mistakes.

> It is important that we go forword and explore outer Space. An astronot may discover a new planet We could find an animal as familiar as a faun. We may even travel aboard a flying sauser!

EDITING MARKS

- ⬭ check spelling
- ≡ capital letter
- / lowercase letter
- ⊙ add a period
- ∧ add
- ୧ take out
- ⁋ indent the paragraph
- ↻ move

For more help, see page 171.

Writing • *About Science*

PREWRITE: Jot down some ideas about the life of an astronaut.

DRAFT: Write a paragraph describing the life of an astronaut.

REVISE: Did you use ideas from your list? Are your ideas in a logical order? Use the **Spelling Thesaurus** on page 182 as you revise.

EDIT/PROOFREAD: Use editing marks to correct your mistakes. Make a clean, final copy.

PUBLISH: Display your paragraphs on the bulletin board.

WORDS WITH /ou/ and /oi/

PHONICS PATTERNS

1. outfit
2. powerful
3. enjoyable
4. convoy
5. background
6. mount
7. couch
8. howl
9. shower
10. hoist
11. appoint
12. eyebrow
13. rejoice
14. sour
15. drowsy
16. turquoise
17. loyalty
18. trousers
19. doubt
20. prowl

Learn Spelling Patterns

LOOK & SAY Listen for the sounds in each word.

PICTURE Close your eyes. See each word in your mind.

STUDY These spelling words have /ou/ and /oi/.

WRITE Sort the words. Which words have /ou/ spelled with the letters below?

ou 1. _____   ow 8. _____

2. _____   9. _____

3. _____   10. _____

4. _____   11. _____

5. _____   12. _____

6. _____   13. _____

7. _____

Which words have /oi/ spelled with the letters below?

oi 14. _____   oy 18. _____

15. _____   19. _____

16. _____   20. _____

17. _____

CHECK Did you spell each word correctly? Circle the letters that stand for /ou/ or /oi/.

Pattern Power

How can /oi/ be spelled in the middle of a word or syllable? 21. _____ How can /oi/ be spelled at the end of a word or syllable? 22. _____ How can /ou/ be spelled? 23. _____ or 24. _____

Other Words

Write words you would like to add to this week's list.

_____

_____

Practice Word Meanings

Analogies

An **analogy** is a comparison between pairs of words that are similar. Example:

Teacher is to *school* as *doctor* is to *hospital.*

A teacher works in a school. Similarly, a doctor works in a hospital. Use spelling words to complete these analogies.

1. *Sleep* is to *bed* as *sit* is to _____.

2. *Sugar* is to *sweet* as *lemon* is to _____.

3. *Dog* is to *bark* as *wolf* is to _____.

4. *Arms* are to *shirt* as *legs* are to _____.

5. *Bird* is to *flock* as *truck* is to _____.

6. *Red* is to *pink* as *blue* is to _____.

7. *Awake* is to *alert* as *sleepy* is to _____.

8. *Powerful* is to *strong* as *select* is to _____.

9. *Mount* is to *climb* as *lift* is to _____.

Challenge Words • *Social Studies*

Write the challenge word that matches each clue below. Use the **Spelling Dictionary** on page 214 to help you. Circle the letters that stand for the /ou/ or /oi/ sounds in each word.

10. the border of a state or country _____

11. a person who rules a colony for a distant king _____

12. a member of a council _____

13. to join with others in refusing to buy from someone

_____

14. a person who shows support for something _____

boycott
viceroy
loyalist
boundary
councilor

Spelling Tip

Here's a spelling rule that you can always count on.
✦ The letter *q* is always followed by the letter *u.*

Which of your spelling words follows this rule?

List Words

outfit
powerful
enjoyable
convoy
background
mount
couch
howl
shower
hoist
appoint
eyebrow
rejoice
sour
drowsy
turquoise
loyalty
trousers
doubt
prowl

Challenge Words

boycott
viceroy
loyalist
boundary
councilor

Review Words

outdoors
allow
voyage
noisy
avoid

Build Vocabulary

Prefixes and Compound Words

The prefix *re-* means "to do again."

re + read = to read again

■ Add *re-* to each underlined word below to make a new word that fits the meaning. Write the new word.

1. <u>mount</u> again _____

2. <u>appoint</u> again _____

3. <u>shower</u> again _____

■ Write the base word of each word below.

4. doubtful _____   6. prowler _____

5. rejoicing _____   7. outfitted _____

■ A **compound word** is formed by joining two words together. Write three list words that are compound words. Draw a line between the two words in each compound word.

8. _____   10. _____

9. _____

Use words you made to complete these sentences.

11. The general may _____ the same officers as before.

12. The soldiers had to _____ their horses and ride farther.

Review Words

Write the review words that have /ou/ spelled as follows:

ou 13. _____

ow 14. _____

Write the review words that have /oi/ spelled as follows:

oy 15. _____

oi 16. _____

17. _____

outdoors
allow
voyage
noisy
avoid

T A K E H O M E

Write your spelling words in three lists according to whether they are nouns, verbs, or adjectives. Some words will appear on more than one list. Circle the spelling of /ou/ or /oi/ in each word. Use your lists to practice at home.

Apply Spelling Skills

Dictionary Skills

Write the spelling word that matches each definition below. Use the **Spelling Dictionary** on page 214 to check your work.

1. climb _____

2. sleepy _____

3. name or select _____

4. strong and lasting affection or support _____

5. having a sharp taste _____

6. pants _____

Pattern Power

Look at the list words in the dictionary activity.

• Circle the letters that spell /ou/ or /oi/.

Proofreading

Check spelling, capital letters, and punctuation. Then rewrite the paragraph. There are six mistakes.

> Do you know the backgroun of the American Revolution? England was powerfel . The colonies decided to end their loyelty to england. They wanted to rejoyce in their freedom

EDITING MARKS

⬭ check spelling

≡ capital letter

∕ lowercase letter

⊙ add a period

∧ add

⤴ take out

¶ indent the paragraph

↻ move

For more help, see page 171.

Writing • *About Social Studies*

PREWRITE: Think about the American Revolution. Jot down your ideas about the patriots.

DRAFT: Make a poster for the patriot cause. Use ideas from your list.

REVISE: Are your ideas clear? Is your poster eye-catching? Use the **Spelling Thesaurus** on page 182 as you revise.

EDIT/PROOFREAD: Use editing marks to correct spelling, capitalization, and punctuation. Make a clean, final copy.

PUBLISH: Display your posters in the classroom.

10

WORDS WITH /är/ and /âr/

1. carve
2. prepare
3. everywhere
4. wherever
5. compare
6. darkness
7. affair
8. carefully
9. remark
10. airline
11. arch
12. beware
13. scar
14. rare
15. target
16. harness
17. arctic
18. tardy
19. barge
20. chart

Learn Spelling Patterns

LOOK & SAY Listen for the sounds in each word.

PICTURE Close your eyes. See each word in your mind.

STUDY These spelling words have /är/ and /âr/.

WRITE Sort the words. Which words have /är/ spelled with the letters below?

ar 1. _____ 7. _____

2. _____ 8. _____

3. _____ 9. _____

4. _____ 10. _____

5. _____ 11. _____

6. _____

Which words have /âr/ spelled with the letters below?

are 12. _____ **air** 17. _____

13. _____ 18. _____

14. _____ **ere** 19. _____

15. _____ **er** 20. _____

16. _____

CHECK Did you spell each word correctly? Circle the letters that stand for /är/ or /âr/.

Pattern Power

How is /är/ usually spelled? 21. _____

How can /âr/ be spelled? 22. _____ or

23. _____ or 24. _____ or 25. _____

Other Words

Write words you would like to add to this week's list.

_____

_____

Practice Word Meanings

Related Meanings

Write the word in each pair that is related in meaning to the word in dark print.

1. **strap**   harness   remark   *harness*

2. **curve**   scar   arch   _____

3. **party**   tardy   affair   _____

4. **boat**   barge   target   _____

5. **table**   airline   chart   _____

6. **cut**   compare   carve   _____

7. **plan**   prepare   beware   _____

8. **anywhere**   carefully   wherever   _____

9. **night**   light   darkness   _____

Challenge Words • *Math*

Write the challenge word that best completes each sentence. Use the **Spelling Dictionary** on page 214 to help you. Circle the letters that stand for the /är/ and /âr/ sounds in each word.

10. A _____ equals about two-and-a-half acres.

11. You get a _____ when you pay less than the usual amount.

12. The rainbow formed a colorful _____ of 180° in the sky.

13. A list of 30 states is a _____ list of all U.S. states.

14. A number that can change over time is called a _____.

arc
bargain
variable
hectare
partial

Spelling Tip

Sometimes you can hear a small word that you know in a longer word. You can use the small word to help you spell the longer word. For example:

✦ Listen to the word *darkness*. You can hear the smaller word *dark* and the suffix *-ness*.

Find other small words, suffixes, or prefixes in your spelling words. Use them to help you remember how to spell the new words.

carve
prepare
everywhere
wherever
compare
darkness
affair
carefully
remark
airline
arch
beware
scar
rare
target
harness
arctic
tardy
barge
chart

Challenge Words

arc
bargain
variable
hectare
partial

Review Words

farther
barnyard
dairy
share
wear

Build Vocabulary

Adjective Endings and Base Words

■ Add -er and -est to each word below. If the word ends in e, drop the final e before adding the ending. Change y to i before adding the ending.

	-er	-est
1. rare		
2. smart		
3. fair		
4. sharp		
5. tardy		

■ Write the spelling word that is the base word of each word below.

6. preparation _____

7. comparison _____

8. remarkable _____

9. scarred _____

10. tardiness _____

Review Words

Write the review words that have /âr/ spelled with the following letters.

air 11. _____

are 12. _____

ear 13. _____

Write the review words that have /är/. Circle the letters that spell /är/.

14. _____

15. _____

farther
barnyard
dairy
share
wear

T A K E   H O M E

Write your spelling words in alphabetical order. Circle the spelling of /är/ or /âr/ in each word. Use your list to practice at home.

42

© McGraw-Hill School Division

Apply Spelling Skills

Dictionary Skills

Find the words below in your **Spelling Dictionary** on page 214.
Write the first definition for each word as a noun and as a verb.

1. chart (n) _____

2. chart (v) _____

3. arch (n) _____

4. arch (v) _____

Proofreading

Proofread the paragraph. Check spelling, capital letters, and
punctuation. Then rewrite the paragraph. There are six mistakes.

> Companies always check the costs of shipping
> They may compair the prices of an airline and a
> barge. Some companies ship all the way to the
> Artic planning carfully can save lots of money.

EDITING MARKS

- ⬭ check spelling
- ≡ capital letter
- / lowercase letter
- ⊙ add a period
- ⌃ add
- ⤲ take out
- ⌗ indent the paragraph
- ↷ move

For more help, see page 171.

Writing • *About Math*

PREWRITE: Imagine you could go anywhere on a vacation. Where
would you go? What would you do? Jot down some ideas.

DRAFT: Write a paragraph that explains your vacation plans. Estimate
the cost of tickets, hotels, and other items.

REVISE: Did you estimate the cost of every item? Did you explain all
of your plans? Use the **Spelling Thesaurus** on page 182 as you
revise.

EDIT/PROOFREAD: Correct your mistakes. Make a neat, final copy.

PUBLISH: Share your dream vacation with your classmates. Take turns
reading your plans in class.

WORDS WITH /îr/ and /ûr/

1. deserve
2. return
3. stir
4. appear
5. career
6. clerk
7. disturb
8. engineer
9. frontier
10. severe
11. shear
12. alert
13. term
14. smear
15. atmosphere
16. purse
17. verse
18. pier
19. peer
20. journey

Learn Spelling Patterns

LOOK & SAY Listen for the sounds in each word.

PICTURE Close your eyes. See each word in your mind.

STUDY These spelling words have /îr/ and /ûr/.

WRITE Sort the words. Which words have /îr/ spelled with the letters below?

eer 1. _____   ere 7. _____

2. _____   8. _____

3. _____   ier 9. _____

ear 4. _____   10. _____

5. _____

6. _____

Which words have /ûr/ spelled with the letters below?

er 11. _____   ur 16. _____

12. _____   17. _____

13. _____   18. _____

14. _____   ir 19. _____

15. _____   our 20. _____

CHECK Did you spell each word correctly? Circle the letters that stand for these sounds.

Pattern Power

How can /îr/ be spelled? 21. _____ or

22. _____ or 23. _____ or 24. _____

How can /ûr/ be spelled? 25. _____ or 26. _____ or

27. _____ or 28. _____

Other Words

Write words you would like to add to this week's list.

_____

_____

Practice Word Meanings

Definitions

Write the spelling word that matches each definition below.

1. very strict _____
2. interrupt _____
3. to mix _____
4. handbag _____
5. to cut _____
6. a country's far edge _____
7. a word or group of words _____
8. to show up _____
9. to come back _____

10. a poem _____
11. a trip _____
12. to spread _____
13. to look _____
14. merit _____

Challenge Words • *Social Studies*

Write the challenge word that completes each analogy. Use the **Spelling Dictionary** on page 214 to help you. Circle the letters that stand for the sound /îr/ or /ûr/ in each word.

15. *Music* is to *composer* as *article* is to _____.

16. *School* is to *teacher* as *hospital* is to _____.

17. *Rocket* is to *astronaut* as *covered wagon* is to _____.

18. *Swim* is to *diver* as *climb* is to _____.

19. *Pay* is to *professional* as *free* is to _____.

volunteer
journalist
pioneer
surgeon
mountaineer

Spelling Tip

Say the words *pier* and *peer.* They sound alike but are spelled differently and have different meanings.

+ For words that sound alike, decide which word is right in your sentence.

+ Use a dictionary to check if you need to.

When you check something you have written, look especially for words that sound the same but are spelled differently.

deserve
return
stir
appear
career
clerk
disturb
engineer
frontier
severe
shear
alert
term
smear
atmosphere
purse
verse
pier
peer
journey

Challenge Words

volunteer
journalist
pioneer
surgeon
mountaineer

Review Words

perfect
cheer
disappear
purpose
fierce

Build Vocabulary

Prefixes

■ The prefixes *in-* and *im-* mean "not."

in + active = inactive; *im* + polite = impolite

Add *-in* or *-im* to each word below to make a new word that fits the meaning. Write the new word.

1. not possible _____

2. not sincere _____

3. not perfect _____

■ The prefix *re-* means "again."

Add *re-* to each word below. Write the new word.

4. turn _____

5. stir _____

6. appear _____

7. alert _____

Review Words

Write the review words with /îr/ spelled as follows:

eer 8. _____

ear 9. _____

ier 10. _____

Write the review words with /ûr/ spelled as follows:

er 11. _____

ur 12. _____

Write the review word you find in each word below.

13. cheerful _____ 15. purposely _____

14. perfection _____ 16. disappearance _____

perfect
cheer
disappear
purpose
fierce

TAKE HOME

Write your spelling words in three lists: words with one, two, and three syllables. Use your lists to practice at home.

46

Apply Spelling Skills

Using the Thesaurus

A **thesaurus** is a special dictionary for writers. It gives **synonyms** and **antonyms** for an entry word. Look at the index for the **Spelling Thesaurus** on page 184. Find a list word that is a synonym or antonym of each word below.

	Synonyms		Antonyms
1. clip	_____	4. disappear	_____
2. wharf	_____	5. leave	_____
3. look	_____	6. mild	_____

Proofreading

Check spelling, capital letters, and punctuation. Then rewrite the paragraph. There are six mistakes.

> What kind of carear interests you You might wish to work with people as a store clurk. Maybe you'd rather work as an enginir in a lab. Choose the work atmospher that pleases, you most.

EDITING MARKS

- ◯ check spelling
- ≡ capital letter
- / lowercase letter
- ⊙ add a period
- ∧ add
- ⤶ take out
- ¶ indent the paragraph
- ↻ move

For more help, see page 171.

Writing • *About Social Studies*

PREWRITE: Make a list of careers that interest you.

DRAFT: Choose one career. Write a paragraph describing the career. Be sure to tell why you like that career.

REVISE: Did you begin with a topic sentence? Did you use vivid words? Use the **Spelling Thesaurus** on page 182 as you revise.

EDIT/PROOFREAD: Use editing marks to correct your mistakes. Make a clean, final copy.

PUBLISH: Set up a "Career Corner" in the classroom. Display your paragraphs for the class.

12 REVIEW Spelling Patterns

Sort the words in each list. Write each word. Circle the spelling pattern.

indicate
creep
roast
nighttime
faith
fable
bolt
theme
flea
gigantic

Lesson 7
Words with the long vowel sound of

/ā/ 1. _____   /ē/ 6. _____

2. _____   7. _____

3. _____   8. _____

/ī/ 4. _____   /ō/ 9. _____

5. _____   10. _____

crawl
saucer
border
aboard
lawn
worn
false
source
chore
broad

Lesson 8
Words with /ô/ spelled   Words with /ôr/ spelled

aw 11. _____   or 16. _____

12. _____   17. _____

a 13. _____   our 18. _____

oa 14. _____   oar 19. _____

au 15. _____   ore 20. _____

outfit
convoy
mount
howl
hoist
appoint
eyebrow
rejoice
loyalty
doubt

Lesson 9
Words with /ou/ spelled   Words with /oi/ spelled

ou 21. _____   oi 26. _____

22. _____   27. _____

23. _____   28. _____

ow 24. _____   oy 29. _____

25. _____   30. _____

carve
prepare
everywhere
wherever
affair
arch
beware
target
harness
chart

Lesson 10

Words with /är/ spelled

ar 31. _____

32. _____

33. _____

34. _____

35. _____

Words with /âr/ spelled

are 36. _____

37. _____

air 38. _____

ere 39. _____

er 40. _____

stir
appear
career
clerk
frontier
alert
atmosphere
purse
peer
journey

Lesson 11

Words with /îr/ spelled

eer 41. _____

42. _____

ear 43. _____

ere 44. _____

ier 45. _____

Words with /ûr/ spelled

er 46. _____

47. _____

ur 48. _____

ir 49. _____

our 50. _____

$\mathcal{S}$pelling Tip

How can you figure out the spelling of a long
word? Long words are easier to spell when you
sound them out one syllable at a time.

gigantic
loyalty

✦ Listen for the first syllable in *indicate.* What
  vowel sound do you hear?

✦ Listen for the next syllable. What vowel sound do
  you hear?

✦ Listen for the last syllable. What vowel sound do you hear?

✦ Remember, each syllable must have a vowel sound.

✦ Write the word one syllable at a time.

in + di + cate = indicate

Write the words *gigantic* and *loyalty* in syllables.

1. _____

2. _____

Word Meaning Mixed Lesson Review

affair
bolt
clerk
creep
saucer
crawl
eyebrow
howl
purse
worn

Analogies
Write the spelling word that completes each analogy.

1. *Thunder* is to *clap* as *lightning* is to _____.

2. *Frog* is to *leap* as *snail* is to _____.

3. *Sock* is to *shoe* as *cup* is to _____.

4. *First* is to *last* as *new* is to _____.

5. *Bird* is to *chirp* as *wolf* is to _____.

6. *Lip* is to *mustache* as *eye* is to _____.

7. *Grown-up* is to *walk* as *baby* is to _____.

8. *Course* is to *class* as *party* is to _____.

9. *Hospital* is to *doctor* as *store* is to _____.

10. *Toys* is to *chest* as *money* is to _____.

broad
carve
gigantic
journey
rejoice

Synonyms
Write a spelling word that is a synonym for each word below.

11. huge _____

12. wide _____

13. celebrate _____

14. cut _____

15. trip _____

appear
everywhere
false
hoist
nighttime

Antonyms
Write a spelling word that is an antonym for each word below.

16. daytime _____

17. true _____

18. lower _____

19. nowhere _____

20. disappear _____

Vocabulary Mixed Lesson Review

Form Plurals

Write the plural form of each word below by adding *-s* or *-es*.
The spelling of the base word may have to change.

1. arch _____

2. atmosphere _____

3. chore _____

4. convoy _____

5. faith _____

6. flea _____

7. harness _____

8. loyalty _____

9. peer _____

10. source _____

Dictionary Skills

Write each spelling word below. Insert hyphens between the syllables to
show where the word can be divided. Use your **Spelling Dictionary**
on page 214 for help.

1. indicate _____ 6. appoint _____

2. fable _____ 7. wherever _____

3. alert _____ 8. prepare _____

4. border _____ 9. career _____

5. outfit _____ 10. frontier _____

Spelling and Writing

A recipe is a form of explanatory writing. The writer explains, step by step, how to prepare a dish.

STATE THE TASK

ORDER WORDS

You can **prepare a tuna platter** that will be a gigantic hit. It's no chore if you follow these simple steps.

1. First, spoon the tuna into a bowl.
2. Next, add the mayonnaise.
3. Then, chop the celery into small pieces. Add them to the bowl.
4. Chop the onion into small pieces. Add them to the bowl.
5. Stir the mixture until it is completely mixed.
6. Later, place the lettuce leaves on a plate. Place the tuna salad on top of the lettuce.
7. Last, cut the cucumber into thin slices. Place them around the border of the plate.

Adjust the amounts according to the number of people you are serving. No doubt your guests will rejoice over your tuna platter!

> Tuna Platter
> (serves 2)
> *Ingredients:*
>
> 1 6-oz. can tuna
>
> 2 tbs. mayonnaise
>
> 1 celery stalk
>
> 1/4 small onion
>
> 1 head lettuce
>
> 1 cucumber

WRITING TIPS!!

Explanatory Writing

- Clearly state the task that is being performed.
- Include every step that is necessary to perform the task.
- Make sure all steps are presented in the right order.
- Use order words such as *first, next, then, later,* and *last.*

Now write your own recipe.

PREWRITE: What delicious food do you know how to prepare? List the ingredients and equipment needed to make it.

DRAFT: Write a paragraph that explains how to make the food. Begin with a topic sentence that mentions the food. Then list the steps in order.

REVISE: Share your paragraph with a classmate. Use your classmate's comments and the Writing Tips shown at the left as you revise.

EDIT/PROOFREAD: Use editing marks to correct your capitalization, spelling, and punctuation. Rewrite your paragraph neatly.

PUBLISH: Add your recipe to a class book of favorite recipes.

SPELLING FUN
CUMULATIVE REVIEW

GET THE PICTURE?

- Choose a word from Lessons 1–6 that suggests a picture.
- Find an original way of writing the word to show its meaning.
- Be as creative as you can!
- Do as many pictures as you like. Create a class art gallery.

CLUE ME IN!

- Choose one word from any list in Lessons 7–11.
- Give a clue about the word to your partner. If you choose *saucer*, you might say, "This word contains a smaller word (*sauce*)."
- If your partner can't guess the word, give another clue. For example: "This word starts with /s/" or "This word has two syllables."
- Continue giving hints until your partner guesses the right word.
- When you're done, switch roles and play again!

SPELLING BEE

- Two teams share the job of writing words from Lessons 1–11 on cards.
- Place the cards in one large pile, face down.
- A player on Team A picks a card and reads it aloud.
- A player on Team B spells the word on the chalkboard.
- If the word is spelled correctly, Team B gets 1 point. If not, a player from Team A gets a chance to spell the word for 1 point.
- Next, a player from Team B picks a card and reads it aloud. A player on Team A spells it on the chalkboard.
- Continue until all words have been used. The team with the most points wins the spelling bee!

WORDS WITH /ù/ and /yù/

1. understood
2. tourist
3. jury
4. assure
5. scrapbook
6. surely
7. yours
8. childhood
9. pudding
10. plural
11. textbook
12. bulletin
13. lure
14. likelihood
15. cushion
16. mature
17. endurance
18. bureau
19. fury
20. rural

Learn Spelling Patterns

LOOK & SAY Listen for the sounds in each word.

PICTURE Close your eyes. See each word in your mind.

STUDY These spelling words have /ù/ or /yù/.

WRITE Sort the words. Which words have /ù/ spelled with the letters below?

u 1. _____   10. _____

2. _____   11. _____

3. _____ ou 12. _____

4. _____ oo 13. _____

5. _____   14. _____

6. _____   15. _____

7. _____   16. _____

8. _____   17. _____

9. _____

Which words have /yù/ spelled with the letters below?

u 18. _____ you 20. _____

19. _____

CHECK Did you spell each word correctly? Circle the letters that stand for /ù/ or /yù/.

Pattern Power

How can /ù/ be spelled? 21. _____ or 22. _____ or

23. _____ How can /yù/ be spelled? 24. _____

or 25. _____

Other Words

Write words you would like to add to this week's list.

_____

_____

Practice Word Meanings

Definitions
Write the spelling word that matches each definition below.

1. more than one _____

2. having to do with the country _____

3. attract _____

4. a soft pillow _____

5. Someone who takes a trip to see different places _____

6. a sweet, soft dessert _____

7. a chest of drawers _____

8. the condition of being expected _____

Challenge Words • *Social Studies*
Write the challenge word that completes each sentence.
Use the **Spelling Dictionary** on page 214 to help you.
Circle the letter or letters that stand for the sounds /ù/ or /yù/ in each word.

9. Hawaii was the last U.S. state to be granted _____.

10. Soldiers stood guard to protect against any _____.

11. The _____ fled his homeland and came to the United States.

12. The new museum brought a great deal of _____ to the city.

13. The job of the police is to provide _____ for people.

refugee
security
statehood
tourism
ambush

Spelling Tip

+ Some words have unusual spellings. In most cases, the ending /shən/ is spelled *-tion*.
+ Listen to the ending sound of the spelling word *cushion.*
+ Notice how /shən/ is spelled.
+ The word *cushion* is one of very few words that have an unusual spelling for /shən/. Remember this difference when you need to write *cushion.*

understood
tourist
jury
assure
scrapbook
surely
yours
childhood
pudding
plural
textbook
bulletin
lure
likelihood
cushion
mature
endurance
bureau
fury
rural

Challenge Words

refugee
security
statehood
tourism
ambush

Review Words

furious
tour
wooden
sure
during

Build Vocabulary

Suffixes and Compound Words

■ The suffix -ance means "the quality or state of."

■ Add -ance to the base words below to form new words. If the base word ends in e, remember to drop the final e before adding the suffix.

1. endure _____ 3. disturb _____

2. assure _____ 4. insure _____

■ Combine a word part in Column A with one in Column B to form a longer word.

A	B	
scrap	stood	5. _____
under	book	6. _____
child	book	7. _____
text	hood	8. _____

■ Use words you made to complete these sentences.

9. Pioneers of long ago had the strength and

_____ to survive.

10. The newcomers to America kept a _____ of photographs.

Review Words

Write the review words that have /ù/ spelled as follows:

oo 11. _____

u   12. _____

    13. _____

ou 14. _____

Write the review word that has /yù/ spelled u.

15. _____

furious
tour
wooden
sure
during

TAKE HOME

Write your spelling words in alphabetical order. Circle the spelling of /ù/ or /yù/ in each word. Use your list to practice at home.

Apply Spelling Skills

Dictionary Skills

Read each sound symbol and the two words that follow it.
Write the word that contains the sound. Use the **pronunciation
key** at the front of your **Spelling Dictionary** on page 215.

1. **/a/** cash, clay _____

2. **/e/** rent, deed _____

3. **/i/** trim, time _____

4. **/ô/** hog, house _____

5. **/ù/** bulletin, turn _____

6. **/yù/** tub, fury _____

Pattern **Power**

Look at the words
you just wrote.
•Circle the letters
that spell /ù/ and
/yù/.

Proofreading

Proofread the paragraph. Check spelling, capital letters, and
punctuation. Then rewrite the paragraph. There are six mistakes.

> My grandmother came to america in her childhud.
> She barely undirstood English at first. Her speech
> improved as she began to matur. Coming to
> America was surley, a very brave thing to do.

EDITING
MARKS

◯ check spelling

≡ capital letter

/ lowercase letter

⊙ add a period

⌃ add

⌦ take out

⌗ indent the
paragraph

↻ move

**For more help,
see page 171.**

Writing • *About Social Studies*

PREWRITE: Imagine that you could learn to speak any language.
What languages would you like to study? Make a list.

DRAFT: Pick one language and write a paragraph explaining why
you would like to learn it. Explain your choice.

REVISE: Did you begin with a topic sentence? Did you explain your
choice well? Use the **Spelling Thesaurus** on page 182 as you revise.

EDIT/PROOFREAD: Use editing marks to correct your mistakes.
Make a clean, final copy.

PUBLISH: Display your paragraphs on a bulletin board. You might
want to make a chart with some words from the language you chose.

14

WORDS WITH /ər/ and /yər/

1. discover
2. polar
3. figure
4. beggar
5. sweater
6. pepper
7. hamburger
8. flavor
9. leather
10. mayor
11. clover
12. spider
13. master
14. failure
15. regular
16. terror
17. shoulder
18. labor
19. particular
20. lawyer

Learn Spelling Patterns

LOOK & SAY Listen for the sounds in each word.

PICTURE Close your eyes. See each word in your mind.

STUDY These spelling words have /ər/ and /yər/.

WRITE Sort the words. Which words have /yər/ spelled with the letters below?

ure 1. _____   yer 3. _____

2. _____

Which words have /ər/ spelled with the letters below?

er 4. _____   or 13. _____

5. _____   14. _____

6. _____   15. _____

7. _____   16. _____

8. _____   ar 17. _____

9. _____   18. _____

10. _____   19. _____

11. _____   20. _____

12. _____

CHECK Did you spell each word correctly? Circle the letter or letters that stand for /ər/ and /yər/.

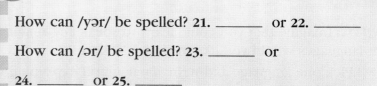

Pattern Power

How can /yər/ be spelled? 21. _____ or 22. _____

How can /ər/ be spelled? 23. _____ or

24. _____ or 25. _____

Other Words

Write words you would like to add to this week's list.

_____

_____

Practice Word Meanings

Analogies

Write the spelling word that completes each analogy.

1. *Rich* is to *king* as *poor* is to _____.

2. *Nest* is to *bird* as *web* is to _____.

3. *Hospital* is to *doctor* as *courtroom* is to _____.

4. *Country* is to *president* as *city* is to _____.

5. *Shirt* is to *cloth* as *shoe* is to _____.

6. *Sock* is to *shoe* as *shirt* is to _____.

7. *Win* is to *lose* as *success* is to _____.

8. *White* is to *salt* as *black* is to _____.

9. *Mustard* is to *hotdog* as *ketchup* is to _____.

10. *Yellow* is to *color* as *eight* is to _____.

Challenge Words • *Health*

Write the challenge words to complete the passage below.
Use the **Spelling Dictionary** on page 214 to help you. Circle the
letters that stand for the /yər / and /ər/ sounds in each word.

People who love to cook must be on their best

11. _____ in the kitchen. Using too much salt, for

example, can 12. _____ someone who has high blood

13. _____. A responsible 14. _____ must

know what is in each food product bought at the store. Likewise, a

responsible food manufacturer must be a helpful 15. _____

who tells buyers what is in each product.

behavior
consumer
educator
pressure
injure

Spelling Tip

✦ It's hard to remember what vowel to use to spell /ər/ at the end
of a word. Think of a related word that you know. Say the word
out loud. Listen for a clue to help you spell the /ər/ sound.

✦ The word *regulate* is related to *regular*.

✦ Say the word *regulate*. You can hear /ā/.

✦ This is a clue that the ending sound of *regular* is spelled *ar*.

List Words

discover

polar

figure

beggar

sweater

pepper

hamburger

flavor

leather

mayor

clover

spider

master

failure

regular

terror

shoulder

labor

particular

lawyer

Challenge Words

behavior

consumer

educator

pressure

injure

Review Words

danger

author

matter

motor

neither

Build Vocabulary

Related Words

■ How are these words similar in spelling and meaning?

polarity

polar

■ Say each word and listen to the sound of the letter *a*. How does the pronunciation of the *a* in *polarity* help you to spell the /ə/ sound in *polar*?

■ Write the spelling word that you see in each word below. Then circle the letter in the longer word that helps you spell the /ə/ sound in the last syllable of the list word. Use the **Spelling Dictionary** page 214 to help you.

1. laborious _____

2. particularity _____

3. regularity _____

Review Words

Write the review words that have /ər/ spelled as follows:

or 4. _____

5. _____

er 6. _____

7. _____

8. _____

danger
author
matter
motor
neither

Circle the letters in each review word that spell /ər/.

Write the review word you find in each word below.

9. authority _____ 11. motoring _____

10. dangerous _____ 12. mattered _____

T A K E   H O M E

Write your spelling words in three lists: words with two, three, or four syllables. Circle the spelling of /ər/ or /yər/ in each word. Use your lists to practice at home.

Apply Spelling Skills

Dictionary Skills

The **schwa** sound /ə/ can be spelled with the letter *a, e, i, o,* or *u.*
Write the words in the box in which /ə/ is spelled as shown below.

> *flavor   particular   clover   terror   regular   shoulder*

e   1. _____   o   5. _____

    2. _____   6. _____

a   3. _____

    4. _____

Circle the letter that spells /ə/ in each word.

Proofreading

Check spelling, capital letters, and punctuation. Then
rewrite the paragraph. There are six mistakes.

> Is there a particulur dish that you like to eat.
> Try to discovar how to make it yourself. you may
> even find a way to give it more flaver than it
> had before. Your labir will pay off!

EDITING MARKS

⬭ check spelling
≡ capital letter
∕ lowercase letter
⊙ add a period
∧ add
℘ take out
⌗ indent the paragraph
↶ move

**For more help,
see page 171.**

Writing • *About Health*

PREWRITE: List some healthy foods that you know how to make.

DRAFT: Write a recipe for one of the foods. List the ingredients.
Give the steps in order.

REVISE: Did you list all the ingredients? Are the steps in the best
order? Use the **Spelling Thesaurus** on page 182 as you revise.

EDIT/PROOFREAD: Use editing marks to correct mistakes. Make a
clean, final copy.

PUBLISH: Collect the class recipes in a class cookbook.
Photocopy enough copies for each class member.

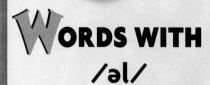

15

WORDS WITH /əl/

1. saddle
2. central
3. shovel
4. barrel
5. tunnel
6. puzzle
7. single
8. council
9. special
10. capitol
11. camel
12. kettle
13. normal
14. medal
15. civil
16. capital
17. crystal
18. syllable
19. informal
20. impossible

Learn Spelling Patterns

LOOK & SAY Listen for the sounds in each word.

PICTURE Close your eyes. See each word in your mind.

STUDY These spelling words have /əl/.

WRITE Sort the words. Which words have /əl/ spelled with the letters below?

le 1. _____   il 11. _____

2. _____   12. _____

3. _____   al 13. _____

4. _____   14. _____

5. _____   15. _____

6. _____   16. _____

el 7. _____   17. _____

8. _____   18. _____

9. _____   19. _____

10. _____   ol 20. _____

CHECK Did you spell each word correctly? Circle the letters that stand for /əl/.

Pattern Power

How can /əl/ be spelled?

21. _____ or 22. _____ or 23. _____ or

24. _____ or 25. _____

Other Words

Write words you would like to add to this week's list.

_____

_____

Practice Word Meanings

Definitions

Write the spelling word that can replace the underlined words.

1. Our <u>Congress building</u> is in Washington, D.C. _____

2. An <u>underground passage</u> leads to the Capitol. _____

3. I use a <u>tool with a scoop</u> to clean the yard. _____

4. Each word has one <u>word part</u>. _____

5. He went over the falls in a <u>wooden container</u>. _____

6. The <u>metal pot</u> whistled. _____

7. I used a leather <u>seat for a rider</u> on the horse. _____

8. There was a <u>lone</u> apple on the tree. _____

9. The <u>glass</u> sculpture was delicate. _____

Challenge Words • *Social Studies*

Write the word that matches each definition. Use the **Spelling Dictionary** on page 214 to help you. Circle the letters that stand for the /əl/ sound in each word.

10. having to do with Congress _____

11. something that stands for something else _____

12. a person who holds an office or position _____

13. allowed by law _____

14. having to do with the nation _____

official
symbol
federal
congressional
legal

Spelling Tip

+ The spelling words *capital* and *capitol* sound alike, but have different spellings and meanings.
+ The word *capital* means "a city where the government is located."
+ The word *capitol* means "a building in which a government meets."
+ You can make up a memory helper to remind yourself of the difference between the two words. The capit*ol* building is very *old*.

saddle

central

shovel

barrel

tunnel

puzzle

single

council

special

capitol

camel

kettle

normal

medal

civil

capital

crystal

syllable

informal

impossible

Challenge Words

official

symbol

federal

congressional

legal

Review Words

terrible

model

hospital

possible

puddle

Build Vocabulary

Related Words

■ How are these words similar in spelling and meaning?

vitality   vital

■ Say each word and listen to the sound of the letter *a*. How does the pronunciation of the *a* in *vitality* help you to spell the /ə/ sound in *vital*?

■ Write the spelling word that you see in each word below. Then circle the letter in the longer word that helps you spell the /ə/ sound in the list word. Use the **Spelling Dictionary** on page 214 to help you.

1. centrality _____

2. normality _____

3. medallion _____

4. informality _____

5. civilian _____

Review Words

Write the review words that have /əl/ spelled as follows:

le 6. _____

7. _____

8. _____

el 9. _____

al 10. _____

Circle the letters in each review word that spell /əl/.

11. Do all the review words follow the pattern?

_____

terrible
model
hospital
possible
puddle

TAKE HOME

Write your spelling words in three lists: nouns, verbs, and adjectives. Several words could be on more than one list. Circle the spelling of /əl/ in each word. Use your lists to practice at home.

Apply Spelling Skills

Dictionary Skills

Write the words in which the underlined letters have the sounds shown below. Use the pronunciation key in your **Spelling Dictionary** on page 215 for help.

p<u>u</u>zzle	bir<u>th</u>	emplo<u>y</u>	<u>c</u>ouncil	norm<u>a</u>l	<u>c</u>amel

/th/ 1. _____birth_____

/ou 2. _____

/oi/ 3. _____

/ə/ 4. _____

/k/ 5. _____

/u/ 6. _____

Pattern Power

Look at the words you just wrote.
• Circle the letters that spell /əl/.

Proofreading

Check spelling, capital letters, and punctuation. Then rewrite the paragraph. There are six mistakes.

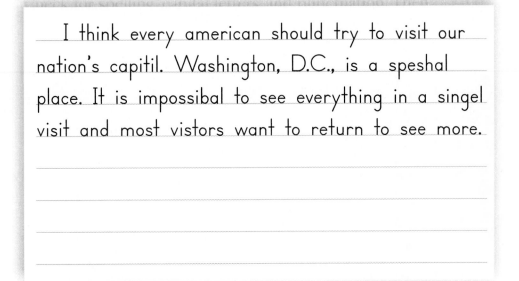

I think every american should try to visit our nation's capitil. Washington, D.C., is a speshal place. It is impossibal to see everything in a singel visit and most vistors want to return to see more.

EDITING MARKS

⬭ check spelling

≡ capital letter

/ lowercase letter

⊙ add a period

∧ add

✗ take out

¶ indent the paragraph

↻ move

For more help, see page 171.

Writing • *About Social Studies*

PREWRITE: Plan a trip to Washington, D.C. Make a list of places to see in the capital.

DRAFT: Choose the places from your list that interest you most. Write a travel brochure for Washington, D.C.

REVISE: Did you pick the most interesting places to see? Did you use language that will make people want to take your trip? Use the **Spelling Thesaurus** on page 182 as you revise.

EDIT/PROOFREAD: Use editing marks to correct spelling, capitalization, and punctuation. Make a clean, final copy.

PUBLISH: Display your brochures in the school so that other classes may see them.

16

WORDS WITH /ən/

PHONICS PATTERNS

1. broken
2. apron
3. falcon
4. fasten
5. sharpen
6. frozen
7. hidden
8. pigeon
9. pardon
10. captain
11. carton
12. canyon
13. oxen
14. burden
15. chosen
16. mountain
17. glisten
18. cinnamon
19. written
20. foreign

Learn Spelling Patterns

LOOK & SAY Listen for the sounds in each word.

PICTURE Close your eyes. See each word in your mind.

STUDY These spelling words have /ən/.

WRITE Sort the words. Which words have /ən/ spelled with the letters below?

en 1. _____

2. _____

3. _____

4. _____

5. _____

6. _____

7. _____

8. _____

9. _____

10. _____

on 11. _____

12. _____

13. _____

14. _____

15. _____

16. _____

17. _____

ain 18. _____

19. _____

eign 20. _____

CHECK Did you spell each word correctly? Circle the letters that stand for /ən/.

Pattern Power

How can /ən/ be spelled?

21. _____ or 22. _____ or 23. _____ or

24. _____

Other Words

Write words you would like to add to this week's list.

_____

_____

Practice Word Meanings

Synonyms and Antonyms

Write a spelling word that is a **synonym** for each word below.

1. cattle _____

2. hill _____

3. shine _____

4. valley _____

5. officer _____

6. chore _____

7. box _____

8. bird _____

Write the spelling word that is an **antonym** for each word below.

9. melted _____

10. blame _____

11. fixed _____

12. native _____

13. flatten _____

14. ignored _____

15. unhook _____

16. exposed _____

Challenge Words • *Science*

Write the challenge word that completes each analogy below.
Use the **Spelling Dictionary** on page 214 to help you.
Circle the letters that stand for the /ən/ sound in each word.

17. *H* is to *hydrogen* as *O* is to _____.

18. *Mistake* is to *error* as *sample* is to _____.

19. *Bricks* are to *wall* as *bones* are to _____.

20. *Flower* is to *rose* as *gas* is to _____.

21. *Fibers* are to *rope* as *tissue* is to _____.

skeleton
tendon
specimen
nitrogen
oxygen

Spelling Tip

Some words have spellings that you don't expect. In most cases, *i* comes before *e* except after *c* or in words that rhyme with *neighbor* or *weigh*.

+ Look at the spelling word *foreign*.
+ Notice how *ei* is spelled.
+ The word *foreign* is one of very few words that does not follow the *i* before *e* rule. Remember this difference when you need to write *foreign*.

List Words

broken

apron

falcon

fasten

sharpen

frozen

hidden

pigeon

pardon

captain

carton

canyon

oxen

burden

chosen

mountain

glisten

cinnamon

written

foreign

Challenge Words

skeleton

tendon

specimen

nitrogen

oxygen

Review Words

women

lion

curtain

reason

siren

Build Vocabulary

Word Endings and Prefixes

■ Add *-ed* and *-ing* to the base words below. You will need to change the spelling of some base words before adding the ending.

	-ed	*-ing*
1. fasten	_____	_____
2. stir	_____	_____
3. pardon	_____	_____
4. carve	_____	_____

■ The prefix *re-* means "again"; *un-* means "not"; *pre-* means "before."

Add the right prefix to each underlined word below to make a word with the meaning given.

5. not <u>broken</u> _____

6. <u>sharpen</u> again _____

7. <u>frozen</u> before _____

■ Use words you made to complete these sentences.

8. The mountain climbers are _____ their belts tightly.

9. The climbers had to _____ their knives before going on.

Review Words

Write the review words that have /ən/ spelled with the letters below.

ain 10. _____

en 11. _____

12. _____

on 13. _____

14. _____

women

lion

curtain

reason

siren

TAKE HOME

Write your spelling words in alphabetical order. Circle the spelling of /ən/ in each word. Use your list to practice at home.

Apply Spelling Skills

Dictionary Skills

Write the spelling words that match the **respellings** below, which show how to pronounce the words. Use your **Spelling Dictionary** on page 214 for help.

1. (ok′sən) _____

2. (kap′tən) _____

3. (fro′zən) _____

4. (sin′ə mən) _____

5. (pij′ən) _____

6. (ā′prən) _____

Proofreading

Check spelling, capital letters, and punctuation. Then rewrite the paragraph. There are six mistakes.

> Last summer, I climbed a tall mountin in colorado. The peak was frozun and covered with snow I enjoyed seeing the snow glissen in the sun. I was so high up that I felt like a falcan!

EDITING MARKS

- ◯ check spelling
- ≡ capital letter
- / lowercase letter
- ⊙ add a period
- ∧ add
- ⌇ take out
- ⌗ indent the paragraph
- ↻ move

For more help, see page 171.

Writing • *About Science*

PREWRITE: List special outdoor places you have visited.

DRAFT: Choose one place. Write a paragraph that describes the place.

REVISE: Did you use descriptive words? Did you tell why you like the place? Use the **Spelling Thesaurus** on page 182 as you revise.

EDIT/PROOFREAD: Use editing marks to correct spelling and punctuation. Make a clean, final copy.

PUBLISH: Read your paragraph to your class. Have others been to that place, too?

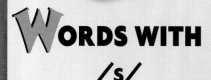

17

WORDS WITH /s/

PHONICS PATTERNS

1. seal
2. scent
3. notice
4. century
5. toss
6. celebrate
7. force
8. soak
9. message
10. medicine
11. scientific
12. case
13. basement
14. gasoline
15. blossom
16. mistake
17. recent
18. basic
19. sandal
20. sword

Learn Spelling Patterns

LOOK & SAY Listen for the sounds in each word.

PICTURE Close your eyes. See each word in your mind.

STUDY These spelling words have /s/. What letters stand for this sound?

WRITE Sort the words. Which words have /s/ spelled with the letters below?

s 1. _____   **ss** 11. _____

2. _____   12. _____

3. _____   13. _____

4. _____   **ce** 14. _____

5. _____   15. _____

6. _____   **c** 16. _____

7. _____   17. _____

8. _____   18. _____

sc 9. _____   19. _____

10. _____

Which word does not fit into any of the patterns above?

20. _____

CHECK Did you spell each word correctly? Circle the letters that stand for /s/.

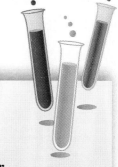

Pattern Power

How can /s/ be spelled? 21. _____ or

22. _____ or 23. _____ or 24. _____ or

25. _____ or **sw**

Other Words

Write words you would like to add to this week's list.

_____

_____

Practice Word Meanings

Definitions

Write the spelling word that matches each definition.

1. to throw _____

2. a sea animal _____

3. a metal weapon _____

4. fundamental _____

5. a communication _____

6. a cellar _____

7. a flower _____

8. a fuel _____

9. a box _____

10. observe a
    special day _____

Challenge Words • Science

Write the challenge word that completes each sentence. Use the
Spelling Dictionary on page 214 to help you. Circle the letter or
letters that stand for the /s/ sounds.

11. Air pollution can cause _____, which can harm
    plants.

12. Chemicals in the air _____ and fall to the ground.

13. There is a _____ for treating plants that are
    diseased.

14. Scientists examine each plant and then _____ its
    disease.

15. Scientists _____ plants that belong in special
    groups.

system
acid rain
classify
diagnose
condense

 pelling Tip

Here is a hint for spelling /s/ followed by a vowel.

✦ The sound /s/ can be spelled *c* only if *c* is followed by *e, i,* or *y.*

Which spelling words follow this rule?

seal
scent
notice
century
toss
celebrate
force
soak
message
medicine
scientific
case
basement
gasoline
blossom
mistake
recent
basic
sandal
sword

Challenge Words

system
acid rain
classify
diagnose
condense

Review Words

across
science
famous
peace
cellar

Build Vocabulary

Prefixes and Suffixes

■ Some words have both a prefix and a suffix.

un + believe + **able** = unbelievable

■ Write the prefix, base word, and suffix in each word below. You may have to add the dropped final *e* to some base words.

	prefix	base word	suffix
1. unscented	_____	_____	_____
2. resealable	_____	_____	_____
3. presoaking	_____	_____	_____
4. unnoticed	_____	_____	_____
5. insincerely	_____	_____	_____
6. unmistakable	_____	_____	_____
7. enforcement	_____	_____	_____

■ Use the base words you wrote to complete these sentences.

8. I couldn't smell the flower because it had no _____.

9. We hoped the recent rainfall would _____ the flowers.

Review Words

Write the review words that have /s/ spelled as follows:

s 10. _____   **ss** 13. _____

ce 11. _____   **sc** 14. _____

12. _____   **c** 15. _____

Write the review word that is related to each word below.

16. infamous _____

17. scientific _____

18. crossing _____

19. peaceful _____

across
science
famous
peace
cellar

T A K E   H O M E

Write your spelling words in four lists: words having one, two, three, or four syllables. Circle the spelling of /s/ in each word. Use your lists to practice at home.

Apply Spelling Skills

Dictionary Skills

Write the spelling word for each respelling below. Use your **Spelling Dictionary** on page 214 for help.

1. (sōk)   _soak_

2. (san′ dəl)   _____

3. (fôrs)   _____

4. (sen′chə rē)   _____

Pattern Power

Look at the list words you just wrote.
• Circle the letters that spell /s/.

Proofreading

Check spelling, capital letters, and punctuation. Then rewrite the paragraph. There are six mistakes.

> The world of medisine has advanced greatly. Many changes have taken place in rescent years Many sientific discoveries have been made. who knows what will occur in the next scentury?

EDITING MARKS

⬭ check spelling
= capital letter
/ lowercase letter
⊙ add a period
⌃ add
✍ take out
¶ indent the paragraph
↻ move

For more help, see page 171.

Writing • *About Science*

PREWRITE: Imagine that you invented a medicine. List some ideas about your discovery.

DRAFT: Use ideas from your list to write a news article about your medicine. Describe what it cures and how it works.

REVISE: Did you write a clear topic sentence? Did you present ideas in a logical order? Use the **Spelling Thesaurus** on page 182 as you revise.

EDIT/PROOFREAD: Use editing marks to correct spelling and punctuation. Make a clean, final copy.

PUBLISH: Publish all the class articles as a "Medicine Forecast." Give a copy to each student.

18 REVIEW Spelling Patterns

Sort the words in each list. Write each word. Circle the spelling pattern.

---

understood
tourist
jury
pudding
plural
textbook
bulletin
cushion
fury
rural

Lesson 13
Words with /ů/ spelled

u   1. _____   6. _____

    2. _____   ou   7. _____

    3. _____   oo   8. _____

    4. _____   9. _____

    5. _____

Words with /yů/ spelled

u   10. _____

---

discover
figure
beggar
pepper
hamburger
spider
regular
terror
shoulder
lawyer

Lesson 14
Words with /yər/ spelled

ure 11. _____   15. _____

yer 12. _____   16. _____

Words with /ər/ spelled   17. _____

er   13. _____   or 18. _____

     14. _____   ar 19. _____

                                 20. _____

---

shovel
puzzle
single
council
capitol
camel
kettle
normal
capital
informal

Lesson 15
Words with /əl/ spelled

le 21. _____   il 26. _____

    22. _____   al 27. _____

    23 _____   28. _____

el 24. _____   29. _____

    25. _____   ol 30. _____

broken
apron
falcon
sharpen
captain
carton
oxen
burden
written
foreign

Lesson 16
Words with /ən/ spelled

en 31. _____   on 36. _____

32. _____   37. _____

33. _____   38. _____

34. _____   ain 39. _____

35. _____   eign 40. _____

scent
force
soak
message
medicine
basement
gasoline
mistake
recent
sword

Lesson 17
Words with /s/ spelled

ss 41. _____   46. _____

sc 42. _____   ce 47. _____

s 43. _____   c 48. _____

44. _____   49. _____

45. _____   sw 50. _____

Spelling Tip

Some words have unusual spellings. For example, the word *cushion* is one of the few words that has an unusual spelling for /shən/. When you are learning a difficult word, find the part of the word that is hardest to spell. Study that part.

Write the word for each respelling. Circle the part of the word that has an unusual spelling.

foreign
sword

1. /sôrd/   _____

2. /fôr′ən/   _____

Word Meaning Mixed Lesson Review

apron
beggar
capital
gasoline
kettle
written
recent
rural
spider
textbook

Context Sentences

Write the spelling word that best completes each sentence.

1. The teacher gave each of us a new _____ with stories in it.

2. Farms are usually found in _____ areas.

3. The _____ stood on the street corner and asked for money.

4. I watched a _____ spin a beautiful web.

5. Austin is the _____ of Texas.

6. We prepared tea by boiling water in a _____.

7. The chef wore an _____ over his clean clothes.

8. Have you _____ your report yet?

9. We filled the car tank with _____ before the long trip.

10. My dog is still recovering from a _____ accident.

camel
captain
cushion
medicine
pepper

Analogies

Write the spelling word that completes each analogy.

11. Lawyer is to law as doctor is to _____.

12. Bed is to pillow as sofa is to _____.

13. Sweet is to sugar as spicy is to _____.

14. Jungle is to lion as desert is to _____.

15. Country is to president as team is to _____.

broken
figure
fury
informal
mistake

Definitions

Write the spelling word that matches each definition.

16. anger _____

17. shape _____

18. not stiff and proper _____

19. not working _____

20. error _____

Vocabulary Mixed Lesson Review

Add Suffixes

Add the suffix to each base word below. Write the new word.

Base Word	Suffix	New Word
1. plural	-ize	_____
2. recent	-ly	_____
3. discover	-y	_____
4. regular	-ly	_____
5. burden	-some	_____
6. puzzle	-ment	_____
7. normal	-ity	_____
8. foreign	-er	_____
9. force	-ful	_____
10. scent	-less	_____

Dictionary Skills

Write the spelling word that matches each respelling below. Use the **Spelling Dictionary** on page 214 for help.

1. /bùl′i tin/ _____
2. /jùr′ē/ _____
3. /shōl′dər/ _____
4. /lô′yər// _____
5. /nôr′məl/ _____

6. /sing′gəl/ _____
7. /kär′tən/ _____
8. /ok′sən/ _____
9. /mes′ij/ _____
10. /sôrd/ _____

Spelling and Writing

Descriptive writing describes a subject. The writer tells how the subject looks, sounds, feels, smells, or tastes.

VIVID WORDS

ADJECTIVES

Do you want to discover an **exciting** place? Take an informal tour of our **local** library. As you walk in, you will see a **large** bulletin board. It points you to the **different** areas of the building. You may want to visit the new Reading Room. There you'll find the most recent books on the shelves. A computer helps you locate all books without any burden. It comes with a list of instructions. They are easily understood. Next, visit the Audio Center. You'll find every single tape and CD you can imagine! The Computer Room offers dozens of computer games. In the basement, the Children's Room has hundreds of books to check out. Also, there is a **huge** carton of old books. They're given away for free! Our local library is a **fascinating** place to visit anytime.

WRITING TIPS!!

Descriptive Writing

- Tell how your subject looks, sounds, smells, tastes, or feels.
- Use vivid words that make the subject easy to picture.
- Use many adjectives as descriptive details.
- Present the details in a good order.

Now write your own description of a place of interest in your neighborhood or town.

PREWRITE: What nearby place do you enjoy visiting? List the different things you find there.

DRAFT: Write a paragraph about the place you chose. Begin with a topic sentence that names the place. Then write sentences that describe it.

REVISE: Share your paragraph with a classmate. Use your classmate's comments and the Writing Tips as you revise.

EDIT/PROOFREAD: Use editing marks to correct your capitalization, spelling, and punctuation.

PUBLISH: Send your description to your local newspaper.

SPELLING FUN
CUMULATIVE REVIEW

RHYME TIME

- Choose a word from Lessons 1–11 that has several rhyming words.
- Write the word. Then write other words that rhyme with your word.
- See how long you can make your rhyming list!
- Pick other spelling words to rhyme. Start a Rhyming Dictionary.

flea	free	ski
be	me	tea
bee	knee	three
see	pea	tree
sea	she	we

PICTURE THIS !

- Choose one word from any list in Lessons 13–17.
- Draw a picture that suggests your word. Show it to your partner.
- Have your partner try to guess your word. If the guess is wrong, draw another picture that suggests the same word.

- Continue until your partner guesses correctly. Then have your partner spell your word.
- Switch roles. You try to guess your partner's word.

Pepper

SPELLING BEE

- Divide the class into two teams.
- Listen as your teacher reads a spelling word from Lessons 1–17 aloud.
- A player from Team A spells the word on the chalkboard. If it is correct, Team A gets 1 point. If it is not correct, a player from Team B gets a chance to spell the word for 1 point.

- Listen as your teacher reads another word aloud. A player from Team B spells the word on the chalkboard.
- Continue play until all words have been used.
- The team with the most points is the winner.

WORDS WITH /z/ and /zh/

PHONICS PATTERNS

1. squeeze
2. zipper
3. visit
4. praise
5. musical
6. pleasure
7. suppose
8. usually
9. freeze
10. surprise
11. tease
12. breeze
13. opposite
14. amuse
15. treasure
16. lizard
17. pause
18. represent
19. amaze
20. dizzy

Learn Spelling Patterns

LOOK & SAY Listen for the sounds in each word.

PICTURE Close your eyes. See each word in your mind.

STUDY These spelling words have /z/ or /zh/.

WRITE Sort the words. Which words have /z/ spelled with the letters below?

s 1. _____   z 11. _____

2. _____   12. _____

3. _____   13. _____

4. _____   14. _____

5. _____   15. _____

6. _____   16. _____

7. _____   zz 17. _____

8. _____

9. _____

10. _____

Which words have /zh/ spelled with the letter below?

s 18. _____   20. _____

19. _____

CHECK Did you spell each word correctly? Circle the letters that stand for /z/ or /zh/.

attern Power

How can /z/ be spelled? 21. _____ or

22. _____ or 23. _____ How is /zh/ usually spelled?

24. _____

Other Words

Write words you would like to add to this week's list.

_____

_____

Practice Word Meanings

Words in Context and Related Meanings

Write the spelling word that best completes each sentence.

1. My jacket has a broken _____.

2. A light _____ blew David's hat off his head.

3. The magician's act will _____ and surprise you.

4. Please tell me what you _____ prepare for dinner.

5. Gina tried to _____ us with her newest joke.

6. We used a map to help us locate the buried _____.

Write the word that is related in meaning to the word in dark print.

7. **music**	muscle	musical	_____
8. **oppose**	opposite	operate	_____
9. **present**	represent	descent	_____
10. **visitor**	advise	visit	_____
11. **please**	pleasure	plead	_____

Challenge Words • Science

Write the challenge word that matches each clue below. Use the **Spelling Dictionary** on page 214 to help you. Circle the letter or letters that stand for the /z/ or /zh/ sound in each word.

12. find out the size of something _____

13. mix with liquid _____

14. a substance used to make crops grow _____

15. a stage in development _____

16. protect something _____

fertilizer
phase
measure
dissolve
preserve

Spelling Tip

Words that are related in meaning are often related in spelling. For example,

+ *please* and *pleasure* are related in meaning
+ *please* has the long vowel sound spelled *ea*
+ *pleasure* has the short vowel sound spelled *ea*

Remembering how to spell *please* can help you spell *pleasure*.

List Words

squeeze

zipper

visit

praise

musical

pleasure

suppose

usually

freeze

surprise

tease

breeze

opposite

amuse

treasure

lizard

pause

represent

amaze

dizzy

Challenge Words

fertilizer

phase

measure

dissolve

preserve

Review Words

pleasant

lazy

whose

usual

quiz

Build Vocabulary

Word Endings

■ Add *-ing* and *-ed* to each base word below. You will need to change the spellings of some base words before you add the endings.

	-ing	*-ed*
1. suppose	_____	_____
2. surprise	_____	_____
3. squeeze	_____	_____
4. zip	_____	_____
5. praise	_____	_____
6. tease	_____	_____

■ Use words you made to complete these sentences.

7. Jack _____ a tube of toothpaste.

8. The coach enjoyed _____ the team for scoring a goal.

Review Words

Write the review word that spells /z/ as in the list word *suppose.*

9. _____

Write the review words that use the letter *s* to spell the sounds below.

10. **/z/**   _____

11. **/zh/**   _____

Write the review words that spell /z/ as in the list word *zipper.*

12. _____

13. _____

pleasant
lazy
whose
usual
quiz

T A K E   H O M E

Write your spelling words in three lists: words with one syllable, two syllables, and three syllables. Circle the letters that stand for /z/ and /zh/. Use your lists to practice at home.

Apply Spelling Skills

Dictionary Skills

When endings are added to base words in the dictionary, the new words are the same part of speech as the entry word. Look up each word below in the **Spelling Dictionary** on page 214. Write the other forms listed for each word.

1. pause   _____   _____

2. freeze   _____   _____   _____

3. treasure   _____   _____

4. amaze   _____   _____

Pattern Power

Look at the words you wrote.

- Circle the letters that spell /z/ and /zh/.

Proofreading

Proofread the paragraph. Check spelling, capital letters, and punctuation. Then rewrite the paragraph. There are six mistakes.

> Do cold temperatures make you feel dizzie. I prayze the sun shining brightly. like my pet lisard, I want to feel the warmth of the sun. The cold air does not bring me pleshure.

EDITING MARKS

⬭ check spelling

= capital letter

/ lowercase letter

⊙ add a period

∧ add

⤶ take out

⌗ indent the paragraph

↻ move

For more help, see page 171.

Writing • *About Science*

PREWRITE: How do you feel about winter? Brainstorm details that support your feeling.

DRAFT: Write a paragraph you might include in a friendly letter. Describe how you feel about winter.

REVISE: Reread your letter. Did you use vivid words with details? Use the **Spelling Thesaurus** on page 182 as you revise.

EDIT/PROOFREAD: Use the editing marks. Then rewrite your paragraph.

PUBLISH: Complete the letter and send it to a friend or family member.

20

Silent Letters and Digraphs

1. wrist
2. naughty
3. whatever
4. flight
5. chalkboard
6. wring
7. whisper
8. wheelchair
9. brighten
10. kneel
11. whine
12. dough
13. wrench
14. wharf
15. bough
16. wreck
17. wrinkle
18. sought
19. knight
20. flashlight

Learn Spelling Patterns

LOOK & SAY Listen for the sounds in each word.

PICTURE Close your eyes. See each word in your mind.

STUDY Some of these spelling words begin with the consonant digraph *wh*. The rest of these spelling words have one or more silent consonants.

WRITE Sort the words. Which words have /hw/ spelled with the letters below?

wh 1. _____   4. _____

2. _____   5. _____

3. _____

Which words have the silent letters below?

w 6. _____   gh 14. _____

7. _____   15. _____

8. _____   16. _____

9. _____   17. _____

10. _____   18. _____

l 11. _____   19. _____

k 12. _____   20. _____

13. _____   21. _____

CHECK Did you spell each word correctly? Circle the letters that stand for /hw/ or the silent consonants.

Pattern Power

How can /hw/ be spelled? 22. _____ Which consonants are sometimes silent? 23. _____ or 24. _____ or 25. _____ or 26. _____

Other Words

Write words you would like to add to this week's list.

_____

_____

84

Practice Word Meanings

Analogies and Synonyms

Use spelling words to complete the analogies below.

1. *Ball* is to *toy* as _____ is to *tool.*

2. *Ankle* is to *leg* as _____ is to *arm.*

3. *Garage* is to *car* as _____ is to *ship.*

4. *Nice* is to *good* as _____ is to *bad.*

5. *Batter* is to *cake* as _____ is to *bread.*

6. *Shout* is to *loud* as _____ is to *soft.*

7. *Cruise* is to *boat* as _____ is to *airplane.*

Write the spelling words that are synonyms for the words below.

8. twist _____   **11.** complain _____

9. crash _____   **12.** crease _____

10. looked _____   **13.** branch _____

Challenge Words • *The Arts*

Write the challenge word that matches each clue below. Use the **Spelling Dictionary** on page 214 to help you. Circle the consonants that are silent in each word.

14. a row of lights along a stage _____

15. understanding _____

16. an author of plays _____

17. write it again _____

18. a traditional story _____

folktale
playwright
rewrite
insight
footlights

Spelling Tip

Some beginning sounds can be spelled more than one way. Knowing the different spellings can help you use the dictionary to find out how to spell a word. For example, /r/ at the beginning of a word can be spelled *r* or *wr.*

Here's a hint to help you decide between *rench* or *wrench.*

✦ Look up a word that starts with /r/ under *r.*

✦ If you don't find it, try *wr.*

wrist
naughty
whatever
flight
chalkboard
wring
whisper
wheelchair
brighten
kneel
whine
dough
wrench
wharf
bough
wreck
wrinkle
sought
knight
flashlight

Challenge Words

folktale
playwright
rewrite
insight
footlights

Review Words

writer
delight
whittle
thorough
whirl

Build Vocabulary

Word Building

■ Combine a word in Column A with one from Column B to form a compound word.

A	B	
what	chair	1. _____
chalk	light	2. _____
wheel	ever	3. _____
flash	board	4. _____

■ Write the spelling word that is a form of each word below.

5. knelt   _____

6. wrung   _____

7. seek   _____

8. wrinkled   _____

Use words you wrote to complete these sentences.

9. The king _____ to wear the crown.

10. The soldier had to _____ before the king.

Review Words

Write the review words that have the sound /hw/.

11. _____

12. _____

Write two review words that have the same silent consonants as the list word *brighten*.

13. _____

14. _____

Write the review word that spells /r/ as in the list word *wrinkle*.

15. _____

writer
delight
whittle
thorough
whirl

TAKE HOME

Write your spelling words in three categories: words with one syllable, words with two syllables, and words with three syllables. Circle the letters that stand for /hw/ or silent consonants. Use your lists to practice at home.

Apply Spelling Skills

Dictionary Skills

Write the spelling word to match each respelling below. You may use the **Spelling Dictionary** on page 214 to help you.

1. (flīt) _____   **5.** (rek) _____

2. (bou) _____   **6.** (nīt) _____

3. (hwīn) _____   **7.** (sôt) _____

4. (nō′tē) _____   **8.** (hwôrf) _____

Proofreading

Check spelling, capital letters, and punctuation. Then rewrite the paragraph. There are six mistakes.

> The knites of the Round Table lived in england. They would neel in front of King Arthur. The king might say, "You briten my kingdom " The knights sawt to please their king.

EDITING MARKS

⬭ check spelling

≡ capital letter

╱ lowercase letter

⊙ add a period

∧ add

⤴ take out

¶ indent the paragraph

↻ move

For more help, see page 171.

Writing • *About the Arts*

PREWRITE: Imagine you could meet King Arthur. Where and when would this meeting take place? Make a list of what you would say or do in his presence.

DRAFT: Write a paragraph from a story in which you or a made-up character has the chance to meet King Arthur.

REVISE: Read your paragraph aloud to a partner. Then allow your partner to read the paragraph silently and write comments for you in a note. Use the **Spelling Thesaurus** on page 182 as you revise.

EDIT/PROOFREAD: Use the editing marks. Then rewrite your paragraph.

PUBLISH: Complete your story. Then create a class anthology of stories called *I Met King Arthur*. Make the anthology available for other classes to read.

21

WORDS WITH /m/ and /n/

PHONICS PATTERNS

1. main
2. navy
3. banner
4. known
5. palm
6. gnaw
7. plum
8. mane
9. grown
10. crumb
11. modern
12. honest
13. committee
14. knead
15. autumn
16. assignment
17. column
18. channel
19. gnat
20. command

Learn Spelling Patterns

LOOK & SAY Listen for the sounds in each word.

PICTURE Close your eyes. See each word in your mind.

STUDY These words have /m/ and /n/. Some of the spellings for /m/ and /n/ have silent consonants.

WRITE Sort the words. Which words have /m/ or /n/ spelled with the letters below?

mm 1. _____   **kn** 14. _____

2. _____   15. _____

mn 3. _____   **n** 16. _____

4. _____   17. _____

mb 5. _____   18. _____

m 6. _____   19. _____

7. _____   20. _____

8. _____   21. _____

9. _____   22. _____

10. _____   23. _____

lm 11. _____   24. _____

nn 12. _____   **gn** 25. _____

13. _____   26. _____

27. _____

CHECK Did you spell each word correctly? Circle the letters that stand for /m/ and /n/.

Pattern Power

Which letters are sometimes silent?

_____, _____, _____, _____,

and _____

Other Words

Write words you would like to add to this week's list.

_____

Practice Word Meanings

Words in Context

Write the spelling word that best completes each sentence below.

1. In the _____, the leaves turn to gold.

2. Coconuts grow only on certain _____ trees.

3. A thief is not _____.

4. Writers will often go on a special _____.

5. Mice have strong, sharp teeth to _____ at food.

6. You must have strong hands to _____ bread dough.

7. It is not easy to swat a _____ as it buzzes by.

8. The _____ is a favorite summer fruit.

9. The horse's long _____ was blowing in the breeze.

10. The chief of police will _____ the police officers.

11. Just one cracker _____ fell on the floor.

12. The town had _____ to twice its original size.

13. The new town hall was more _____ than the old one.

Challenge Words • *Social Studies* -

Write the challenge word that is a synonym for each word below. Use the **Spelling Dictionary** on page 214 to help you. Circle the letters that stand for /n/ and underline the letters that stand for /m/ in each word.

14. significance _____

15. blame _____

16. change _____

17. foreigner _____

18. ability _____

knack
condemn
amendment
immigrant
importance

Spelling Tip

Sometimes the sounds you hear in a related spelling word can help you to decide how to spell a word with a silent letter.

✦ To remember how to spell *crumb*, think of the related word *crumble*.

✦ You can hear the *b* in *crumble*. That sound can help you remember to spell the final /m/ in *crumb* with *mb*.

main
navy
banner
known
palm
gnaw
plum
mane
grown
crumb
modern
honest
committee
knead
autumn
assignment
column
channel
gnat
command

Challenge Words

knack
condemn
amendment
immigrant
importance

Review Words

cream
limb
knife
nature
drum

Build Vocabulary

Prefixes

■ The prefix *un-* means *not.* The prefix *re-* means *again.* Add one of these two prefixes to each underlined word below to form a word that fits the meaning given.

1. not <u>wrinkled</u>   _____

2. not <u>sought</u>   _____

3. not <u>amused</u>   _____

4. not <u>known</u>   _____

5. <u>assign</u> again   _____

6. <u>channel</u> again   _____

7. <u>appoint</u> again   _____

■ Use words you made to complete these sentences.

8. The citizens decided to _____ the mayor for a second term.

9. The mayor was _____ by the egg-throwing on Halloween.

Review Words

Write the review words that spell /m/ like the list words below.

crumb 10. _____

mane 11. _____

12. _____

Write the review words that spell /n/ as in the list words below.

13. modern _____

14. knead _____

cream
limb
knife
nature
drum

T A K E   H O M E

Write your spelling words in three lists: words with one syllable, two syllables, and three syllables. Circle the letters that spell /m/ and /n/. Use your lists to practice at home.

Apply Spelling Skills

Dictionary Skills

Look at the dictionary entry for the word *column* in the **Spelling Dictionary** on page 214. Notice that an example sentence often follows a definition and helps explain a word's meaning.

1. Write the example sentence given for definition 1.

_____

2. Write the example sentence given for definition 4.

_____

3. Write your own example sentence for definition 3.

_____

Pattern Power

Find the list word you wrote in sentence 2. Circle the silent letter.

Proofreading

Check spelling, capital letters, and punctuation. Then rewrite the paragraph. There are six mistakes.

> The mane purpose of the meeting was to plan a parade A navey ship will unload officers. They would like to carry a baner. the head of the parade comittee has approved this plan.

EDITING MARKS

- ◯ check spelling
- ≡ capital letter
- / lowercase letter
- ⊙ add a period
- ∧ add
- ✐ take out
- ⌗ indent the paragraph
- ↻ move

For more help, see page 171.

Writing • *About Social Studies*

PREWRITE: What special activities could your town or city do for students? Brainstorm ideas. Then list details and examples.

DRAFT: Present your idea in a paragraph. Think of the paragraph as a speech you would give at a town meeting.

REVISE: Go over your paragraph with a small group of classmates. Have group members comment on your paragraph. Use the **Spelling Thesaurus** on page 182 as you revise.

EDIT/PROOFREAD: Use the editing marks. Then rewrite your paragraph.

PUBLISH: Complete your speech and present it aloud to the class.

22

WORDS WITH /j/ and /f/

PHONICS PATTERNS

1. gem
2. stage
3. agent
4. margin
5. hinge
6. lodge
7. trophy
8. budge
9. gopher
10. fudge
11. paragraph
12. physical
13. telegraph
14. emergency
15. manage
16. shortage
17. postage
18. ledge
19. average
20. triumph

Learn Spelling Patterns

LOOK & SAY Listen for the sounds in each word.

PICTURE Close your eyes. See each word in your mind.

STUDY These spelling words have /j/ and /f/.

WRITE Sort the words. Which words have /j/ spelled with the letters below?

dge 1. _____   ge 9. _____
2. _____   10. _____
3. _____   11. _____
4. _____   12. _____
g 5. _____   13. _____
6. _____   14. _____
7. _____
8. _____

Which words have /f/ spelled with the letters below?

ph 15. _____   18. _____
16. _____   19. _____
17. _____   20. _____

CHECK Did you spell each word correctly? Circle the letters that stand for /j/ and /f/.

Pattern Power

How can /f/ be spelled with two different consonants? 21. _____ To make the sound /j/, which vowels may follow g? 22. _____ or 23. _____ or **y**.

Other Words

Write words you would like to add to this week's list.

_____

_____

Practice Word Meanings

Words in Context

Write the spelling word that best completes each sentence below.

1. A drought is a _____ of water.

2. The cost of _____ depends on the weight.

3. A _____ can send a message faster than mail.

4. To _____ means to win.

5. A _____ is a small animal that digs tunnels.

6. Many people have an _____ for business.

7. She was awarded a _____ for her efforts.

8. To take care of, or to supervise, is to _____.

9. A yearly _____ exam is a good idea.

10. Find the _____ of the three numbers.

Challenge Words • *Physical Education*

Write the challenge words that match the clues. Circle the letters that stand for /j/ and /f/ in each word.

11. doctor _____

12. physical build _____

13. a strong material in the body _____

14. breaking down food _____

15. able to move quickly _____

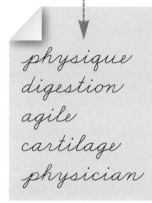

physique
digestion
agile
cartilage
physician

Spelling Tip

The history of the parts of a word can help you remember how to spell the word.

✦ The word *telegraph* is made up of two Greek words.
✦ The word part *tele* means "at a distance."
✦ The word part *graph* means "to write."
✦ The word *telegraph* means "to write from a distance."

gem

stage

agent

margin

hinge

lodge

trophy

budge

gopher

fudge

paragraph

physical

telegraph

emergency

manage

shortage

postage

ledge

average

triumph

Build Vocabulary

Plurals

■ Write the plural form of these nouns. You may have to change the base-word spelling before you add -s or -es.

1. stage _____

2. ledge _____

3. shortage _____

4. emergency _____

5. paragraph _____

6. trophy _____

7. triumph _____

8. hinge _____

9. gem _____

10. lodge _____

11. margin _____

12. wrench _____

13. gopher _____

14. agent _____

■ Use words you made to complete these sentences.

15. _____ dug tunnels under my lawn.

16. After three _____, the track team lost today's meet.

Review Words

Write the review words that spell /j/ with the letters below.

ge   17. _____

dge   18. _____

j   19. _____

Write two review words that spell /f/ as in the list word *triumph.*

20. _____

21. _____

phone
bandage
bridge
alphabet
jealous

T A K E H O M E

Write your spelling words in alphabetical order. Circle the letters that stand for /j/ and /f/. Use your lists to practice at home.

Apply Spelling Skills

Dictionary Skills

In many dictionaries, the part of speech for each entry word follows the entry or the respelling. Each spelling word below can be used as more than one part of speech. Using the **Spelling Dictionary** on page 214, write the parts of speech listed for each word.

1. stage   _____   _____

2. hinge   _____   _____

3. average   _____   _____

                   _____

4. lodge   _____   _____

Proofreading

Check spelling, capital letters, and punctuation. Then rewrite the paragraph. There are six mistakes.

> The team members did not buje. the coach read a paragraf from the local newspaper. There was no shortadge of praise for the runners. then the coach gave the team homemade fuge as a reward.

EDITING MARKS

⬭ check spelling
≡ capital letter
/ lowercase letter
⊙ add a period
∧ add
✄ take out
¶ indent the paragraph
↻ move

For more help, see page 171.

Writing • *About Physical Education*

PREWRITE: Make a list of Olympic sports. Decide on your favorite.

DRAFT: Make a poster for your sport. Use color and exciting words.

REVISE: Will your poster attract attention?

EDIT/PROOFREAD: Correct your mistakes. Make a final copy.

PUBLISH: Display the posters in the school gym.

23

WORDS WITH /sh/ and /ch/

PHONICS PATTERNS

1. shine
2. stitch
3. manufacture
4. cheap
5. especially
6. speech
7. shake
8. ditch
9. shove
10. patient
11. clutch
12. ancient
13. bench
14. polish
15. adventure
16. English
17. orchard
18. caution
19. purchase
20. sketch

Learn Spelling Patterns

LOOK & SAY Listen for the sounds in each word.

PICTURE Close your eyes. See each word in your mind.

STUDY These spelling words have /sh/ and /ch/.

WRITE Sort the words. Which words have /sh/ spelled with the letters below?

sh 1. _____   **ci** 6. _____

2. _____   7. _____

3. _____   **ti** 8. _____

4. _____   9. _____

5. _____

Which words have /ch/ spelled with the letters below?

tch 10. _____   **ch** 14. _____

11. _____   15. _____

12. _____   16. _____

13. _____   17. _____

18. _____

Which words have /chər/ spelled with the letters below?

ture 19. _____   20. _____

CHECK Did you spell each word correctly? Circle the letters that stand for /sh/ and /ch/.

Pattern Power

How can /sh/ be spelled? 21. _____ or

22. _____ or 23. _____ How can /ch/ be spelled?

24. _____ or 25. _____

Other Words

Write words you would like to add to this week's list.

_____

_____

Practice Word Meanings

Definitions

Write the spelling word that matches each definition below.

1. very old _____

2. to push hard _____

3. to make shiny _____

4. to tremble _____

5. from England _____

6. a place where fruit trees grow _____

7. a long seat for several people _____

8. a talk made in public _____

9. a long, narrow hole dug in the

    ground _____

10. mainly _____

11. low in price _____

Challenge Words • *The Arts*

Write the challenge word that best completes each analogy.
Use the **Spelling Dictionary** on page 214 to help you. Circle
the letters that stand for /sh/, /ch/, and /chər/.

12. *Locate* is to *location* as *create* is to _____.

13. *Sound* is to *music* as *image* is to _____.

14. *Icing* is to *cake* as *glitter* is to _____.

15. *Singer* is to *concert* as *speaker* is to _____.

16. *Job* is to *professional* as *hobby* is to _____.

amateur
creation
lecture
motion picture
decoration

pelling Tip

Here's a spelling rule that you can rely on.

✦ When you hear /chər/ at the end of a word, it is almost always
   spelled with *ture*.

What spelling words can you find that follow this rule?

shine
stitch
manufacture
cheap
especially
speech
shake
ditch
shove
patient
clutch
ancient
bench
polish
adventure
English
orchard
caution
purchase
sketch

amateur
creation
lecture
motion picture
decoration

picture
brushes
reach
chance
coaches

Build Vocabulary

Plurals

■ Write the plural forms of these nouns. Use your **Spelling Dictionary** on page 214 to check your work.

1. adventure   _____

2. polish   _____

3. sketch   _____

4. patient   _____

5. stitch   _____

6. speech   _____

7. ditch   _____

8. bench   _____

9. orchard   _____

10. purchase   _____

■ Use words you made to complete these sentences.

11. Gold thread was used for the _____.

12. With three _____, a customer gets a free gift.

Review Words

Write the review word that spells /sh/ with the letters below.

sh 13. _____

Write the review words that spell /ch/ as in the list word *purchase*.

14. _____   16. _____

15. _____

Write the review word that spells /chər/ as in the list word *manufacture*.

17. _____

picture
brushes
reach
chance
coaches

T A K E   H O M E

Write your spelling words in alphabetical order. Circle the letters that stand for /ch/ and /sh/ in each word. Use your lists to practice at home.

Apply Spelling Skills

Dictionary Skills

Sometimes a word has different meanings, depending on its part of speech. Find the words below in your **Spelling Dictionary** on page 214. Write a definition for each word, first as a noun and then as a verb.

1. shake (n) _____

2. shake (v) _____

3. sketch (n) _____

4. sketch (v) _____

Proofreading

Check spelling, capital letters, and punctuation. Then rewrite the paragraph. There are six mistakes.

> To manufachure tables, Mr. Grays company uses a new power tool. Workers have to cluch the table top. They must use caushun. when the table top has a perfect shin, it is stamped.

Writing • *About the Arts*

PREWRITE: Invent a new kind of chair. Jot down some ideas about it.

DRAFT: Write an ad that will persuade people to buy your chair.

REVISE: Improve your word choices. Use the **Spelling Thesaurus** on page 182 as you revise.

EDIT/PROOFREAD: Use the editing marks. Then rewrite your paragraph.

PUBLISH: Record your ad as a radio commercial. Play the commercial for classmates.

Pattern Power

Look at the list words in the dictionary activity.

• Circle the spelling words that have the /sh/ sound.

EDITING MARKS

⬯ check spelling

= capital letter

/ lowercase letter

⊙ add a period

⌃ add

⌒ take out

⌗ indent the paragraph

⟲ move

For more help, see page 171.

24 REVIEW Spelling Patterns

Sort the words in each list. Write each word. Circle the spelling pattern. In Lesson 21, circle all spellings of /m/ and /n/. (Some words have two or three.)

---

squeeze	**Lesson 19**
zipper	**Words with /z/ spelled**
visit	
pleasure	s 1. _____
usually	2. _____
breeze	3. _____
opposite	
amuse	z 4. _____
treasure	5. _____
dizzy	

6. _____

7. _____

Words with /zh/ spelled

s   8. _____

9. _____

10. _____

---

whatever	**Lesson 20**
chalkboard	**Words with silent letters**
whisper	
wheelchair	w 11. _____
kneel	12. _____
whine	l 13. _____
dough	
wrench	gh 14. _____
wrinkle	15. _____
flashlight	

k 16. _____

Words with /hw/ spelled

wh 17. _____

18. _____

19. _____

20. _____

---

banner	**Lesson 21**
known	**Words with /m/ and /n/ in alphabetical order**
palm	
gnaw	21. _____
mane	22. _____
committee	23. _____
autumn	24. _____
assignment	25. _____
channel	
command	

26. _____

27. _____

28. _____

29. _____

30. _____

gem
agent
margin
budge
gopher
physical
emergency
ledge
average
triumph

Lesson 22
Words with /j/ spelled

ge 31. _____

g 32. _____

33. _____

34. _____

35. _____

dge 36. _____

37. _____

Words with /f/ spelled

ph 38. _____

39. _____

40. _____

shine
stitch
manufacture
cheap
especially
ancient
adventure
English
caution
purchase

Lesson 23
Words with /sh/, /ch/ or /chər/ spelled

sh 41. _____

42. _____

ci 43. _____

44. _____

ti 45. _____

ch 46. _____

47. _____

tch 48. _____

ture 49. _____

50. _____

Spelling Tip

Some beginning sounds can be spelled more than one way. Knowing the different spellings can help you use the dictionary to find out how to spell a word. For example, /r/ at the beginning of a word can be spelled r or *wr*.

Here's a hint to help you decide between *rench* or *wrench*.

✦ Look up a word that starts with /r/ under *r*.

✦ If you don't find it, try *wr*.

Try spelling the following respelled word:

(ring′kəl) _____

Word Meaning Mixed Lesson Review

Word Categories

Write the word in each group below that is not related in meaning to the other words.

mane
ancient
usually
whisper
triumph
breeze
wrench
cheap
wrinkle
whatever

1. shoe   breeze   shirt   _____
2. spoon   knife   wrench   _____
3. expensive   cheap   costly   _____
4. flat   smooth   wrinkle   _____
5. ancient   new   modern   _____
6. seldom   usually   rarely   _____
7. shout   scream   whisper   _____
8. whatever   truly   exactly   _____
9. defeat   triumph   lose   _____
10. bald   hairless   mane   _____

Analogies

Use spelling words to complete the analogies below.

shine
stitch
treasure
kneel
manufacture

11. *Scuff* is to *dull* as *polish* is to _____.

12. *Pencil* is to *write* as *needle* is to _____.

13. *Cheap* is to *trash* as *valuable* is to _____.

14. *Up* is to *stand* as *down* is to _____.

15. *School* is to *teach* as *factory* is to _____.

Context Sentences

Write a spelling word to complete each sentence below.

channel
average
purchase
opposite
chalkboard

16. We wrote our answers on the _____.

17. The boat passed through a narrow _____.

18. If something isn't the same, it may be the _____.

19. To _____ the hat, you will need ten dollars.

20. For all five tests, Angela's _____ score was eighty-five.

Vocabulary Mixed Lesson Review

Suffixes

Add the suffixes to each base word below to form new words.

	–ed	–ing	–er or -or
1. gnaw	*gnawed*	*gnawing*	*gnawer*
2. squeeze			
3. command			
4. visit			
5. shine			

Look at the words you have just written. Circle the words in which you dropped a final *e* and added an ending.

Plurals

Write the plural forms of these nouns.

6. zipper _____   9. autumn _____

7. wheelchair _____   10. committee _____

8. flashlight _____

Dictionary Skills

Look at the sample dictionary entries for the word *palm*.

palm[1] The inside surface of the hand between the wrist and the fingers. *Noun.* –
1. To hold or hide in the hand. The magician *palmed* the cards so we would think they had disappeared. **2.** To get rid of by fooling someone. The crook *palmed* off the cheap stone as a diamond. *Verb.* **palm** (päm) *noun, plural* **palms;** *verb,* **palmed, palming**
palm[2] Any of a number of trees, shrubs, or vines with fanning leaves that grow in warm climates. **palm** (päm) *noun, plural* **palms.**

1. What parts of speech would *palm* be? _____

2. Write the verb forms for the verb *palm*. _____

3. Write an example sentence for the first definition of *palm*.

_____

Spelling and Writing

In a friendly letter, you may discuss two related subjects, like movies or television programs. When you show how each is similar or different, you are making comparisons and contrasts.

SUBJECTS OF COMPARISON

DETAILS SHOW SIMILARITIES OR DIFFERENCES

Dear Emanuel,

  The two movies I treasure from this past month are *Bumping into My Past* and *Night Among the Pharaohs*. Both movies have historical settings. In *Bumping into My Past*, the main character experiences a surprise. She goes into a one-minute photograph machine, becomes dizzy, then ends up as a princess in the Middle Ages. In *Night Among the Pharaohs*, the main character accidentally gets locked in a museum overnight. The statues from the ancient Egyptian room come alive to visit with him. Whatever problems these movies may have, both are far above average. *Bumping into My Past* will amuse you with its fast pace. On the other hand, *Night Among the Pharaohs* is usually serious and, sometimes, a little sad. If I were you, I'd choose the historical period that interests you and then see that film. Both movies are a triumph.

Your pal,

Joey

WRITING TIPS!!

Comparison and Contrast

- Name subjects to be compared and contrasted.
- Use details from each subject for clear comparisons.
- Present details of one subject, then details of the other. Or present a general topic, then present a related detail from each subject.
- Include the proper heading and closing for a friendly letter.

Now write a friendly letter in which you compare and contrast two movies or television shows.

PREWRITE: Brainstorm a list of movies or television shows you enjoy. Choose two to compare and contrast.

DRAFT: Write a paragraph from a letter to a friend or family member about these two movies or television shows. Name the two movies or television shows at the beginning. Then use details from each to show how they are similar and different.

REVISE: Share your paragraph with a partner. Use your partner's comments and the Writing Tips as you revise.

EDIT/PROOFREAD: Use editing marks to correct your capitalization, spelling, and punctuation.

PUBLISH: Complete your letter and mail it.

SPELLING FUN
CUMULATIVE REVIEW

WHAT'S MY WORD?

- Play with up to four players. Each player chooses a word from a list in Lessons 1-17. *(for example, spoon).*
- Draw pictures or show classroom objects with the same spelling pattern as the word you have chosen. *(for example, moon)*
- Have players identify the spelling pattern. Then have each player write the spelling word they think you have chosen.
- Every correctly chosen and spelled word earns a player one point.
- Take turns presenting words and clues. The player who earns 5 points first wins!

RHYMING QUIZ

- Choose a word from any list in Lessons 19-23.
- Brainstorm four words that rhyme with your word. Check spellings in the dictionary.
- Say your first rhyming word, then write it down to show your partner.
- Allow one minute for your partner to guess and spell your word correctly.
- Continue with each of the four rhymes.
- Exchange tasks. See how many rhymes it takes you to guess and spell a chosen word.

SPELLING BEE

- Divide into Teams A and B.
- Write selected words from Lessons 1-23 on an even number of cards. Divide the cards so each team has the same amount.
- A member of Team A calls out a word from Team B's stack.
- A member of Team B spells the word on the board. If it is correct, the card is removed. If it is not correct, the card remains.
- The next member of Team B calls a word from Team A's stack.
- The next member of Team A spells the word on the board. If it is correct, the card is removed. If it is not correct, the card remains.
- The first team to finish the other team's pile wins!

Consonant Clusters

1. strength
2. thrown
3. scribble
4. script
5. strain
6. straighten
7. threaten
8. screech
9. stray
10. scheme
11. sprang
12. strawberry
13. strategy
14. throughout
15. throne
16. scramble
17. stripe
18. sprint
19. schedule
20. scrape

Learn Spelling Patterns

LOOK & SAY Listen for the sounds in each word.

PICTURE Close your eyes. See each word in your mind.

STUDY These spelling words begin with consonant sounds spelled with three consonant letters. These letters are called **consonant clusters**.

WRITE Sort the words. Which words have consonant clusters spelled with the letters below?

scr 1. _____
2. _____
3. _____
4. _____
5. _____

str 6. _____
7. _____
8. _____
9. _____
10. _____
11. _____
12. _____

spr 13. _____
14. _____

sch 15. _____
16. _____

thr 17. _____
18. _____
19. _____
20. _____

CHECK Did you spell each word correctly? Circle each cluster.

Pattern Power

What are five common consonant clusters with three letters? 21. _____, 22. _____, 23. _____, 24. _____, and 25. _____

Other Words

Write words you would like to add to this week's list.

_____

Practice Word Meanings

Sentence Context

Write the spelling word that best completes each
sentence below.

1. The king made many enemies _____ his palace.

2. He would often _____ the guards.

3. Many guards secretly began to _____ against
   the king.

4. They planned to remove the ruler from his _____.

5. One morning, the guards _____ into action.

6. The king was overpowered by their _____.

7. The king let out a loud _____ as he tried
   to escape.

8. His favorite _____ plant was trampled in
   the fight.

9. The _____ of gold on his royal coat was torn.

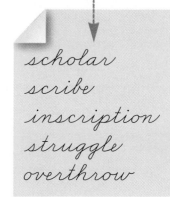

Challenge Words • *Social Studies*

Write the challenge word that matches each clue. Use the **Spelling
Dictionary** on page 214 to help you. Circle the letters that stand
for the consonant clusters you hear in each word.

10. something that is written _____

11. a person with much knowledge _____

12. to defeat _____

13. to fight _____

14. a person who writes or copies _____

scholar
scribe
inscription
struggle
overthrow

pelling Tip

The words *thrown* and *throne* are homophones. They sound
alike, but are spelled differently and have different meanings. To
use homophones correctly in your writing:

✦ After you write something, read it over. Do you see any
  homophones?

✦ Decide if you used the right word.

✦ Check the dictionary.

strength
thrown
scribble
script
strain
straighten
threaten
screech
stray
scheme
sprang
strawberry
strategy
throughout
throne
scramble
stripe
sprint
schedule
scrape

Challenge Words

scholar
scribe
inscription
struggle
overthrow

Review Words

thread
straight
split
spray
stew

Build Vocabulary

Word Endings

■ Add *-ed* and *-ing* to each base word below. Write the new words. You will need to change the spellings of some base words before adding the endings.

	-ed	-ing
1. scrape	_____	_____
2. threaten	_____	_____
3. scramble	_____	_____
4. stray	_____	_____
5. scribble	_____	_____
6. sprint	_____	_____
7. scheme	_____	_____
8. straighten	_____	_____
9. script	_____	_____

■ Use words you made to complete these sentences.

10. The guards _____ down their plans on a piece of paper.

11. They claimed to be _____ out a crooked government.

Review Words

Write the review words that have these consonant clusters.

spr 12. _____   str 15. _____

thr 13. _____   spl 16. _____

st 14. _____

17. Which review word appears within a list

word? _____

thread
straight
split
spray
stew

T A K E   H O M E

Write your spelling words in alphabetical order. Circle the consonant cluster in each word. Use your list to practice at home.

Apply Spelling Skills

Dictionary Skills

Use the two dictionary entries to complete the activity below.

throne The chair for a king or queen.
thrown Past participle of **throw.**

Write the word that completes each sentence.

1. The old king was _____ out of the palace.

2. A new king now sits on the _____.

3. Write a sentence that uses the word *throne*.

_____

4. Write a sentence that uses the word *thrown*.

_____

Pattern Power

Look at the list words you just wrote.

• Circle the consonant cluster at the beginning of each word.

Proofreading

Use editing marks. Check spelling, capital letters, and punctuation. Then rewrite the paragraph. There are six mistakes.

It can be very dangerous to sceme against a king. the stratigy must be timed perfectly. If it's not on skedule, the plotters may fail The stress and strane of plotting are great.

EDITING MARKS

⬭ check spelling
≡ capital letter
/ lowercase letter
⊙ add a period
∧ add
✂ take out
⌗ indent the paragraph
↻ move

For more help, see page 171.

Writing • *About Social Studies*

PREWRITE: Think of a problem in your town. Jot down ideas to fix it.
DRAFT: Choose one idea. Write a paragraph that explains why your town would try your idea.
REVISE: Try to make your language persuasive. Use the **Spelling Thesaurus** on page 182 as you revise.
EDIT/PROOFREAD: Use editing marks. Then rewrite your paragraph.
PUBLISH: Read your paragraph to your class. Discuss your ideas and solutions.

WORDS WITH Prefixes

1. prevent
2. produce
3. review
4. provide
5. protect
6. prefix
7. program
8. preview
9. refill
10. repay
11. recover
12. remain
13. recall
14. preschool
15. protest
16. prepaid
17. pretest
18. prehistoric
19. rebuild
20. propose

Learn Spelling Patterns

LOOK & SAY Listen for the sounds in each word.

PICTURE Close your eyes. See each word in your mind.

STUDY Each spelling word has a prefix. A **prefix** is a word part added to the beginning of a base word or root that changes its meaning. For example, the prefix *pre-* means "before," *re-* usually means "again," and *pro-* means "forward" or "out."

WRITE Sort the words. Which words have prefixes spelled with the letters below?

pre 1. _____ 11. _____

2. _____ 12. _____

3. _____ 13. _____

4. _____ 14. _____

5. _____ pro 15. _____

6. _____ 16. _____

7. _____ 17. _____

re 8. _____ 18. _____

9. _____ 19. _____

10. _____ 20. _____

CHECK Did you spell each word correctly? Circle each prefix.

Pattern Power

What are three common prefixes?

21. _____, 22. _____, and 23. _____

Other Words

Write words you would like to add to this week's list.

_____

Practice Word Meanings

Definitions

Write the spelling word that matches each definition below.

1. a play or performance _____

2. to remember _____

3. to pay back _____

4. to make _____

5. to stop something before it happens _____

6. to see or show in advance _____

7. to object to _____

8. to stay back _____

9. to fill again _____

10. to suggest something _____

Challenge Words • *Math*

Write the challenge words to complete the paragraph. Use the **Spelling Dictionary** on page 214 to help you. Circle the letters that make up the prefixes in each word.

Plan carefully if you wish to **11.** _____ your room.

First make a drawing, a sort of **12.** _____ of your new

design. Use a **13.** _____ to measure angles in your

drawing. Even with planning, **14.** _____ exactly how

your room will turn out can be difficult. Keep a **15.**

_____ for every item you buy, in case you need to

return it later.

predicting
projection
rearrange
receipt
protractor

Spelling Tip

The /k/ sound at the end of a word can be spelled *ck*, *c*, or *k*. If a word ends with the letter *k*, you often have to put a *c* before the *k*. Exceptions include words that have the letters *oo* before the letter *k*, as in *look*.

✦ What word on your spelling list ends with /k/?

✦ How is it spelled?

prevent
produce
review
provide
protect
prefix
program
preview
refill
repay
recover
remain
recall
preschool
protest
prepaid
pretest
prehistoric
rebuild
propose

Challenge Words

predicting
projection
rearrange
receipt
protractor

Review Words

repair
report
unknown
unfair
disappoint

Build Vocabulary

Prefixes

■ Combine each base word below with the given prefix or prefixes to make new words. Write each new word.

Prefixes	Base Word		New Words	
pre-, pro-	test	1. _____	2. _____	
pre-, re-	view	3. _____	4. _____	
re-	fill	5. _____		
re-	cover	6. _____		
pre-, re-	pay	7. _____	8. _____	
pre-	historic	9. _____		
pre-	school	10. _____		

■ Use words you made to complete these sentences.

11. I thought I would never _____ from the flu.

12. I got a _____ of how my new room will look.

Review Words

Write the review words that have the following prefixes.

un 13. _____   **re** 16. _____

14. _____   17. _____

dis 15. _____

Write the review words that rhyme with these words.

stair 18. _____

19. _____

sort 20. _____

own 21. _____

joint 22. _____

repair
report
unknown
unfair
disappoint

⌂ T A K E   H O M E ⌂

Write your spelling words in three lists: nouns, verbs, and adjectives. Some words belong on more than one list. Circle the prefix in each word. Use your lists to practice at home.

Apply Spelling Skills

Using the Thesaurus

When you write, a **thesaurus** can help you find the exact word you want. Look in your **Spelling Thesaurus** on page 182 to find synonyms and antonyms for each of the following list words.

Look in your **Spelling Thesaurus** on page 182 to find

Synonyms	Antonyms
1. provide _____	4. prevent _____
2. recall _____	5. remain _____
3. protest _____	6. prehistoric _____

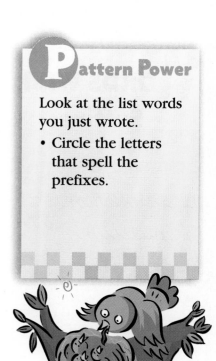

Complete each sentence with a list word that is a **synonym** or **antonym** of the word in dark type.

7. **recollect** I _____ that the room used to be purple.

8. **encourage** You can't _____ me from painting the room pink.

Proofreading

Check spelling, capital letters, and punctuation. Then rewrite the paragraph. There are six mistakes.

> When you redecorate your house, measure the rooms to privent error. Pruvide yourself with exact figures. This way, you pratect yourself. you won't have to rebild items that don't fit

Writing • *About Math*

PREWRITE: Make a list of foods for a class picnic. Estimate amounts.

DRAFT: Write a plan to buy the food on your list. Give the price of each item. Avoid junk food—it is expensive!

REVISE: Reread your plan. Is it too expensive? How could you cut the cost?

EDIT/PROOFREAD: Use editing marks. Then rewrite your plan.

PUBLISH: Compare your plan with others'.

27

WORDS WITH Suffixes

1. education
2. position
3. correction
4. invention
5. imagination
6. direction
7. invitation
8. population
9. discussion
10. collection
11. expression
12. explosion
13. mission
14. conviction
15. instruction
16. information
17. suggestion
18. concentration
19. attention
20. selection

Learn Spelling Patterns

LOOK & SAY Listen for the sounds in each word.

PICTURE Close your eyes. See each word in your mind.

STUDY Each spelling word has a suffix. A **suffix** is a word part added to the end of a base word that changes its meaning. For example, the suffixes *-ion* and *-ation* mean "act or process of."

WRITE Sort the words. Which words have base words that *do not* change when these suffixes are added?

ion 1. _____   7. _____

2. _____   8. _____

3. _____   9. _____

4. _____   10. _____

5. _____   ation 11. _____

6. _____

Which words have base words that *do* change when these suffixes are added?

ion 12. _____   16. _____

13. _____   ation 17. _____

14. _____   18. _____

15. _____

Which words have **-ion** as part of the base word?

19. _____   20. _____

CHECK Did you spell each word correctly? Circle each suffix.

Pattern Power

Which vowel letter is often dropped when the suffix *-ion* or *-ation* is added to a base word? 21. _____

Other Words

Write words you would like to add to this week's list.

_____

Practice Word Meanings

Suffixes

The suffix *-ion* means "the act of" or "the process of." For example, *collection* means "the act or process of collecting."

Write the word that means the same as each definition below.

1. the act or process of educating _____

2. the act or process of selecting _____

3. the act or process of instructing _____

4. the act or process of directing _____

5. the act or process of suggesting _____

6. the act or process of inventing _____

7. the act or process of exploding _____

8. the act or process of correcting _____

Challenge Words • *Science* -

Write the challenge words to complete each sentence. Use the **Spelling Dictionary** on page 214 to help you.

9. I heard a good _____ of how the solar system works.

10. The entire _____ involves the sun, moon, and planets.

11. A force called _____ keeps planets in their orbits.

12. Stars in the sky form a group called a _____.

13. Every _____ learns more about the solar system.

explanation
generation
gravitation
constellation
operation

Spelling Tip

There are different ways to spell the sound /shən/ that you hear at the end of *education* and *expression*. These rules will help you when you need to spell a word that ends with /shən/.

✦ This sound is never spelled *shun*.

✦ Most of the time it is spelled *tion*.

✦ Sometimes it is spelled *ssion*.

Which spelling words follow these rules?

education
position
correction
invention
imagination
direction
invitation
population
discussion
collection
expression
explosion
mission
conviction
instruction
information
suggestion
concentration
attention
selection

explanation
generation
gravitation
constellation
operation

action
vacation
question
station
election

Build Vocabulary

Related Words

■ How are these words similar in spelling and meaning?

conduct   **conduction**

Say each word and listen to the sound of the letter *t*. How does the pronunciation of the *t* in *conduct* help you spell the /sh/ sound in *conduction*?

■ Write the spelling word that is related to each word below. Then circle the letter or letters in the shorter word that help you spell the /sh/ sound in the list word. Use the **Spelling Dictionary** on page 214 to help you.

1. populate _____

2. convict _____

3. direct _____

4. collect _____

5. instruct _____

6. select _____

7. discuss _____

8. express _____

9. correct _____

10. invite _____

Review Words

Write the review words that are related to the words below.

11. quest _____

12. act _____

13. elect _____

14. vacate _____

15. state _____

action
vacation
question
station
election

TAKE HOME

Write your spelling words in four lists: words with two, three, four, or five syllables. Circle the *-ion* or *-ation* ending in each word. Use your lists to practice at home.

Apply Spelling Skills

Dictionary Skills

In a dictionary, the entries often list other forms of an entry word. They appear in dark print at the very end of the entry. Look up these entry words in your **Spelling Dictionary** on page 214. Write the word form given at the end of each entry.

1. instruction _____

2. direction _____

3. information _____

4. education _____

Proofreading

Check spelling, capital letters, and punctuation. Then rewrite the paragraph. There are five mistakes.

In school we paid a lot of atention to the solar system We learned about the pozition of the planets. we also learned what astronauts do on a space mision.

E DITING MARKS

⬭ check spelling

= capital letter

/ lowercase letter

⊙ add a period

∧ add

⌇ take out

⌗ indent the paragraph

↻ move

For more help, see page 171.

Writing • *About Science*

PREWRITE: Imagine that you visited another planet.

DRAFT: Write a paragraph that describes your visit. Tell what you saw and did there.

REVISE: Be sure you write good descriptive sentences.

EDIT/PROOFREAD: Use editing marks. Then rewrite your paragraph.

PUBLISH: Draw a picture to go with your paragraph. Put the class paragraphs together in a folder.

28

WORDS WITH Suffixes

1. allowance
2. entertainment
3. wonderful
4. settlement
5. painful
6. movement
7. peaceful
8. statement
9. treatment
10. dreadful
11. amusement
12. harmful
13. argument
14. grateful
15. announcement
16. equipment
17. government
18. graceful
19. entrance
20. performance

Learn Spelling Patterns

LOOK & SAY Listen for the sounds in each word.

PICTURE Close your eyes. See each word in your mind.

STUDY These spelling words have suffixes. The suffixes *-ance* and *-ment* mean "state or quality of." The adjective suffix *-ful* means "full of."

WRITE Sort the words. Which words have the suffixes below?

ance 1. _____   ment 11. _____

2. _____   12. _____

3. _____   13. _____

ful 4. _____   14. _____

5. _____   15. _____

6. _____   16. _____

7. _____   17. _____

8. _____   18. _____

9. _____   19. _____

10. _____   20. _____

CHECK Did you spell each word correctly? Circle each suffix.

Pattern Power

Which suffixes mean "state or quality of"? 21. _____ and

22. _____ Which suffix means "full of"? 23. _____

Other Words

Write words you would like to add to this week's list.

_____

_____

Practice Word Meanings

Synonyms and Antonyms

Write the spelling word that is a **synonym** for each word below.

1. sentence _____ 4. tools _____

2. entertainment _____ 5. care _____

3. thankful _____ 6. fight _____

Write the spelling word that is an **antonym** for each word below.

7. clumsy _____

8. exit _____

9. stillness _____

10. safe _____

11. terrible _____

12. noisy _____

Challenge Words • *Social Studies*

Write the challenge word that completes each analogy. Use the **Spelling Dictionary** on page 214 to help you. Circle the letters that spell the suffix in each word.

13. *Scholar* is to *wisdom* as *fool* is to _____.

14. *Collect* is to *collection* as *assist* is to _____.

15. *Timid* is to *brave* as *boring* is to _____.

16. *Settle* is to *settlement* as *establish* is to _____.

17. *End* is to *destruction* as *growth* is to _____.

development
assistance
establishment
eventful
ignorance

Spelling Tip

Some words that we use a lot are hard to spell. Often these words have short vowel sounds that are spelled in unexpected ways. One of these words is *wonderful*. The /u/ sound in the first syllable is spelled *o*. One way to remember hard to spell words is:

✦ Look at the word letter by letter.

✦ Close your eyes. Try to see each letter in the word.

✦ Open your eyes and write the word.

✦ Check to see if you are right.

List Words

allowance
entertainment
wonderful
settlement
painful
movement
peaceful
statement
treatment
dreadful
amusement
harmful
argument
grateful
announcement
equipment
government
graceful
entrance
performance

Build Vocabulary

Base Words and Suffixes

■ Write the base word for each spelling word below.

1. government   _____

2. argument   _____

3. entertainment   _____

4. harmful   _____

5. announcement   _____

6. performance   _____

7. dreadful   _____

8. amusement   _____

9. entrance   _____

10. painful   _____

Which base words change their spelling when the suffix is added?

11. _____   12. _____

■ Add -*ly* to the spelling words below to change them from adjectives to adverbs.

13. grateful _____   15. wonderful _____

14. graceful _____   16. peaceful _____

Review Words

Write the review words that have these base words.

17. beauty   _____

18. care   _____

19. thought   _____

20. hand   _____

21. appoint   _____

thoughtful
handful
beautiful
careful
appointment

Challenge Words

development
assistance
establishment
eventful
ignorance

Review Words

thoughtful
handful
beautiful
careful
appointment

T A K E   H O M E

Write your spelling words in two lists: nouns and adjectives. Circle the suffix in each word. Use your lists to practice at home.

© McGraw-Hill School Division

Apply Spelling Skills

Dictionary Skills

Write each spelling word below. Insert a hyphen between syllables to show where the word can be divided at the end of a writing line. Use your **Spelling Dictionary** on page 214 for help.

1. entrance _____
2. allowance _____
3. wonderful _____
4. painful _____
5. settlement _____
6. equipment _____

Proofreading

Check spelling, capital letters, and punctuation. Then rewrite the paragraph. There are six mistakes.

> we are lucky that our goverment provides us with courts. They are wunderful places for people. We can settle an arguement there The courts keep our nation peacefull.

EDITING MARKS

- ⬭ check spelling
- ≡ capital letter
- / lowercase letter
- ⊙ add a period
- ∧ add
- ℘ take out
- ⌐ indent the paragraph
- ↻ move

For more help, see page 171.

Writing • *About Social Studies*

PREWRITE: Make a list of ways to help students end an argument.

DRAFT: Choose the five best rules. Write a paragraph explaining how your rules will end an argument.

REVISE: Be sure you have selected the best rules. Be sure your paragraph is clear.

EDIT/PROOFREAD: Use editing marks to correct your writing. Make a clean copy.

PUBLISH: Present your rules to your class. Make a classroom list of the best rules from everyone's lists. Display this list in the classroom.

29

CONTRACTIONS

1. hasn't
2. they've
3. you'll
4. we'd
5. would've
6. they're
7. haven't
8. she'd
9. must've
10. they'll
11. you'd
12. shouldn't
13. should've
14. you've
15. what'll
16. who'd
17. needn't
18. how's
19. mustn't
20. what'd

Learn Spelling Patterns

LOOK & SAY Listen for the sounds in each word.

PICTURE Close your eyes. See each word in your mind.

STUDY Each spelling word is a **contraction**, or the shortened form of two words.

WRITE Sort the words. Which words contain shortened forms of the words below?

will 1. _____ had/would 11. _____
2. _____ 12. _____
3. _____ 13. _____
not 4. _____ 14. _____
5. _____ did/would 15. _____
6. _____ have 16. _____
7. _____ 17. _____
8. _____ 18. _____
are 9. _____ 19. _____
is 10. _____ 20. _____

CHECK Did you spell each word correctly? Circle the shortened part of each word.

Pattern Power

What is used to show where a letter or letters have been left out in a contraction? 21. _____

What letter does the apostrophe replace when *not* is combined with a verb? 22. _____

Other Words

Write words you would like to add to this week's list.

_____

_____

122

Practice Word Meanings

Contractions

Write the contractions formed by the words in parentheses.

1. There are people (who would) _____ listen to pop music all day.

2. When others were asked, (what did) _____ they say?

3. They said they (need not) _____ hear any music but folk.

4. Who knew (we would) _____ have so much music to choose from?

5. If you ask (how is) _____ that possible, it is!

Challenge Words • *Language Arts*

Write the challenge word that matches each word or pair of words. Use the **Spelling Dictionary** on page 214 to help you. Circle the letters and apostrophes that stand for the shortened forms.

6. might have   _____

7. could have   _____

8. who will   _____

9. that will   _____

10. over   _____

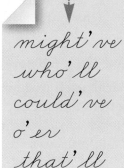

might've
who'll
could've
o'er
that'll

Spelling Tip

Use words you know how to spell to help you spell new words. For example, if you want to spell the contraction *mustn't*:

✦ Think about what the word means. **mustn't = must not**

✦ Remember that the first *t* in *mustn't* is silent.

✦ Add the apostrophe and letters to replace the word *not*.

hasn't
they've
you'll
we'd
would've
they're
haven't
she'd
must've
they'll
you'd
shouldn't
should've
you've
what'll
who'd
needn't
how's
mustn't
what'd

might've
who'll
could've
o'er
that'll

we've
who's
wouldn't
there's
they'd

Build Vocabulary

Contractions

■ Write the pair of words for each contraction below.

1. should've _____

2. she'd _____

3. you've _____

4. haven't _____

5. you'd _____

6. what'll _____

7. hasn't _____

8. must've _____

9. would've _____

10. they'll _____

■ Use contractions given above to complete these sentences.

11. A song won't be a hit if it _____ got a catchy tune.

12. What song do you feel _____ been a hit but wasn't?

Review Words

Write each review word. Next to it, write the letter or letters that are replaced by the apostrophe (').

13. _____ _____

14. _____ _____

15. _____ _____

16. _____ _____

17. _____ _____

we've
who's
wouldn't
there's
they'd

TAKE HOME

Write your spelling words in alphabetical order. Circle the apostrophe (') in each word. Use your list to practice at home.

Apply Spelling Skills

Dictionary Skills

The **accent mark** in a dictionary entry shows you which syllable in a word is accented.   ə pos′ trə fē

Sometimes a word has a primary (stronger) accent and a secondary (weaker) accent.

man′ yə fak′ chər

Write the words that are respelled below, leaving space between syllables. Then add the accent marks. Use the **Spelling Dictionary** on page 214 for help.

1. shùd′ənt   _____

2. si lek′shən   _____

3. ej′ ə kā′shən   _____

4. en′tər tān′mənt   _____

Proofreading

Check spelling, capital letters, and punctuation. Then rewrite the paragraph. There are six mistakes.

> Contractions are very common. here are some that you're likely to hear and must'nt forget: youl'l (you will) theyv'e (they have), and their (they are).

EDITING
MARKS

⬭ **check spelling**

= **capital letter**

/ **lowercase letter**

⊙ **add a period**

∧ **add**

⤶ **take out**

¶ **indent the paragraph**

↻ **move**

For more help, see page 171.

Writing • *About Language Arts*

PREWRITE: List your favorite writers and poets.

DRAFT: Choose one writer or poet. Write a paragraph that tells why you like that person's writing so much.

REVISE: Use colorful and exciting words. Use the **Spelling Thesaurus** on page 182 as you revise.

EDIT/PROOFREAD: Use editing marks. Then rewrite your paragraph.

PUBLISH: Put a photo or drawing of the writer with your paragraph. Display the paragraphs in a classroom folder.

Sort the words in each list. Write each word. Circle the spelling pattern. In Lesson 26, circle the prefixes. In Lessons 27 and 28, circle the suffixes. In Lesson 29, circle the word that has not been shortened.

thrown
scribble
strain
screech
scheme
sprang
strategy
throughout
scramble
stripe

Lesson 25
Words that begin with these consonant clusters

scr   1. _____   str   6. _____

        2. _____   7. _____

        3. _____   8. _____

spr   4. _____   thr   9. _____

sch   5. _____   10. _____

prevent
review
program
preview
repay
remain
preschool
protest
prehistoric
propose

Lesson 26
Words with these prefixes

pre-   11. _____   16. _____

        12. _____   17. _____

        13. _____   pro-   18. _____

        14. _____   19. _____

re-   15. _____   20. _____

education
correction
imagination
direction
invitation
expression
explosion
instruction
information
concentration

Lesson 27

Words in which the base word changes with the suffix

Words in which the base word does not change with the suffix

-ion   21. _____   -ion   26. _____

        22. _____   27. _____

        23. _____   28. _____

-ation   24. _____   29. _____

        25. _____   -ation   30. _____

allowance
entertainment
wonderful
peaceful
treatment
harmful
argument
equipment
government
performance

Lesson 28
Words with these suffixes

-ance 31. _____

32. _____

-ful 33. _____

34. _____

35. _____

-ment 36. _____

37. _____

38. _____

39. _____

40. _____

you'll
they're
haven't
she'd
must've
you'd
should've
what'll
needn't
how's

Lesson 29
Words with shortened forms of these words

will 41. _____

42. _____

not 43. _____

44. _____

is 45. _____

are 46. _____

had 47. _____

48. _____

have 49. _____

50. _____

Spelling Tip

Remember: Long words are easier to spell when you divide them into syllables. Say each of the words respelled below. What syllables do you hear? Listen for prefixes and suffixes you know how to spell. Try writing the words one syllable at a time. Circle any prefix or suffix you find.

1. /i majʹə nāʹshən/ _____

2. /ə louʹəns/ _____

3. /prēʹhis tôrʹik/ _____

prehistoric
imagination
allowance

Word Meaning Mixed Lesson Review

harmful
information
invitation
peaceful
remain
repay
scribble
should've
sprang
you'll

Definitions

Write the spelling word that matches each definition below.

1. to write in a messy way _____

2. jumped or popped up _____

3. to pay back _____

4. to stay _____

5. a request _____

6. facts, knowledge _____

7. calm and quiet _____

8. damaging _____

9. you will _____

10. should have _____

allowance
education
equipment
explosion
prehistoric
review
they're
throughout
thrown
you'd

Context Sentences

Write the spelling word that completes each sentence.

11. Rain falls on many days _____ the year.

12. The baseball player has _____ a curve ball.

13. You should _____ your notes before taking a test.

14. Dinosaurs lived in _____ times.

15. It's hard to get a good job without a good

    _____.

16. The _____ of the bomb could be heard for miles.

17. Jane gets a weekly _____ for doing jobs at home.

18. The workers used many pieces of _____.

19. You shouldn't eat foods if _____ spoiled.

20. If you want to have friends, _____ better be nice.

Vocabulary Mixed Lesson Review

Add Prefixes and Suffixes

Add the prefix or suffix to each base word below. Write the new word. In some cases, the spelling of the base word will change when you add a suffix.

Prefix	Base Word	Suffix	New Word
1. —	scheme	-er	_____
2. re-	strain	—	_____
3. —	prevent	-able	_____
4. pro-	pose	-al	_____
5. mis-	direct	ion	_____
6. —	expression	-less	_____
7. —	government	-al	_____
8. pre-	perform	-ance	_____
9. pre-	school	-er	_____
10. mis-	treat	-ment	_____

Dictionary Skills

Write the spelling word that matches each respelling below. Using the word you wrote, circle the syllable that has the primary accent. Underline the syllable with a secondary accent mark. Use your Spelling Dictionary on page 214 for help.

argument	haven't	preview	scramble	entertainment
correction	instruction	program	concentration	wonderful

1. skram′bəl _____

2. kon′sən trā′shən _____

3. prō′gram _____

4. prē′vu _____

5. kə rek′shən _____

6. in struk′shən _____

7. wun′dər fəl _____

8. är′gyə mənt _____

9. hav′ənt _____

10. en′tər tān′mənt _____

Spelling and Writing

A book review is a form of persuasive writing. The writer gives reasons for reading the book.

USE CONVINCING WORDS

PRESENT THE FACTS

STATE AN OPINION

The book *A Dog for Davey* by Bill E. Neder **is wonderful entertainment.** If you're like me, you'll both laugh and cry throughout the story. It starts when Davey finds a dog. It has been thrown out of the house by a cruel owner. **Davey's parents decide the dog can remain in their home.** The family gets a quick education. The dog nearly eats all their shoes! They also discover that the dog snores loudly. Davey and his parents visit a veterinarian. They ask for information on handling their new pet. If you haven't guessed by now, the book has a happy ending. The author has a great imagination. **Some of the scenes are hilarious.** At one point, Davey chases the dog through a giant mud puddle. But the story also turns serious when the dog gets sick. I urge you to read *A Dog for Davey*. You won't regret it!

WRITING TIPS!!

Persuasive Writing

- Use convincing words and phrases.
- Clearly state an opinion.
- Give good facts and reasons for your opinion.
- Present the facts and reasons in a clear order.

Now write your own persuasive review.

PREWRITE: What book have you read that your friends might enjoy? List what you liked most about the book.

DRAFT: Write a paragraph about the book. Begin with a topic sentence that states your opinion. Give reasons to support your opinion.

REVISE: Share your paragraph with a classmate. Use your classmate's comments and the Writing Tips as you revise.

EDIT/PROOFREAD: Use editing marks to correct your capitalization, spelling, and punctuation. Rewrite your paragraph neatly.

PUBLISH: Post your book review in the school library.

SPELLING FUN
CUMULATIVE REVIEW

LETTER PERFECT

- Choose a word from Lessons 1–23 that has a lot of letters.
- List other words that have some of the letters in your word.
- See how many other words you can spell using the letters in your word.
- Try as many spelling words as you like. See who can make the longest lists.

SCRAMBLED WORDS

- Choose one word from any list in Lessons 25–29.
- Mix up the order of the letters. Write your scrambled word on paper.
- Show the scrambled word to your partner. See if your partner can guess your word.
- When you're done, switch roles. You try to guess a word that your partner has scrambled!

SPELLING BEE

- On a piece of paper, draw a Bingo card with twenty-five squares.
- Write a different spelling word from Lessons 1–29 in each square.
- Listen as your teacher says each word aloud. If you have that word, cover it with a marker.
- If you cover five words across, down, or diagonally, shout "Bingo!" Then spell your five words correctly.

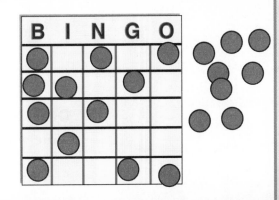

31

Homophones, Homographs

1. break
2. male
3. record
4. bore
5. stable
6. refuse
7. wound
8. file
9. contest
10. stock
11. waste
12. vault
13. brake
14. foul
15. mail
16. fowl
17. pain
18. waist
19. range
20. pane

Learn Spelling Patterns

LOOK & SAY Listen for the sounds in each word.

PICTURE Close your eyes. See each word in your mind.

STUDY These words are **homophones** and **homographs**.

WRITE Write the homophone pairs in which /ā/ and /ou/ are pronounced the same but spelled differently.

/ā/ 1. _____ 6. _____

2. _____ 7. _____

3. _____ 8. _____

4. _____ /ou/ 9. _____

5. _____ 10. _____

The remaining words are homographs. For each one, there is another word that is spelled the same but has a completely different meaning. Write the words.

11. _____ 16. _____

12. _____ 17. _____

13. _____ 18. _____

14. _____ 19. _____

15. _____ 20. _____

CHECK Did you spell each word correctly? Circle the letters in the homophones that are pronounced the same but are spelled differently.

Pattern Power

What kinds of words sound alike but have different meanings and spellings?

21. _____

Other Words

Write words you would like to add to this week's list.

_____

_____

Practice Word Meanings

Homophones and Homographs

Write the homophone in each pair that relates in meaning to the word in dark print.

1. **window**   pain   pane   _____

2. **chicken**   fowl   foul   _____

3. **fracture**   break   brake   _____

4. **unpleasant** foul   fowl   _____

5. **man**   male   mail   _____

Write the homograph in each pair below that relates in meaning to *both* words in dark print.

6. **injury/clock** wound solve   _____

7. **reject/trash** refuse garbage   _____

8. **write/music** report record   _____

Challenge Words • *Language Arts* --------------------

Write the homograph that answers each riddle. Use the **Spelling Dictionary** on page 214 to help you.

9. I can make you warm or mark your trail. _____

10. I can hold dirty socks or stop progress. _____

11. When a ball is hit with me, spectators can cause me with their

    loud cheers. _____

12. I am a kind of fish with a deep voice. _____

13. It might take this amount of time for something my size to

    move a few inches. _____

racket
hamper
bass
minute
blaze

$\bigcirc$pelling Tip

A computer Spellchecker finds words that are spelled incorrectly, not words that are used incorrectly.

✦ If you wrote, "The *pain* of glass was broken," the Spellchecker would not correct you, because *pain* is a correctly spelled word.

Always check to be sure you have used the correct homophone.

break

male

record

bore

stable

refuse

wound

file

contest

stock

waste

vault

brake

foul

mail

fowl

pain

waist

range

pane

Challenge Words

racket

hamper

bass

minute

blaze

Review Words

weak

week

punch

tire

sink

Build Vocabulary

Word Endings

■ Write the plural forms of the following nouns by adding *-s* or *-es*.

1. waist _____   4. jury _____

2. brake _____   5. entrance _____

3. stable _____

■ Add *-ed* or *-ing* to the following verbs.

	-ed	-ing
6. mail	_____	_____
7. contest	_____	_____
8. bore	_____	_____
9. vault	_____	_____
10. range	_____	_____
11. stock	_____	_____

■ Use words you made to complete these sentences.

12. In all the _____ across the valley, the horses began to speak.

13. One horse, who became _____, started to sing "Home, Home on the Range."

Review Words

Write the two review words that sound alike but have different spellings and meanings.

14. _____   15. _____

Write three review words that have the same spelling as other words with different meanings.

16. _____

17. _____

18. _____

weak
week
punch
tire
sink

T A K E   H O M E

Write your spelling words in three lists: words with four letters, words with five letters, words with six or more letters. Circle the letters that stand for /ā/ or /ou/. Underline homographs. Use your lists to practice at home.

Apply Spelling Skills

Dictionary Skills

Some **homographs** have different meanings because they have different *etymologies*, or root words. Read the dictionary entries below.

file[1] [from Early French *fil*, meaning "thread"] To arrange in order. (fīl) *verb*, **filed, filing.**

file[2] [from Old English *fēol*, meaning "file"] A tool used for smoothing rough surfaces. (fīl) *noun, plural* **files.**

1. Write the two foreign words that are the root words for *file*.

_____

2. Write the two languages that the word *file* came from.

_____

Proofreading

Proofread the paragraph. Check spelling, capital letters, and punctuation. Then rewrite the paragraph. There are six mistakes.

> Its a waist of time installing that software?
> That computer fil gave me pane. sometimes
> I wish computers were just a fad.

EDITING MARKS

- ⬭ check spelling
- ≡ capital letter
- / lowercase letter
- ⊙ add a period
- ∧ add
- ✂ take out
- ¶ indent the paragraph
- ↷ move

For more help, see page 171.

Write • *About Language Arts*

PREWRITE: Think about a funny conversation you could have with a friend. List words that have more than one meaning that could cause confusion and create humor.

DRAFT: Write the dialogue between you and your friend.

REVISE: Try out your dialogue with a partner. Read it aloud, each taking a part. Allow your partner to make comments. Use the **Spelling Thesaurus** on page 182 as you revise.

EDIT/PROOFREAD: Use editing marks. Rewrite your dialogue.

PUBLISH: When you finish the dialogue, choose a partner with whom you can perform it for the class.

135

32

Compound Words

1. cupboard
2. ice-skating
3. mailbox
4. wallpaper
5. homesick
6. all right
7. no one
8. twenty-five
9. goldfish
10. post office
11. pocketbook
12. housework
13. somebody
14. field trip
15. nobody
16. peanut butter
17. nightgown
18. merry-go-round
19. vice president
20. teaspoon

Learn Spelling Patterns

LOOK & SAY Listen for the sounds in each word.

PICTURE Close your eyes. See each word in your mind.

STUDY These spelling words are **compound words**, words made up of more than one word.

WRITE Sort the words. Which words are made up of two words and written as one word?

1. _____   7. _____

2. _____   8. _____

3. _____   9. _____

4. _____   10. _____

5. _____   11. _____

6. _____

Which words are made up of two separate words?

12. _____   15. _____

13. _____   16. _____

14. _____   17. _____

Which contain two or more words joined by hyphens?

18. _____   20. _____

19. _____

CHECK Did you spell each word correctly? Circle the words that make up each compound word.

Pattern Power

How can compound words be written?

As 21. _____ word, as 22. _____ words, or with 23. _____ .

Other Words

Write words you would like to add to this week's list.

_____

_____

Practice Word Meanings

Word Context

Write the spelling word that best completes each sentence.

1. The temperature in the _____ rink was 30˚F.

2. The local branch of the _____ is open until 6 PM.

3. Jelly goes well with _____.

4. The kitchen walls have flowered _____.

5. Twelve times two, plus one, is _____.

6. A _____ is a measurement often used in cooking.

7. The _____ is one of the oldest carnival rides.

8. I keep all my cups in a _____.

9. I need _____ to walk the dog today.

10. People often become _____ on vacation.

11. You can drop your letter in the _____ outside the movie theater.

12. My pet _____ is in that bowl.

Challenge Words • *Physical Education*

Write the challenge word that best fits in each group of compound words. Circle the separate words in each compound word you write.

13. baseball, kickball, _____

14. mouthwash, mouthwatering, _____

15. chessboard, billboard, _____

16. quarter-deck, quarterfinal, _____

17. hand-me-down, hoedown, _____

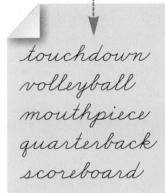

touchdown
volleyball
mouthpiece
quarterback
scoreboard

Spelling Tip

It is hard to know whether a compound word should be written as one word, as two separate words, or with hyphens. Think of tricks to help you.

✦ The compound word *all right* is written as two separate words.

✦ This saying can help you remember how to write this word: Be *right all* the time.

List Words

cupboard

ice-skating

mailbox

wallpaper

homesick

all right

no one

twenty-five

goldfish

post office

pocketbook

housework

somebody

field trip

nobody

peanut butter

nightgown

merry-go-round

vice president

teaspoon

Challenge Words

touchdown

volleyball

mouthpiece

quarterback

scoreboard

Review Words

sunshine

herself

somewhere

newspaper

fireplace

Build Vocabulary

Compound Words

■ Combine a word in Column A with a word in Column B to form a compound spelling word.

	A	B	
1.	house	president	_____
2.	pocket	gown	_____
3.	twenty	trip	_____
4.	field	work	_____
5.	night	book	_____
6.	tea	spoon	_____
7.	no	five	_____
8.	vice	body	_____

■ Use words you made to complete these sentences.

9. The _____ gave a speech on television.

10. There were _____ students in the class.

Review Words

Write the review word that fits in each group.

11. somebody, someone,

_____

12. itself, himself,

_____

13. sunscreen, sunglasses,

_____

14. newscast, newsprint,

_____

15. firefly, fireworks, _____

sunshine
herself
somewhere
newspaper
fireplace

TAKE HOME

Write your spelling words in three lists: words with two syllables, words with three syllables, and words with four syllables. Circle the separate words within each compound word. Use your lists to practice at home.

Apply Spelling Skills

Dictionary Skills

Write the spelling word from the box that you would find on a page with each set of guide words below.

| housework | all right | field trip | cupboard |
| teaspoon | peanut butter | wallpaper | somebody |

1. ace-apple _____

2. walk-waste _____

3. table-tool _____

4. crunch-custard _____

5. patriot-physical _____

Pattern Power

Look at the compound words you just wrote.

• Circle the separate words in each compound word.

Proofreading

Check spelling, capital letters, and punctuation. Then rewrite the paragraph. There are six mistakes.

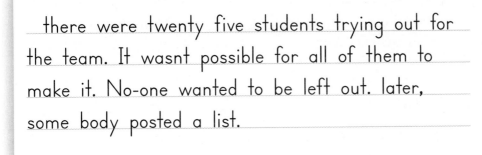

there were twenty five students trying out for the team. It wasnt possible for all of them to make it. No-one wanted to be left out. later, some body posted a list.

EDITING MARKS

⬭ check spelling

≡ capital letter

/ lowercase letter

⊙ add a period

∧ add

⌇ take out

⌗ indent the paragraph

↻ move

For more help, see page 171.

Write • *About Physical Education*

PREWRITE: What are two sports you like? Take notes about ways they are similar and different.

DRAFT: Write a paragraph you could include in an article that compares these two sports.

REVISE: Ask a classmate to read your paragraph and make comments on the details about each sport you compared and contrasted. Use the **Spelling Thesaurus** on page 182 as you revise.

EDIT/PROOFREAD: Use editing marks. Rewrite your paragraph.

PUBLISH: Illustrate your article with drawings or photographs from newspapers or magazines. Display your work in a class "sports page."

33

State Names

1. Idaho
2. South
3. Hawaii
4. East
5. Kansas
6. Iowa
7. North
8. Florida
9. Alaska
10. West
11. California
12. Connecticut
13. Delaware
14. Colorado
15. Arkansas
16. Illinois
17. Alabama
18. Indiana
19. Georgia
20. Arizona

Learn Spelling Patterns

LOOK & SAY Listen for the sounds in each word.

PICTURE Close your eyes. See each word in your mind.

STUDY These spelling words are state names or the names of geographical regions.

WRITE Sort the words. Which words are state names? Write them in alphabetical order.

1. _____ 9. _____
2. _____ 10. _____
3. _____ 11. _____
4. _____ 12. _____
5. _____ 13. _____
6. _____ 14. _____
7. _____ 15. _____
8. _____ 16. _____

Which words are geographical regions? Write them in alphabetical order.

17. _____ 19. _____
18. _____ 20. _____

CHECK Did you spell each word correctly? Circle each capital letter.

Pattern Power

What kind of letter is at the beginning

of the name of a state or the name of a region?

21. _____

Other Words

Write words you would like to add to this week's list.

_____

_____

Practice Word Meanings

Abbreviations

It is often easier to use abbreviations than to write full state names. The post office uses a two-letter abbreviation for each state name to make mail delivery easier. Write the full state name that matches each abbreviation below.

1. IA _Iowa_

2. AK _____

3. AZ _____

4. AR _____

5. IN _____

6. CO _____

7. GA _____

8. DE _____

9. FL _____

10. CT _____

11. HI _____

12. AL _____

13. IL _____

14. CA _____

15. ID _____

16. KS _____

Challenge Words • *Social Studies*

Write the challenge word that best completes each sentence. Use the **Spelling Dictionary** on page 214 to help you. Circle the capital letters in each word.

17. _____ is a city in California.

18. _____ is a city in Kansas.

19. _____ is a city in Arizona.

20. _____ is a city in Florida.

21. _____ is a city in Illinois.

Topeka
Miami
Los Angeles
Chicago
Phoenix

Spelling Tip

Words or word parts that are spelled the same are not always pronounced the same.

✦ *Kansas* is part of the name of *Arkansas*.

✦ *Kansas* is pronounced kan′ zəs.

✦ *Arkansas* is pronounced är′ kən sô′.

✦ You can use the smaller word *Kansas* to help you spell *Arkansas*. Just be sure to remember the difference in pronunciation when you say or hear *Arkansas*.

List Words

Idaho

South

Hawaii

East

Kansas

Iowa

North

Florida

Alaska

West

California

Connecticut

Delaware

Colorado

Arkansas

Illinois

Alabama

Indiana

Georgia

Arizona

Challenge Words

Topeka

Miami

Los Angeles

Chicago

Phoenix

Review Words

February

Saturday

October

Wednesday

August

Build Vocabulary

Suffixes

■ A suffix can be added to a state name to form a word that names or describes something or someone from the state. If the state name ends with a vowel, the suffix *-an* is usually added. For example, a person from Idaho is called an Idahoan.

Add the suffix *-an to* the state names below. You may have to drop the final *a* of the base word when you add the suffix.

1. Georgia _____

2. California _____

3. Hawaii _____

4. Iowa _____

5. Indiana _____

6. Alaska _____

■ Use words you made to complete these sentences.

7. You may have visited San Francisco if you're a

_____ .

8. A _____ might live in Honolulu.

Review Words

Write the review words that are days of the week.

9. _____

10. _____

Write the review words that are months of the year.

11. _____

12. _____

13. _____

February
Saturday
October
Wednesday
August

TAKE HOME

Write your spelling words in four lists: words with one syllable, words with two syllables, words with three syllables, and words with four syllables. Circle the capital letters in each word. Use your lists to practice at home.

Apply Spelling Skills

Dictionary Skills

Write each spelling word below. Insert a hyphen between syllables to show where the word can be divided at the end of a writing line. Use your **Spelling Dictionary** on page 214 for help.

1. Alaska _____
2. Florida _____
3. Hawaii _____
4. Arizona _____
5. Iowa _____
6. Illinois _____
7. Arkansas _____
8. Colorado _____

Pattern Power

Look at the list words you just wrote.

• Circle the capital letters in each word.

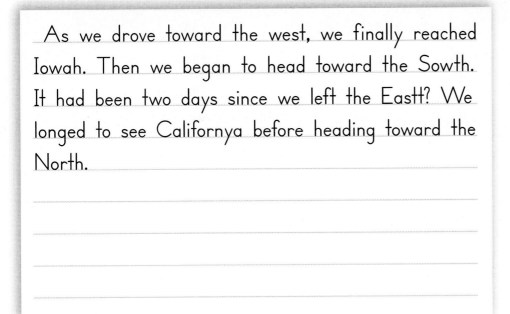

Proofreading

Check spelling, capital letters, and punctuation. Then rewrite the paragraph. There are six mistakes.

As we drove toward the west, we finally reached Iowah. Then we began to head toward the Sowth. It had been two days since we left the Eastt? We longed to see Californya before heading toward the North.

Write • About Social Studies

PREWRITE: Which state do you live in? Brainstorm some of its outstanding characteristics.

DRAFT: Create a public service announcement for people who plan to visit your state. Write a paragraph you would include in this announcement.

REVISE: In a small group, read your paragraph aloud and take notes on helpful comments by group members. Use the **Spelling Thesaurus** on page 182 as you revise.

EDIT/PROOFREAD: Use the editing marks. Then rewrite your paragraph.

PUBLISH: When you finish your public service announcement, record it or read it aloud to the class as a radio or television commercial.

EDITING MARKS

⬭ check spelling
= capital letter
/ lowercase letter
⊙ add a period
∧ add
⌇ take out
¶ indent the paragraph
↻ move

For more help, see page 171.

34

State Names

1. Northwest
2. New York
3. Maine
4. Southeast
5. Kentucky
6. Missouri
7. Southwest
8. Maryland
9. Nevada
10. Northeast
11. Montana
12. Michigan
13. Louisiana
14. Minnesota
15. Nebraska
16. New Mexico
17. New Jersey
18. Massachusetts
19. Mississippi
20. New Hampshire

Learn Spelling Patterns

LOOK & SAY Listen for the sounds in each word.

PICTURE Close your eyes. See each word in your mind.

STUDY The spelling words are state names or the names of geographical regions.

WRITE Sort the words. Which words are state names? Write them in alphabetical order.

1. _____   9. _____

2. _____   10. _____

3. _____   11. _____

4. _____   12. _____

5. _____   13. _____

6. _____   14. _____

7. _____   15. _____

8. _____   16. _____

Which words are geographical regions? Write them in alphabetical order.

17. _____   19. _____

18. _____   20. _____

CHECK Did you spell each word correctly? Circle each capital letter.

Pattern Power

When the first part of a state name is *New*, how many capital letters do you need to write the name of the state? 21. _____

Other Words

Write words you would like to add to this week's list.

_____

_____

Practice Word Meanings

Abbreviations

Each state has a two-letter abbreviation. Write the full state name that goes with each abbreviation below.

1. LA *Louisiana*

2. MD _____

3. KY _____

4. ME _____

5. MO _____

6. NJ _____

7. NM _____

8. NH _____

9. NY _____

10. NV _____

11. MS _____

12. NE _____

13. MT _____

14. MN _____

15. MA _____

16. MI _____

Challenge Words • *Social Studies*

For each state abbreviation, write the challenge word that is a city in that state. Circle the capital letters in each answer.

17. MI _____

18. NY _____

19. LA _____

20. MD _____

21. MO _____

Which cities have two capital letters?

22. _____

23. _____

Albany
Baltimore
St. Louis
Detroit
New Orleans

ⓢpelling Tip

Many state names have unusual spellings. Memory helpers such as these can help you remember them.

✦ *Mississippi* has four *i*'s and four *s*'s.

✦ <u>Louis</u> is from <u>Louis</u>iana.

✦ To get to Maine, go <u>main</u>ly <u>e</u>ast.

Try to think of your own memory helpers for other state names.

Northwest
New York
Maine
Southeast
Kentucky
Missouri
Southwest
Maryland
Nevada
Northeast
Montana
Michigan
Louisiana
Minnesota
Nebraska
New Mexico
New Jersey
Massachusetts
Mississippi
New Hampshire

Challenge Words

Albany
Baltimore
St. Louis
Detroit
New Orleans

Review Words

Thanksgiving
Fourth of July
Valentine's Day
Labor Day
Memorial Day

Build Vocabulary

Plurals

■ The plurals of letters, numerals, symbols, and words used as words are formed by adding an apostrophe and *s*. Look at these examples.

Letters:	one *g*	two *g*'s
Numerals:	one 6	two 6's
Symbols:	one $	two $'s
Words:	one *and*	two *and*'s

Write the plural form of the word or letter in parentheses below.

1. The computer found all the (Southeast) _____ I had misspelled.

2. Remember to cross your (t) _____ and dot your (i) _____ in Massachusetts and Mississippi.

■ Use plurals you made to complete these sentences.

3. There were fifty _____ listed in the geography book.

4. Remember to lowercase all the _____ in Mississippi.

Review Words

Write each holiday next to the month in which it takes place. Use your **Spelling Dictionary** on page 214 if you need help. Then circle the capital letters in the holiday names.

5. November _____

6. July _____

7. September _____

8. February _____

9. May _____

Thanksgiving
Fourth of July
Valentine's Day
Labor Day
Memorial Day

TAKE HOME

Write your spelling words in two lists: words that are compound words and words that are not compounds. Circle the capital letter in each word. Use your lists to practice spelling the words at home.

Apply Spelling Skills

Dictionary Skills

The syllables of an entry word are separated by bullets (•). Use your **Spelling Dictionary** on page 214 to write each of the following words by syllables.

1. New Mexico _____

2. Minnesota _____

3. Louisiana _____

4. Mississippi _____

Pattern Power

Look at the list words you just wrote.

• Circle the syllables that begin with capital letters.

Proofreading

Check spelling, capital letters, and punctuation. Then rewrite the paragraph. There are six mistakes.

Have you ever visited the states of the northeast. My favorite is Mayne Shawn, my sister, enjoys the mountains of the northwest. Reggie, my brother, prefers to visit the Soutwest.

EDITING MARKS

⬭ check spelling

≡ capital letter

/ lowercase letter

⊙ add a period

∧ add

ໆ take out

indent the paragraph

↻ move

For more help, see page 171.

Write • About Social Studies

PREWRITE: Choose a region of the country you would like to visit with your class. List some things you would like to do or see there.

DRAFT: Choose the most exciting or interesting items from your list. Write a persuasive paragraph that will make your classmates want to visit the region you've chosen.

REVISE: Ask a partner to read your paragraph and make suggestions about ways you can make it more persuasive. Use the **Spelling Thesaurus** on page 182 as you revise.

EDIT/PROOFREAD: Use editing marks to correct your paragraph. Then rewrite it.

PUBLISH: Have the class vote on which region of the country they would like to visit. Ask volunteers to explain what persuaded them to vote for a particular region.

35

State Names

1. Oregon
2. America
3. Ohio
4. Texas
5. Virginia
6. Vermont
7. Oklahoma
8. Utah
9. Tennessee
10. Wyoming
11. United States
12. Washington
13. Pennsylvania
14. North Dakota
15. South Dakota
16. South Carolina
17. West Virginia
18. Wisconsin
19. North Carolina
20. Rhode Island

Learn Spelling Patterns

LOOK & SAY Listen for the sounds in each word.

PICTURE Close your eyes. See each word in your mind.

STUDY These spelling words are state names and other proper nouns.

WRITE Sort the words. Which words are state names? Write them in alphabetical order.

1. _____ 10. _____
2. _____ 11. _____
3. _____ 12. _____
4. _____ 13. _____
5. _____ 14. _____
6. _____ 15. _____
7. _____ 16. _____
8. _____ 17. _____
9. _____ 18. _____

Which words are other proper nouns? Write them in alphabetical order.

19. _____ 20. _____

CHECK Did you spell each word correctly? Circle each capital letter.

Pattern Power

When the first part of a state name is the name of a region, how many capital letters do you need to write the name of the state? 21. _____

Other Words

Write words you would like to add to this week's list.

_____

_____

Practice Word Meanings

Abbreviations

Write the full state name that goes with each abbreviation given below.

1. OH _____*Ohio*_____   10. WI _____

2. PA _____   11. WY _____

3. VT _____   12. OR _____

4. UT _____   13. OK _____

5. VA _____   14. TN _____

6. RI _____   15. WA _____

7. NC _____   16. WV _____

8. SC _____   17. ND _____

9. TX _____   18. SD _____

Challenge Words • *Social Studies*

Write the challenge word that matches each clue. Circle the capital letters.

19. I have two *t*'s in the middle of my name. _____

20. I have /f/ spelled with two letters, two times. _____

21. I begin with /ô/. _____

22. I have /sh/ in the middle of my name. _____

23. Land is part of my name. _____

Cleveland
Austin
Nashville
Seattle
Philadelphia

Spelling Tip

One way to remember hard-to-spell state names is to create memory helpers such as these:

+ *Tennessee* has two *n*'s, two *s*'s and four *e*'s. It starts with *Ten* and ends with *see*.
+ They do a <u>ton</u> of washing in Washington.
+ There is <u>ore</u> in Oregon.

What memory helpers can you make up to remember spellings of other hard-to-spell state names?

List Words

Oregon
America
Ohio
Texas
Virginia
Vermont
Oklahoma
Utah
Tennessee
Wyoming
United States
Washington
Pennsylvania
North Dakota
South Dakota
South Carolina
West Virginia
Wisconsin
North Carolina
Rhode Island

Challenge Words

Cleveland
Austin
Nashville
Seattle
Philadelphia

Review Words

Thursday
January
September
December
November

Build Vocabulary

Suffixes

■ By adding a suffix to a state name, you can form a word that names or describes something or someone from that state. Common suffixes are *-an*, *-ian*, and *-er*. Follow each pattern below to form a new word from the state name.

1. South Dakota   – *a* + *an* = _____

2. Tennessee   – *e* + *an* = _____

3. Washington   + *ian* = _____

4. Oregon   + *ian* = _____

5. Vermont   + *er* = _____

6. Rhode Island   + *er* = _____

7. Texas   – *as* + *an* = _____

■ Use words you made to complete these sentences.

8. An _____ from Portland addressed our class.

9. Is that rodeo rider a _____ from Houston?

Review Words

Write the review words that end with the /ər/ sound spelled *er.*

10. _____

11. _____

12. _____

Write the review word that has /ûr/ spelled with the letters ur.

13. _____

Write the review word that ends with /ē/ spelled with the letter y.

14. _____

Thursday
January
September
December
November

TAKE HOME

Write your spelling words in three lists: words with three or fewer syllables, words with four syllables, words with five syllables. Circle the capital letters. Use your lists to practice spelling the words at home.

Apply Spelling Skills

Dictionary Skills

An **idiom** is an expression that cannot be understood by the meaning of its separate words. "You're pulling my leg" is an idiom. To find the meaning of an idiom, look up the key word. Use your **Spelling Dictionary** on page 214 to look up the entry for *scrape*.

1. Where in the entry does the idiom *scrape by* appear?

_____

2. What does the idiom *scrape by* mean? _____

3. Write your own example sentence for the idiom *scrape by*.

_____

Proofreading

Check spelling, capital letters, and punctuation. Then rewrite the paragraph. There are five mistakes.

Many names in the United Steates have an interesting story? Oheio is a Native American name. Amurica comes from Amerigo Vespucci, a Italian explorer.

EDITING MARKS

⬭ check spelling

= capital letter

/ lowercase letter

⊙ add a period

∧ add

⤴ take out

⌗ indent the paragraph

↻ move

For more help, see page 171.

Write • *About Social Studies*

PREWRITE: Brainstorm problems you think your state needs to solve. Choose one problem and list examples that support your opinion.

DRAFT: Write a letter to your state governor describing the problem and explaining why the state should solve it.

REVISE: Is your letter polite and reasonable? Did you use strong examples? Use the **Spelling Thesaurus** on page 182 as you rewrite.

EDIT/PROOFREAD: Use editing marks to correct your letter. Then rewrite it.

PUBLISH: Share your letter with the class and with your friends and family. You may also wish to send it to your governor.

36 REVIEW Spelling Patterns

Sort the words. Write each word. Circle the spelling patterns in Lesson 31. Circle the separate words in the compound words in Lesson 32. Circle the capital letters in the state names in Lessons 33, 34, and 35.

---

break
record
bore
refuse
contest
waste
foul
mail
fowl
pain

Lesson 31
Homophones with /ā/ or /ou/

a-e   1. _____

ea   2. _____

ai   3. _____

4. _____

ou   5. _____

ow   6. _____

Homographs

7. _____

8. _____

9. _____

10. _____

---

cupboard
all right
no one
twenty-five
post office
nobody
nightgown
merry-go-round
vice president
teaspoon

Lesson 32
Compound Words: as one word, two words, or with hyphens

one   11. _____   16. _____

12. _____   17. _____

13. _____   18. _____

14. _____   hyphen 19. _____

two   15. _____   20. _____

Kansas
Idaho
Iowa
Hawaii
Florida
California
Connecticut
Arkansas
Indiana
Arizona

Lesson 33
State names alphabetically

21. _____   26. _____

22. _____   27. _____

23. _____   28. _____

24. _____   29. _____

25. _____   30. _____

Kentucky
Maine
New York
Nevada
Missouri
Michigan
Louisiana
New Mexico
Massachusetts
Mississippi

Lesson 34
State names alphabetically

31. _____   36. _____

32. _____   37. _____

33. _____   38. _____

34. _____   39. _____

35. _____   40. _____

America
Texas
Oklahoma
Tennessee
Wyoming
United States
Pennsylvania
South Dakota
West Virginia
Rhode Island

Lesson 35
State names alphabetically

46. _____

41. _____   47. _____

42. _____   48. _____

43. _____   **Other proper nouns**

44. _____   49. _____

45. _____   50. _____

Spelling Tip

Compound words are not always written as one word. Sometimes they have a hyphen between them, and sometimes they are written as two separate words.

no one
ice-skating
teaspoon

◆ The compound word *all right* is written as two separate words.

◆ This saying can help you remember how to write this word: Be *right all* the time.

Make up your own sayings for the following compound words: *no one, ice-skating,* and *teaspoon.*

Word Meaning Mixed Lesson Review

record
all right
no one
foul
fowl
waste
cupboard
break
nightgown
mail

Synonyms

Write the word or words in each group below that are related in meaning to the words in dark print.

1. **nasty**   fowl   foul   _____

2. **trash**   waist   waste   _____

3. **bird**   fowl   foul   _____

4. **okay**   all done   all right   _____

5. **cabinet**   cupboard   boardwalk   _____

6. **account**   record   refuse   _____

7. **sleepwear**   shoes   nightgown   _____

8. **nobody**   someone   no one   _____

9. **divide**   brake   break   _____

10. **letter**   male   mail   _____

Kansas
Tennessee
Oklahoma
Hawaii
Mississippi
Massachusetts
Connecticut
Nevada
Louisiana
Rhode Island
California
Texas

Abbreviations

Write the state names that have the following abbreviations.

11. LA _____

12. MS _____

13. TN _____

14. OK _____

15. RI _____

16. CA _____

17. MA _____

18. KS _____

19. HI _____

20. NV _____

21. CT _____

22. TX _____

Vocabulary Mixed Lesson Review

Compound Words
Combine a word from Column A with one from Column B to
form a real compound word.

A	B	
all	president	1. _____
twenty	States	2. _____
night	board	3. _____
United	right	4. _____
cup	five	5. _____
vice	gown	6. _____

> vice president
> nightgown
> cupboard
> all right
> twenty-five
> United States

Suffixes
Write the words formed by adding the suffixes shown to the
following words. You will have to make some base word spelling changes.

7. Kansas   **(-n)**   *Kansan*   10. refuse **(-al)** _____

8. Missouri   **(-an)** _____   11. bore **(-dom)** _____

9. Pennsylvania **(-n)** _____

Dictionary Skills

Read the dictionary entry and complete the items below.

> **record 1.** A written account. The bank keeps a *record* of every deposit. **2.** All the facts
> about what a person or group does. My school has an excellent test *record*. **3.** An act
> better than all others. The team set a new *record* for home runs. **4.** A disk for
> recording music. *Noun.*
> —**1.** To write down. I'll *record* my daily activities. **2.** To put music on a disk.
> My favorite group will *record* a new hit song. *Verb.*
> **rec•ord** (rek'ərd for *noun*; ri kôrd' for *verb*) *noun, plural* **records;** *verb,* **recorded,**
> **recording**

1. What word is defined in this entry? _____

2. What parts of speech can this word be? _____

3. In the noun *record*, which syllable is accented? _____

4. Does the entry have an etymology, or word history? _____

Spelling and Writing

A written report presents researched information on a selected topic. The information is organized logically. Below you'll find the beginning of a longer report about a famous historical figure. The researched information is organized chronologically.

An American Legend: Abraham Lincoln

WRITE AN INTRODUCTION — **Abraham Lincoln was the sixteenth president of the United States.** He was born in Kentucky in 1809 and raised in Illinois.

ORGANIZE INFORMATION — **Lincoln's career in politics began when he was elected to Congress in 1846.** He served in Congress for one term. In 1854, his interest in politics returned.

In 1860, Lincoln was elected president of the United States. He led the Union through the Civil War. **INCLUDE FACTS AND DETAILS** — **His famous *Gettysburg Address* was delivered during the war, in 1863.**

Lincoln won a second term as president in 1864. On April 14, 1865, at Ford's Theater in Washington, D.C., John Wilkes Booth shot the president. The wound caused Lincoln's death the next morning. Vice President Andrew Johnson took over as president.

A pioneer of democracy, Lincoln is an American legend. The Lincoln Memorial in Washington, D.C., was built to honor the "prairie" lawyer who became a symbol of freedom and democracy.

WRITING TIPS!!

Research Report
- Research a topic and take notes.
- Organize information logically.
- Write an introduction about the most important findings in your research, a body for the report that includes details of your research, and a conclusion.
- Include facts and details in your sentences.

Now write your own report. Organize your research logically.

PREWRITE: Think about interesting people or events related to the state you live in. Choose one and research the topic in the encyclopedia and other resources.

DRAFT: Write one long or three short paragraphs as the beginning of your report. Organize your researched information by order of importance, or chronologically.

REVISE: Share the beginning of your report with a classmate. Use your classmate's comments and the Writing Tips as you revise.

EDIT/PROOFREAD: Use editing marks to correct your capitalization, spelling, and punctuation. Rewrite your paragraph neatly.

PUBLISH: Complete your report, give it a title, and place it in the classroom library.

SPELLING FUN
CUMULATIVE REVIEW

SPELLING CIRCLE

- Choose a word from lessons 1–29.
- Create a "spelling circle" by drawing a circle and making boxes for the letters around the perimeter. Fill in all the letters from your chosen word, along with some others.
- See how many words of more than three letters a partner can create from the spelling circle.

- See if your partner finds the list word you chose and spells it correctly!

  Now, let your partner make a spelling circle and see what words you find.

WORD BINGO

- Make sure all players have the word lists for Lessons 31–35. Each member of a group draws a square divided into twenty-five smaller squares (five across and five down).
- A player says the first letter of a list word. Everyone writes the letter in any square.
- The next player adds a second letter to the first to form a list word, without giving away the word. Everyone writes that letter in any square.
- Continue until all the squares are filled. Then each player writes all the words that can be formed by putting together letters from the big square.
- Each formed word earns a point. A formed list word earns two points.

SPELLING BEE

- Two teams share the job of writing selected words from Lessons 1–35 on cards. Each team gets half the cards.
- A player from Team A says a word from one of its cards.
- A player from Team B writes the word on the board.

- If the word is spelled correctly, the card is removed from Team A's pile. If it is misspelled, the card is returned to the pile.
- Then another player from Team B says a word from its pile for a player from Team A to write. Continue.
- The first team to finish the other team's pile of cards wins!

Spelling Resources

Writing Handbook

Common Spelling Patterns

This list shows different ways sounds are spelled. Use this list when you can't find words in the dictionary to see how else the sound may be spelled.

/a/	a	active, apple	/j/	j	jar, jury		sh	shower, polish
/ā/	a	agent, able					ti	ratio, patient
	a-e	amaze, page	/k/	c	coin, act	/spr/	spr	spring, sprang
	ai	drain, afraid		ck	track, knuckle	/str/	str	strength, strain
	ay	maybe, day		k	kitchen, weak	/th/	th	thankful, thumb
	ei	veil, weigh		lk	walk, talk	/th/	th	breathe, they
/är/	ar	party, cart	/m/	lm	palm, calm	/u/	u	upset, must
/âr/	air	affair, haircut		m	mailbox, plum	/ù/	oo	look, book
	are	dare, care		mb	crumb, dumb		ou	tour, yours
	ear	wear, pear		mm	comma, committee		u	ambush, put
	eir	their		mn	autumn, column	/ü/	u-e	flute, rule
	ere	there, where	/n/	gn	gnaw, assignment		ew	drew, flew
/ch/	ch	chore, cheese		kn	kneel, knives		o-e	prove, lose
	tch	clutch, catch		n	nobody, mane		oo	monsoon, moose
/e/	e	pressure, beg		nn	banner, channel		ui	fruit, suit
	ea	pleasure, bread	/o/	o	lodge, hobby		u	truly, cruel
/ē/	e	create, we'll	/ō/	o	Oklahoma, ocean	/ū/	ew	new, few
	ea	appear, eagle		o-e	overthrow, owe		u	bureau, pupil
	ee	agree, meet		oa	oak, boat		ue	avenue, fuel
	ey	chimney, money		ow	own, slow	/ûr/	er	preserve, perfect
	ie	believe, fields	/ô/	a	all right, ball		ir	firm, birth
	y	Albany, angry		au	caution, cause		ur	turn, nurse
/f/	f	fancy, leaf		aw	claw, awful	/yù/	ur	endure, furious
	ff	office, cliff		o	coffee, lost	/z/	s, se	plasma, tease
	gh	laughter, cough	/oi/	oi	appoint, moist		z	zipper, lazy
	ph	phone, trophy		oy	loyalty, annoy		ze	squeeze, daze
/hw/	wh	whittle, whale	/ôr/	or	order, born		zz	buzz, sizzle
/i/	i	spin, window		ore	Baltimore, before	/zh/	s	pleasure, usually
/ī/	i	triumph, I'm	/ou/	ou	outfit, house	/əl/	al	petal, royal
	i-e	scribe, like		ow	eyebrow, anyhow		el	shovel, travel
	ie	die, pie	/r/	wr	wrap, wrinkle		il	evil, council
	y	reply, shy	/s/	c	recent, race		le	apple, purple
/îr/	ear	disappear, fear		ce	slice, peace		ol	capitol, pistol
	eer	engineer, peer		s	sketch, send	/ən/	an	island, organ
	ere	severe, here		sc	scene, science		ain	bargain, mountain
	ier	pier, fierce		se	else, case		en	chicken, broken
/j/	dge	bridge, edge		ss	possible, kiss		on	ribbon, apron
	g	pigeon, giraffe	/sk/	sch	scheme, schedule	/ər/	ar	grammar, polar
	ge	agent, generous	/skr/	scr	scribble, scripts		er	copper, sweater
			/sh/	ci	ancient, especially		or	honor, flavor

Spelling Tips: Rules

Learning these spelling rules can help you spell many words.

1. When words end in silent *e*, drop the *e* when adding an ending that begins with a vowel. *(argue + ed = argued)* When adding an ending that begins with a consonant, keep the silent *e*. *(like + ly = likely)*

2. When a base word ends with a consonant followed by *y*, change the *y* to *i* when adding any ending except endings that begin with *i*. *(cry + es = cries; cry + ing = crying)*

3. When a base word ends with a vowel followed by *y*, do not change the ending when adding suffixes or endings. *(monkey + s = monkeys)*

4. When a one-syllable word ends in one vowel followed by one consonant, double the consonant before adding an ending that begins with a vowel. *(run + ing = running)*

5. The letter *q* is always followed by *u*. *(quilt, quiet)*

6. No English words end in *j*, *q*, or *v*.

7. Add *-s* to most words to form plurals or to change the tense of verbs. Add *-es* to words ending in *x*, *z*, *s*, *sh*, or *ch*. *(cup + s = cups; laugh + s = laughs; glass + es = glasses)*

8. To make plurals of words that end with one *f* or *fe*, you often need to change the *f* or *fe* to *v* and add *-es*. *(wife + es = wives)*

9. When choosing *ei* or *ie*, remember that *i* comes before *e* except after *c* or when sounded like /ā/ as in *neighbor* or *weigh*.

10. When the /s/ sound is spelled *c*, *c* is always followed by *e*, *i*, or *y*. *(peace, citizen, fancy)*

11. When the /j/ sound is spelled *g*, *g* is always followed by *e*, *i*, or *y*. *(gem, engine, energy)*

12. If the /ch/ sound immediately follows a short vowel in a one-syllable word, it is spelled *tch*. *(clutch, sketch)* There are a few exceptions in English: *much, such, which,* and *rich*.

13. The /f/ sound at the end of a word may be spelled *f*, *ph*, or *gh*. *(chief, graph, laugh)*

Spelling Tips

Spelling Tips: Strategies

These strategies can help you become a better speller.

1. Learn common homophones and make sure you have used the correct homophone in your writing.
   They brought <u>their</u> own books.
   Move the books over <u>there</u>.
   <u>It's</u> a sunny day.
   The earth gets <u>its</u> light from the sun.

2. Think of a word you know that has the same spelling pattern, such as a rhyming word. *(blue, clue, glue)*

3. Use words that you know how to spell to help you spell new words. *(<u>fl</u>ower + <u>ock</u> = <u>flock</u>)*

4. Make up clues to help you remember the spelling. *(ache = <u>a</u> <u>c</u>at <u>h</u>as <u>e</u>ars; <u>u</u> and <u>i</u> b<u>ui</u>ld a house; a p<u>ie</u>ce of p<u>ie</u>; the princip<u>al</u> is your p<u>al</u>)*

5. Think of a related word that can help you spell a word with a silent letter or a hard-to-hear sound. *(sign-signal; relative-related)*

6. Divide the word into syllables. *(sub scrip tion)*

7. Learn how to spell prefixes and suffixes you use often in writing.

8. Look for word chunks or smaller words that help you remember the spelling of the word. *(hippopotamus = hippo pot am us)*

9. Change the way you say the word to yourself to help with the spelling. *(knife = /kə nīf/; beauty = /bē ə ū tē/)*

10. Think of times you may have seen the word in reading, on signs, or in another textbook. Try to remember how it looked. Write the word in different ways to see which one looks correct. *(~~havy, hevy,~~ heavy)*

11. If you are working on a computer, use the spell-check program. Remember, though, that spell-checkers are not perfect. If you write *your* instead of *you're*, a spell-check will not catch the mistake.

12. Keep a Personal Word List in a Spelling Journal. Write words you have trouble spelling.

> One more strategy will always help you: Become familiar with the dictionary and use it often.

Many words, like *durable* and *endure*, are close in meaning. They are also close in spelling. Such words are called related words. Sometimes two related words can have different pronunciations but the same spelling. You can use this fact to help you remember how to spell many related words.

1. The underlined letter in the first word in each group below stays the same in other words in the group. How does the sound change?

criti<u>c</u>
criti<u>c</u>ize—to make judging or critical remarks about a person or thing
criti<u>c</u>ism—judgments or critical remarks

domesti<u>c</u>
domesti<u>c</u>ity—having to do with matters of the household

electri<u>c</u>
electri<u>c</u>ity—a form of energy composed of electric power
electri<u>c</u>ian—a person who repairs electrical objects and systems

mathemati<u>c</u>s
mathemati<u>c</u>ian—someone who studies and teaches mathematics

musi<u>c</u>
musi<u>c</u>ian—someone who plays music

In each group, the sound of the letter *c* changes from /k/ to /s/ or /sh/.

■ To remember how to spell *criticize*, think of the related word *critic*.

■ If you know that *critic* ends with the letter *c*, it can help you remember to spell /s/ in *criticize* with the letter *c*.

■ Use this tip with other related words that follow the same pattern as *critic* and *criticize*.

Spelling and Meaning Connections

2. Here's another sound-letter pattern. What changes about the underlined letter in each word in the group? What stays the same?

cooperate
cooperation—the act or process of cooperating

create
creation—the act or process of creating something

decorate
decoration—the act or process of decorating

depart
departure—the act of departing

direct
direction—the act or process of directing or instructing

except
exception—something that is excepted; something to which a rule does not apply

fact
factual—having the quality of being based on facts

habit
habitual—being done by habit

invent
invention—something that is invented

narrate
narration—the act or process of narrating or telling something

object
objection—the act of objecting or protesting something

part
partial—being only a part; not full or total

In all the words you just read, the sound of the letter *t* changes from /t/ to /sh/ or /ch/.

■ To remember how to spell *cooperation,* think of the related word *cooperate.*

■ If you know that *cooperate* contains the letter *t,* it can help you remember to spell /sh/ in cooperation with the letter *t.*

■ Use this tip with other related words that follow the same pattern as *cooperate* and *cooperation.*

3. Look at the letter that is underlined in the words in each group below. How does the sound of that letter change from the first word in the group to the other word or words?

autum<u>n</u>al —having to do with autumn

autum<u>n</u>

autum<u>n</u>s

crum<u>b</u>le—to break into pieces or crumbs

crum<u>b</u>

crum<u>b</u>s

fas<u>t</u>—firmly attached; securely fastened

fas<u>t</u>en

fas<u>t</u>ener

unfas<u>t</u>en

has<u>t</u>e—speed or hurry

has<u>t</u>en

in<u>h</u>erit—to receive money or property when someone dies

<u>h</u>eir

mus<u>c</u>ular—having strong or well-developed muscles

mus<u>c</u>le

mus<u>c</u>les

reception—the act of receiving something

recei<u>p</u>t

signal—a light, movement, or other form of communication

si<u>g</u>n

sof<u>t</u>—easy to shape; not hard

sof<u>t</u>en

sof<u>t</u>ener

In each group, the underlined letter is sounded in the first word and silent in the word or words that follow.

■ To remember how to spell *autumn,* think of the sound of the related word *autumnal.*

■ You can hear the *n* in *autumnal.* That sound can help you remember to spell final /m/ in *autumn* with *mn.*

■ Use this tip with other related words that have silent and sounded letters.

© McGraw-Hill School Division

4. Each word in this group has one or more vowels underlined. Decide how the vowels change in other words in the group.

cl<u>ea</u>n—not dirty
cl<u>ea</u>nse
cl<u>ea</u>nser

comp<u>e</u>te—to try to win or gain something
comp<u>e</u>tition
comp<u>e</u>titive

dr<u>ea</u>m—to see images and events in one's sleep
dr<u>ea</u>mt

h<u>ea</u>l—to get better or make something get better
h<u>ea</u>lth
h<u>ea</u>lthy

m<u>ea</u>n—to have in mind
m<u>ea</u>nt

m<u>i</u>nus—less, decreased by
m<u>i</u>nimum

n<u>a</u>tion—a country that has its own government
n<u>a</u>tional
intern<u>a</u>tional

n<u>a</u>ture—all the things, like trees, that are not made by people
n<u>a</u>tural
unn<u>a</u>tural

pl<u>ea</u>se—to give pleasure to
pl<u>ea</u>sure
pl<u>ea</u>sant

s<u>o</u>le—only; lone
s<u>o</u>litary
s<u>o</u>litude

un<u>i</u>te—to join into a single unit
un<u>i</u>t
un<u>i</u>ty

w<u>i</u>se—having or showing good judgment
w<u>i</u>sdom

A long vowel sound in one word can sometimes change to a short vowel sound in a related word, without a change in spelling.

- *Clean* and *cleanse* are related in meaning.
- *Clean* has the long vowel sound spelled *ea*.
- *Cleanse* has the short vowel sound spelled *ea*.
- Remembering how to spell *clean* can help you spell *cleanse*.
- Can you think of a word that will help you spell *breath*?

5. The underlined letter in the first word in each group has /ə/. What kind of vowel sound does the underlined letter spell in the other words in each group?

admiration—the act of admiring
admire
admirer

composition—a piece of writing or music that is composed
compose
composer

definition—a phrase or sentence that defines a word
define
indefinable

equal—the same or even
equation—a mathematical sentence in which both parts are equal

relative—a person like a sister or cousin who is related to you
relate
related

supposition—something that is assumed or supposed
suppose
supposing

In related words, /ə/ in one word can sometimes change to a long vowel sound in a related word, without a change in spelling.

■ *Admiration* and *admire* are related words.

■ *Admiration* has /ə/ spelled with the letter *i.*

■ *Admire* has a long vowel sound spelled with the letter *i.*

■ Remembering how to spell *admire* can help you spell *admiration.*

■ Can you think of a word that will help you spell *ability*?

6. The underlined letter in the first word in each group has /ə/. What kind of vowel sound does the underlined letter spell in the other word or words in each group?

comp<u>e</u>te—to try to win or gain something from another person or group
comp<u>e</u>tition

fin<u>a</u>l—last
fin<u>a</u>lity
fin<u>a</u>lities

hum<u>a</u>n—having to do with people
hum<u>a</u>nity

individu<u>a</u>l—one person
individu<u>a</u>lity

leg<u>a</u>l—done according to the law
leg<u>a</u>lity

med<u>a</u>l—a flat, coin-shaped object given for excellence or victory
med<u>a</u>llion

met<u>a</u>l—a hard, shiny material like gold or iron
met<u>a</u>llic
nonmet<u>a</u>llic

perf<u>e</u>ct—without fault or flaw
perf<u>e</u>ction
imperf<u>e</u>ction

person<u>a</u>l—having to do with a particular person; private
person<u>a</u>lity

In related words, /ə/ in one word can sometimes change to a short vowel sound in a related word, without a change in spelling.

■ *Compete* and *competition* are related words.

■ *Compete* has /ə/ spelled with the letter *o.*

■ *Competition* has a short vowel sound spelled with the letter *o.*

■ Remembering how to spell *competition* can help you spell *compete.*

■ Can you think of a word that will help you spell *resident*?

Spelling and Meaning Connections

Difficult Words

Easily Confused Words

Easily confused words are words that are often mistaken for another because they are spelled similarly or sound alike. These words have different definitions and can mix up the meaning of a sentence. Use this list to make sure you know the meaning of the words in each pair.

accept	all together	conscience	formally	picture	use
except	altogether	conscious	formerly	pitcher	used
accuse	angel	costume	hour	quiet	very
excuse	angle	custom	our	quite	vary
adapt	any more	dairy	later	recent	weather
adopt	anymore	diary	latter	resent	whether
advice	any way	desert	lay	respectively	your
advise	anyway	dessert	lie	respectfully	you're
affect	breath	expect	loose	sink	
effect	breathe	suspect	lose	zinc	
alley	cloth	farther	of	than	
ally	clothe	further	off	then	
all ready	close	finale	personal	though	
already	clothes	finally	personnel	through	

Troublesome Words

Some words are more difficult to spell than others. Use this list to check you spelling or to test yourself to see how many of these words you can spell correctly.

a lot	college	favorite	let's	right	tried
afraid	control	field	library	separate	truly
again	different	finally	minute	should	until
already	disappear	friend	Mom	since	upon
always	divide	government	myself	sincerely	usually
another	doesn't	grabbed	off	successful	vacation
aren't	early	happened	once	sure	we're
athlete	especially	heard	one	surprise	weird
beautiful	everybody	hero	our	their	went
because	everyone	himself	outside	they	what's
before	everything	instead	people	they're	where
believe	except	it's	piece	threw	which
buy	excited	knew	probably	through	whole
caught	exciting	know	radio	to	you're
clothes	family	knowledge	really	too	

Common Homophones

Homophones are words with the same pronunciation as another, but with a different meaning and spelling. *Know* and *no* are homophones. Use this list of homophones to help you decide which word to use.

ad	chews	grate	knew	rap	vary
add	choose	great	new	wrap	very
aisle	coarse	hair	knot	ring	wade
I'll	course	hare	not	wring	weighed
isle	council	hall	lead	some	wail
allowed	counsel	haul	led	sum	whale
aloud	days	heal	lessen	stationary	*waist
base	daze	heel	lesson	stationery	*waste
*bass	dew	herd	*mail	their	weave
boar	do	heard	*male	there	we've
*bore	die	higher	main	they're	whose
*brake	dye	hire	mane	threw	who's
*break	find	hole	missed	through	
capital	fined	whole	mist	throne	
capitol	flew	in	*pane	thrown	
cent	flu	inn	*pain	toad	
sent	*foul	its	peak	towed	
scent	*fowl	it's	peek		

Words printed in color appear in Spelling lessons.
* These homophones appear in Lesson 31.

Writing Plan

Writing is a way for you to share facts, ideas, or feelings. Follow these steps to create good, clear writing.

Prewrite

Choose your topic.
Decide on your audience.
What is your purpose for writing?

- to express feelings
- to give information
- to describe a person, place, thing, or event
- to persuade

Quickly write down what you already know about your topic.
Then see what more you can learn.

- Read books, magazines, and newspapers. Use the computer Internet.
- Talk to people. Ask questions. Interview an expert.
- If you need to, take a trip to see the real thing.

How will you remember details you see and organize information?

- Take notes.
- Make a list or outline.
- Make a diagram.
- Create a story map.
- Draw pictures.
- Make a word web.
- Draw a chart or graph.

Draft

Now that you have gathered and organized your information, write it in sentence form. Let your thoughts flow. Get them all down on paper.

Revise

Read over your writing. Think about your audience and purpose.

- Are all the important points covered?
- Did you present your ideas in a logical order? Do you need to move, take out, or add anything?
- Does the writing have a clear beginning, middle, and end?
- Do all the sentences express complete thoughts?

To help you revise, you could have a friend look at what you wrote.

Writing Plan

Edit/Proofread

As you reread your writing, look carefully at these things:

- spelling
- punctuation—commas, apostrophes, quotation marks, end marks
- capital letters—to start a sentence and for proper nouns
- indenting of paragraphs
- handwriting—dotting *i*'s and *j*'s, crossing *t*'s and *x*'s.

Use these editing marks as you revise, edit, and proofread.

¶The Ship Titanic sank in 1912, But its rek was not found until after a few years ago.
It was found by robert Ballard his and crew in the Atlantic Ocean.

The ship Titanic sank in 1912, but its wreck was not found until a few years ago. It was found by Robert Ballard and his crew in the Atlantic Ocean.

EDITING MARKS

- ⬭ check spelling
- ≡ capital letter
- / lowercase letter
- ⊙ add a period
- ⌃ add
- ⭂ take out
- ¶ indent the paragraph
- ↷ move

Publish

Think about your audience as you put your writing into final form. How do you want to share your work?

- Read it aloud.
- Hang it on the wall.
- Illustrate it.
- Record it on tape.
- Give it to a friend.
- Create a book of writings.
- Act it out.
- Mail it.

Writing Plan

Types of Writing

Narrative Writing

A story is narrative writing—writing that tells about something that happens.

- Does the story have memorable characters who face an interesting challenge?
- Will the action hold readers' attention?
- Are the events related in an order that readers can follow?
- Does the characters' dialog help move the story forward?
- Have you written in a style that is uniquely your own?

Report

A report gives information about a subject. It presents facts in a clear, well-organized way.

- Does your report present the main idea in an introduction?
- Does the body of the report contain facts that are logically organized?
- Do you conclude with a strong summary of the facts?

Explanatory Writing

Explanatory writing tells how to make or do something.

- Did you begin by clearly expressing your purpose?
- Have information and details been presented in the right order?
- Do you need to add any details to make your explanation clearer?
- Should you include any pictures or diagrams?

Persuasive Writing

Persuasive writing tries to get readers to share the writer's opinion or to take some action. Advertising, movie reviews, letters to a newspaper, and book reports are all examples of persuasive writing.

- Did you use facts and persuasive language to make your point?
- What is the most convincing part of your writing?
- Are readers likely to adopt your viewpoint?

Comparison/Contrast Writing

Comparison/contrast writing presents information about two things to show how they are alike and how they are different.

- Do you begin by presenting a main idea?
- Do you make your comparisons and contrasts clearly? Are they in an order that readers can understand?
- Do the comparisons and contrasts help express the main idea?
- Have you finished with a clear conclusion?

Descriptive Writing

Descriptive writing creates a word picture of a person, place, thing, or event. The words help readers use all their senses to "get the picture."

- Have you created a vivid word picture of your subject?
- Have you used details to add power to your description?
- Does your writing express a feeling about the subject?

Capitalization and Punctuation Tips

Abbreviation An abbreviation is a short form of a word. Most abbreviations begin with a capital letter and end with a period. *Ave.* is an abbreviation for *Avenue.*

Use abbreviations for titles of people, addresses, days of the week, and months of the year.

Mr. and Mrs. Santana   19 Pine St.   Tues.   Feb.

Some abbreviations, such as the U.S. Postal Service abbreviations for the names of states, contain all capital letters and no periods.

Alabama—AL	Missouri—MO
Alaska—AK	Montana—MT
Arizona—AZ	Nebraska—NE
Arkansas—AR	Nevada—NV
California—CA	New Hampshire—NH
Colorado—CO	New Jersey—NJ
Connecticut—CT	New Mexico—NM
Delaware—DE	New York—NY
District of	North Carolina—NC
Columbia—DC	North Dakota—ND
Florida—FL	Ohio—OH
Georgia—GA	Oklahoma—OK
Hawaii—HI	Oregon—OR
Idaho—ID	Pennsylvania—PA
Illinois—IL	Rhode Island—RI
Indiana—IN	South Carolina—SC
Iowa—IA	South Dakota—SD
Kansas—KS	Tennessee—TN
Kentucky—KY	Texas—TX
Louisiana—LA	Utah—UT
Maine—ME	Vermont—VT
Maryland—MD	Virginia—VA
Massachusetts—MA	Washington—WA
Michigan—MI	West Virginia—WV
Minnesota—MN	Wisconsin—WI
Mississippi—MS	Wyoming—WY

Apostrophe An apostrophe is a punctuation mark used with *s* to show possession.

When an apostrophe with *s* is used after a person's name, it shows that something belongs to that person.

Karen's computer   the computer that belongs to Karen

Use an apostrophe alone to form the possessive of a plural noun that ends in *-s*.

the students' tapes   tapes that belong to the students

Use an apostrophe to show where letters have been left out in a contraction.

didn't   did not

Capitalization   Capitalization is the writing of the first letter of a word in its uppercase form.

Capitalize the first word in a sentence.

An eagle is a beautiful bird.

Capitalize the first letter of a proper noun.

Geraldo Mr. Aquino Korea

Capitalize days of the week, months, and holidays.

Wednesday August   Memorial Day

Colon   A colon is a punctuation mark used to introduce a list, an explanation, or an example.

These are the names of the first three Presidents: Washington, Adams, and Jefferson.

A colon is also used to separate hours and minutes when writing time in numerals.

The class ends at 2:25.

Capitalization and Punctuation Tips

Comma A comma is a punctuation mark that indicates a pause or separation between parts of a sentence.

Use a comma between the city and the state in an address.

Augusta, Maine

Use a comma between the day and the year in a date.

November 2, 1998

Use commas to separate three or more items in a series.

That store sells videos, CD ROMs, and music tapes.

Use a comma after the greeting in a friendly letter and the closing in all letters.

Dear Iris,   Yours truly,

End punctuation The punctuation mark at the end of a sentence tells you what kind of sentence it is.

A **period** is used at the end of a statement, a mild command, or a polite request.

Isabel won the science contest.   Please pass the milk.

An **exclamation mark** is used at the end of a strong command or an exclamatory sentence.

Watch out!   What an amazing song that is!

A **question mark** is used at the end of an interrogative sentence, or question.

Is this the paper I should use?

Hyphen Use a hyphen to show the division of a word at the end of a line. Divide the word between syllables.

Do you know the first words the astro-naut said when she landed on the moon?

A hyphen can also be used to form some compound words.

go-cart long-range ready-made

Initial An initial is the first letter of a name. A period is used after an initial.

T. S. Eliot

Quotation Marks In a direct quotation, quotation marks go before and after the exact words that someone said.

Manuel said, "This is a great movie."

Capitalization and Punctuation Tips

Grammar Glossary

Adjective An adjective is a word that can describe a noun or pronoun. It tells what kind, how many, or which one.

The rock is <u>large</u> and <u>solid</u>.

Adverb An adverb is a word that can describe a verb, an adjective, or another adverb. It tells how, when, where, or how much.

Ms. Bannerjee spoke <u>quietly</u> and <u>calmly</u>.

Article An article is a special adjective. *A* and *an* are called **indefinite articles** because they refer to any of a group of people, places, things, or ideas. *The* is called a **definite article**, because it identifies a particular person, place, thing, or idea.

Comparative Adjective A comparative adjective is a form of an adjective that can compare two or more things. To compare two persons or things, form the comparative by adding *-er* to some adjectives. To compare more than two persons or things, you use the superlative form by adding *-est* to some adjectives.

The Congo River is <u>long</u>, but the Amazon River is <u>longer</u>.

The Yellow River and the Mississippi River are <u>long</u>, but the Nile River is the <u>longest</u> river on Earth.

For some other adjectives, add the word *more* or *less* to form the comparative and the word *most* or *least* to form the superlative.

Swimming is the <u>most difficult</u> sport for me, and running is the <u>least difficult</u>.

Comparative Adverb The comparative form of an adverb compares two actions or qualities. Form a comparative adverb by adding *-er* to some adverbs. To compare more than two actions or qualities, add *-est* to some adverbs.

Kofi arrived <u>early</u>, but Yolanda arrived <u>earlier</u>.

Of the three, Jenny arrived <u>earliest</u>.

For some adverbs, add the word *more* or *less* to form the comparative, and the word *most* or *least* to form the superlative:

Chris works <u>more carefully</u> when he is rested and <u>less carefully</u> when he is tired.

Complete Predicate The complete predicate is the simple predicate and all the words in a sentence that tell what the subject is or does.

My mother <u>is not feeling well</u>.

Complete Subject The complete subject is the simple subject and all the words in a sentence that tell what or whom the sentence is about.

<u>Six beautiful gray horses</u> pulled the coach.

Compound Predicate A compound predicate occurs when a sentence contains more than one equally important predicate, or verb. The coordinating conjunctions *and, but,* or

Grammar Glossary

© McGraw-Hill School Division

or can be used to join a compound predicate.

I <u>stood and waited</u> on the porch.

Compound Sentence   A compound sentence is formed by joining two or more sentences with a coordinating conjunction such as *and, but,* or *or.* In a compound sentence, a comma comes before the conjunction that joins the sentences.

<u>The dog lay on the rug,</u> *and* <u>the cat sat on the chair.</u>

Compound Subject   A compound subject occurs when a sentence contains more than one equally important subject. The coordinating conjunctions *and, but,* or *or* can be used to join a compound subject.

<u>Bill and Carlos</u> are captains of the football team.

Compound Word   A compound word is formed by putting two or more words together to make a new word. A compound word can be a hyphenated compound, an open compound, or a closed compound.

round dance   round-robin roundup

Conjunction   A conjunction is a word that is used to join words or word groups. **Coordinating conjunctions** such as *and, but,* and *or* can be used to make compound sentences, subjects, and predicates.

Contraction   A contraction is a short form of two words. An apostrophe takes the place of letters that are left out.

Haven't is a contraction for <u>have not.</u>

Declarative Sentence   A declarative sentence is a statement. It is followed by a period.

The deer ran through the woods.

Dependent Clause   A dependent clause is a group of words with a subject and a verb that cannot stand on its own as a separate sentence.

I have been taking piano lessons <u>since I was five years old.</u>

Double Negatives   Some adverbs, like *no* and *not,* are called negatives because they negate the meaning in the rest of a sentence. Using two negatives in the same sentence is considered a mistake because they cancel one another.

Some negative words: **no, not, nobody, none, no one, nothing**

Correct: **We had <u>no</u> rain.** Correct: **We did <u>not</u> have any rain.**

Mistake: **We did <u>not</u> have <u>no</u> rain today.**

Exclamatory Sentence   An exclamatory sentence shows excitement, surprise, or strong feeling. It is followed by an exclamation mark.

I can't believe I won this race!

Homographs   Homographs are words that have the same spelling but completely different meanings. *Case* is a homograph because it can mean "a box for holding something" or "a situation or set of circumstances."

Grammar Glossary

Homophones Homophones are words that sound the same but are spelled differently and have different meanings. The words *heel* and *heal* are homophones.

Imperative Sentence An imperative sentence gives a command or makes a strong request. It is followed by a period or exclamation mark.

Follow the leader. Don't do that!

Independent Clause An independent clause is a group of words with a subject and a verb that can stand on its own as a separate sentence.

You can call him up, or you can write him a letter.

Interrogative Sentence An interrogative sentence asks a question. It is followed by a question mark.

Where is the mustard?

Irregular Verb An irregular verb is a verb that does not follow the rule of forming the past tense and the past participle by adding *-ed* or *-d* to the base form of the word.

base form: **eat**   past tense: **ate**
past participle: **eaten**

Noun A noun is the name of a person, place, thing, or idea.

girl   city   house   courage

Paragraph A paragraph is a group of sentences that tells about one main idea. It usually begins with a topic sentence that states the main idea. All other sentences in the paragraph tell more about, or support, the topic sentence. The first word in a paragraph is indented, or set in from the margin.

Parts of Speech The English language is divided into eight parts of speech. Each word is a part of speech: a noun, a verb, an adjective, an adverb, a conjunction, a pronoun, an interjection, or a preposition. Some words can be used as more than one part of speech.

Aim can be a noun or a verb.

East can be a noun, an adjective, or an adverb.

Plural Plural means "more than one." The plurals of most nouns are formed by adding *-s* or *-es* to the noun. Some plurals are formed by changing the spelling of the noun. Some nouns can be both singular and plural.

**hat hats   fox foxes
child children   sheep sheep**

Prefix A prefix is a meaningful unit of letters added to the beginning of a base word to form a new word.

re + build = rebuild

Pronoun A pronoun is a word or group of words that takes the place of a noun or a group of words acting as a noun.

**Mr. DeStefano went shopping.
He bought a radio.**

Proper Noun A proper noun is the name of a particular person, place, or thing. Capitalize the first letter of each important word in a proper noun.

**Harriet Tubman   Georgia
White House**

Question A question, or interrogative sentence, asks about something. It is followed by a question mark.

Did you follow the directions?

Quotation A quotation includes the words that someone says. A direct quotation is the exact words that someone says. Quotation marks are used before and after a direct quotation. Commas are used to set it off from the rest of the sentence. The first word in a direct quotation is capitalized.

Mrs. Avila said, "The last train leaves at 10 o'clock."

Sentence A sentence is a group of words that tells one complete thought. The first word in a sentence begins with a capital letter. A sentence may end with a period, a question mark, or an exclamation mark.

Simple Predicate The simple predicate, or verb, is contained in the complete predicate of a sentence. It tells what the subject of the sentence is or does.

Tomas <u>swims</u> at the pool every day.

Simple Subject The simple subject is the main word in the complete subject of a sentence. It tells what the sentence is about.

A tall young <u>man</u> walked into the library.

Subject/ Verb Agreement The form of verbs changes depending on the number of people or things performing the action. This is called subject/verb agreement. If one person or thing is performing the action, the verb is **singular.** If more than one person or thing is performing the action, the verb is **plural.**

The plant <u>grows</u>. The plants grow.

Suffix A suffix is a meaningful letter or group of letters added to the end of a word to change its meaning or part of speech.

depend + <u>able</u> = dependable

Verb A verb is a word that expresses action or state of being. The simple predicate in a sentence is a verb. The principal parts of verbs are the forms the verb has to show present, past, or future tense.

walk   walked   will walk
is   was   will be

Grammar Glossary

How to Use the Spelling Thesaurus

Thesaurus Entry

Have you ever looked for just the right word to make a sentence more interesting or exciting? You could find that word in a thesaurus. A **thesaurus** is a collection of synonyms and antonyms. It can help you with your writing. Read this sentence:

The cat looked *carefully* at the barking dog before walking *carefully* past the large animal.

The sentence would be better if the word *carefully* wasn't used twice. You need another word that means the same or almost the same as *carefully*. You can find one in your **Spelling Thesaurus**.

Read the thesaurus entry below. There are three synonyms for *carefully*. You can use several of those synonyms to rewrite the sentence like this:

The cat looked *warily* at the barking dog before walking *cautiously* past the large animal.

Look at this entry for *carefully*.

part of speech

main entry word — **carefully** *Adverb.* paying close attention to avoid danger or risk: The tourists stayed *carefully* away from the edge of the cliff. — **definition**

cautiously using care: The bicyclist *cautiously* avoided the potholes.

synonyms — *gingerly* with great delicacy or care: *Gingerly*, I pulled the cactus spine from my thumb.

warily with care and caution: The mouse *warily* poked its nose out of the cupboard in case the cat was near.

antonyms: carelessly, heedlessly, recklessly — **antonyms**

A few **Spelling Thesaurus** entries have so many synonyms that you'll find a box full of synonyms instead of sentences. The box also has some antonyms.

gigantic

Adjective. very big and powerful, like a giant.

colossal	monumental
enormous	mountainous
huge	towering
immense	tremendous
mammoth	vast

antonyms: tiny, minute, microscopic

Thesaurus Index

The index can help you find what is in your **Spelling Thesaurus**. The index is a listing of every word in the **Spelling Thesaurus**, including every synonym and every antonym. All the words are in alphabetical order.

Each **entry word** is listed in red:
carefully *Adverb*

To find this entry word, look in the **Spelling Thesaurus** under **C.**

Each *synonym* is listed in italic print. Next to the synonym is the synonym's entry word.
cautiously carefully *Adverb*

To find the meaning of the word *cautiously,* look up the thesaurus entry for **carefully.**

Each antonym is listed in black print. Next to the antonym is its entry word.
carelessly carefully *Adverb*

To find this word, look up the entry for **carefully.**

Shades of Meaning

Take a moment to look through your **Spelling Thesaurus.** You'll find something interesting about synonyms. While some synonym pairs have exactly the same meaning, others don't. For example, two synonyms of **damp** are *humid* and *dank. Humid* means "having a lot of water vapor in the air." *Dank* means "uncomfortably wet and chilly." You might describe a hot day as *humid,* but you wouldn't describe it as *dank.* The definitions and sample sentences with each word will help you figure out whether the synonyms have slightly different meanings.

Try This: Replace each underlined word with a more exact word. Use your **Spelling Thesaurus** to help you. Then write your new sentence.

1. Instead of a uniform, the worker wore <u>informal</u> clothes.

2. The girl and her younger sister had on <u>twin</u> hats.

3. Nathan put a <u>narrow</u> slice of cheese in his sandwich.

4. If you are <u>alert</u>, you can remember more details of what you see.

5. The post office will <u>provide</u> mail on Saturdays.

Spelling Thesaurus

Spelling Thesaurus Index

A

abandon **receive** *Verb*
accept **receive** *Verb*
accord **argument** *Noun*
acquire **receive** *Verb*
adventure *Noun*
agreeable **enjoyable** *Adjective*
agreement **argument** *Noun*
aim **goal** *Noun*
alert *Adjective*
allow **prevent** *Verb*
amaze *Verb*
ancient **prehistoric** *Adjective*
annoy **tease** *Verb*
antiquated **modern** *Adjective*
antique **modern** *Adjective*
appear *Verb*
appreciative **grateful** *Adjective*
argument *Noun*
arid **damp** *Adjective*
asleep **alert** *Adjective*
assemble **manufacture** *Verb*
assignment **mission** *Noun*
association **club** *Noun*
astonish **amaze** *Verb*
astound **amaze** *Verb*
attach **fasten** *Verb*
attentive **alert** *Adjective*
attire **outfit** *Noun*
attract **lure** *Verb*
award **trophy**

B

barge **prowl** *Verb*
basic *Adjective*

belief **faith** *Noun*
bellow **howl** *Noun*
beneficial **useful** *Adjective*
bind **fasten** *Verb*
blaze **brighten** *Verb*
blunder **mistake** *Noun*
boost **raise** *Verb*
border *Noun*
bore **amaze** *Verb*
boring **dull** *Adjective*
boundary **border** *Noun*
brighten *Verb*
bring down **raise** *Verb*
build **create** *Verb*
burden *Noun*

C

carefully *Adverb*
carelessly **carefully** *Adverb*
casual **informal** *Adjective*
category **type** *Noun*
cautiously **carefully** *Adverb*
cease **remain** *Verb*
celebrate *Verb*
center **border** *Noun*
central **basic** *Adjective*
chat **discussion** *Noun*
chiefly **especially** *Adverb*
choice **special** *Adjective*
chore *Noun*
circle **club** *Noun*
class **type** *Noun*
clear **hidden** *Adjective*
clip **shear** *Verb*
clothing **outfit** *Noun*
club *Noun*

Spelling Thesaurus

Spelling Thesaurus

early tardy *Adjective*
earn deserve *Verb*
easygoing severe *Adjective*
effort labor *Noun*
emerge appear *Verb*
encourage prevent *Verb*
endure remain *Verb*
energy strength *Noun*
enjoyable *Adjective*
enjoyable wonderful *Adjective*
enormous gigantic *Adjective*
ensemble outfit *Noun*
entertainment *Noun*
error mistake *Noun*
especially *Adverb*
essential basic *Adjective*
exceptional special *Adjective*
excite amaze *Verb*
exciting dull *Adjective*
exciting wonderful *Adjective*
excursion journey *Noun*
expedition journey *Noun*
exploit adventure *Noun*
explore *Verb*
extraordinary special *Adjective*

faith *Noun*
fascinating dull *Adjective*
fascinating wonderful *Adjective*
fashion create *Verb*
fasten *Verb*
fault mistake *Noun*
favorable wonderful *Adjective*
feat adventure *Noun*

feebleness strength *Noun*
fight argument *Noun*
finish remain *Verb*
flabbergast amaze *Verb*
foam *Noun*
follow obey *Verb*
force *Verb*
force strength *Noun*
forget recall *Verb*
form create *Verb*
frayed worn *Adjective*
fresh modern *Adjective*
frontier border *Noun*
frosty frozen *Adjective*
froth foam *Noun*
frozen *Adjective*
fun entertainment *Noun*
fundamental basic *Adjective*
furnish provide *Verb*

garbage waste *Noun*
gaze peer *Verb*
gem jewel *Noun*
generate create *Verb*
get receive *Verb*
gigantic *Adjective*
gingerly carefully *Adverb*
give receive *Verb*
gleam brighten *Verb*
glide prowl *Verb*
go away return *Verb*
goal *Noun*
good naughty *Adjective*
grateful *Adjective*
gratifying wonderful *Adjective*
grim severe *Adjective*
guess imagine *Verb*
guide leader *Noun*

harmful *Adjective*
haul **drag** *Verb*
heave **raise** *Verb*
heed **notice** *Verb*
heedlessly **carefully** *Adverb*
helpful **useful** *Adjective*
hidden *Adjective*
hinder **prevent** *Verb*
hoist *Verb*
honor **celebrate** *Verb*
hot **frozen** *Adjective*
howl *Noun*
huge **gigantic** *Adjective*
humid **damp** *Adjective*
hurtful **harmful** *Adjective*

icy **frozen** *Adjective*
identical **twin** *Adjective*
ignore **celebrate** *Verb*
ignore **obey** *Verb*
imagine *Verb*
immense **gigantic** *Adjective*
inattentive **alert** *Adjective*
informal *Adjective*
inside **border** *Noun*
interesting **dull** *Adjective*
interior **border** *Noun*
invent **create** *Verb*
investigate **explore** *Verb*
issue **subject** *Noun*

jewel *Noun*
job **chore** *Noun*
journey *Noun*
joyful **wonderful** *Adjective*

key **basic** *Adjective*
kind **severe** *Adjective*
kind **type** *Noun*
known *Verb*

labor *Noun*
last **remain** *Verb*
late **tardy** *Adjective*
lather **foam** *Noun*
leader *Noun*
leave **return** *Verb*
let **prevent** *Verb*
lift **hoist** *Verb*
lift **raise** *Verb*
lighten **brighten** *Verb*
load **burden** *Noun*
look **peer** *Verb*
lower **raise** *Verb*
loyalty *Noun*
lure *Verb*
lurk **prowl** *Verb*

Spelling Thesaurus

mammoth gigantic *Adjective*
manufacture *Verb*
march **prowl** *Verb*
mark **notice** *Verb*
marvelous **wonderful** *Adjective*
matching **twin** *Adjective*
medal **trophy** *Noun*
merit **deserve** *Verb*
microscopic **gigantic** *Adjective*
mild **severe** *Adjective*
mimic **tease** *Verb*
minute **gigantic** *Adjective*
mischievous **naughty** *Adjective*
mission *Noun*
mistake *Noun*
modern *Adjective*
modern **prehistoric** *Adjective*
moist **damp** *Adjective*
monumental **gigantic** *Adjective*
mountainous **gigantic** *Adjective*
murmur **howl** *Noun*

narrow *Adjective*
naughty *Adjective*
neglect **celebrate** *Verb*
new **modern** *Adjective*
new **prehistoric** *Adjective*
noteworthy **special** *Adjective*
notice *Verb*
novel **modern** *Adjective*

obedient **naughty** *Adjective*
obey *Verb*
objection **protest** *Noun*
objective **goal** *Noun*
observant **alert** *Adjective*
observe **notice** *Verb*
obsolete **modern** *Adjective*
obtain **receive** *Verb*
obvious **hidden** *Adjective*
offer **provide** *Verb*
old **modern** *Adjective*
old-fashioned **modern** *Adjective*
on time **tardy** *Adjective*
open **hidden** *Adjective*
ordinary **special** *Adjective*
originate **create** *Verb*
outdated **modern** *Adjective*
outfit *Noun*
out-of-date **modern** *Adjective*
outstanding **special** *Adjective*
overdue **tardy** *Adjective*
overlook **celebrate** *Verb*
overwhelm **amaze** *Verb*

parade **prowl** *Verb*
particularly **especially** *Adverb*
peer *Verb*
permit **prevent** *Verb*
pier *Noun*
plan **create** *Verb*
pleasant **enjoyable** *Adjective*
pleasant **wonderful** *Adjective*
pleasing **wonderful** *Adjective*

pleasurable wonderful *Adjective*
poetry verse *Noun*
power strength *Noun*
precious stone jewel *Noun*
prehistoric Adjective
present modern *Adjective*
prevent *Verb*
primarily especially *Adverb*
primitive prehistoric Adjective
prize trophy *Noun*
problem subject *Noun*
produce create *Verb*
produce manufacture *Verb*
prompt tardy *Adjective*
protest *Noun*
provide *Verb*
prowl *Verb*
prune shear Verb
purpose goal *Noun*

refreshing wonderful *Adjective*
relaxed informal *Adjective*
remain *Verb*
remarkable special *Adjective*
remember recall *Verb*
repel lure *Verb*
require force *Verb*
research explore *Verb*
return *Verb*
revisit return *Verb*
rhyme verse *Noun*
ridicule tease *Verb*
rubbish waste *Noun*
rude grateful *Adjective*

quarrel argument *Noun*

ragged worn *Adjective*
raise *Verb*
raise hoist *Verb*
rare special *Adjective*
recall *Verb*
receive *Verb*
recent modern *Adjective*
recklessly carefully *Adverb*
recognized known *Verb*
recollect recall *Verb*
recreation entertainment *Noun*
recur return *Verb*

safe harmful *Adjective*
safe vault *Noun*
safe-deposit box vault *Noun*
satisfying wonderful *Adjective*
scrap waste *Noun*
scream howl *Noun*
screech howl *Noun*
secret hidden *Adjective*
separate fasten *Verb*
settlement argument *Noun*
severe Adjective
shabby worn *Adjective*
shape create *Verb*
shear *Verb*
shout howl *Noun*
show appear *Verb*
shriek howl *Noun*
single twin *Adjective*
skulk prowl *Verb*
slender narrow *Adjective*
slim narrow *Adjective*
slink prowl *Verb*
sneak prowl *Verb*

Spelling Thesaurus

sort type *Noun*
special *Adjective*
splendid wonderful *Adjective*
stare peer *Verb*
stay remain *Verb*
steadfastness loyalty *Noun*
steal prowl *Verb*
steaming frozen *Adjective*
stern severe *Adjective*
stop prevent *Verb*
stop remain *Verb*
strength *Noun*
strict severe *Adjective*
stride prowl *Verb*
strut prowl *Verb*
study explore *Verb*
stun amaze *Verb*
subject *Noun*
suds foam *Noun*
superfluous basic *Adjective*
superior special *Adjective*
supply provide *Verb*
suppose imagine *Verb*
suspicions faith *Noun*
swagger prowl *Verb*

take down raise *Verb*
talk discussion *Noun*
tardy *Adjective*
task chore *Noun*
taunt tease *Verb*
tease *Verb*
tedious dull *Adjective*
tempt lure *Verb*
terrific wonderful *Adjective*
thankful grateful *Adjective*
thin narrow *Adjective*
thrashing upset *Noun*

threadbare worn *Adjective*
thrill amaze *Verb*
thwart prevent *Verb*
tiny gigantic *Adjective*
tiresome dull *Adjective*
toil labor *Noun*
topic subject *Noun*
tow drag *Verb*
towering gigantic *Adjective*
trash waste *Noun*
treasure jewel *Noun*
trek journey *Noun*
tremendous gigantic *Adjective*
trim shear *Verb*
trip journey *Noun*
trophy *Noun*
trust faith *Noun*
twin *Adjective*
type *Noun*

uncommon special *Adjective*
understanding argument *Noun*
understood known *Verb*
unfasten fasten *Verb*
ungrateful grateful *Adjective*
unimportant basic *Adjective*
unique special *Adjective*
unnecessary basic *Adjective*
unpleasant enjoyable *Adjective*
unpleasant wonderful *Adjective*
unremarkable special *Adjective*
unsatisfied grateful *Adjective*
up-to-date modern *Adjective*
up-to-the-minute modern *Adjective*
upset *Noun*
useful *Adjective*
usual special *Adjective*

Spelling Thesaurus

valuable useful *Adjective*
vanish appear *Verb*
vanish remain *Verb*
vast gigantic *Adjective*
vault *Noun*
venture adventure *Noun*
verse *Noun*
vigilant alert *Adjective*
vigor strength *Noun*

wail howl *Noun*
warily carefully *Adverb*
waste *Noun*

watchful alert *Adjective*
weakness strength *Noun*
weight burden *Noun*
wharf pier *Noun*
whimper whine *Verb*
whine *Verb*
whisper howl *Noun*
wonderful *Adjective*
work labor *Noun*
worn *Adjective*

yell howl *Noun*
yowl howl *Noun*

Spelling Thesaurus

Spelling Thesaurus

adventure

Noun. something that a person does that is difficult or exciting:
The camping trip was an *adventure* for the whole family.

exploit a brave deed or act:
The newspaper article described the *exploit* of the rescue squad in great detail.

feat an act or deed that shows great courage, strength, or skill:
Crossing the river on horseback was a *feat* for even the strongest rider.

venture a task or undertaking that involves risk or danger:
Taking part in a *venture* such as the search for a sunken ship needs great courage.

alert

Adjective. watching and listening carefully:
The deer was *alert* to every slight sound in the forest.

attentive watching, listening, or concentrating carefully:
The *attentive* student heard the directions the first time.

observant noticing:
The *observant* witness remembered the make and color of the speeding car.

watchful paying close attention:
The boy sat next to his sleeping baby sister in *watchful* silence.

vigilant paying close attention, usually with the idea of watching for danger:
The *vigilant* guards never fell asleep at their posts.

> antonyms: asleep, drowsy, inattentive

amaze

Verb. to surprise greatly; to fill with wonder.

> *astonish*
> *astound*
> *confound*
> *dazzle*
> *excite*
> *flabbergast*
> *overwhelm*
> *stun*
> *thrill*

antonym: bore

appear

Verb. to come into sight:
As soon as the first buds *appear,* she thinks it's spring.

emerge to come into view:
In the night sky, the moon was trying to *emerge* from behind the scattered clouds.

show to be in sight, to be
visible:
If you use such thin cloth for the
curtains, the light will *show*
through them.

antonyms: disappear, vanish

argument

Noun. a discussion of something
by people who do not agree:
They had an *argument* about
who was better at solving
problems.

disagreement a difference of opinion:
We resolved our *disagreement* by
taking turns.

conflict a strong disagreement:
Sometimes a minor problem
can lead to a more serious
conflict.

fight an angry disagreement:
Let's not *fight* over which movie
to see.

quarrel an angry argument or
disagreement:
The broken window set off a
quarrel over who should get
it fixed.

antonyms: agreement, accord,
settlement, understanding

basic

Adjective. forming the most
important part:
Air, water, and food are *basic* needs
for life.

central very important, main:
The *central* idea of the paragraph is
usually found in the first sentence.

essential necessary:
Extra water is *essential* if you want
to hike in the desert during the
summer.

fundamental serving as a basis,
essential:
Listening closely is a *fundamental*
part of following directions.

key chief:
The *key* ingredient of an enjoyable
game is enthusiasm.

antonyms: dispensable,
unnecessary, unimportant,
superfluous

border

Noun. a line where one area begins
and another ends:
The train crossed the *border*
between the United States and
Canada.

boundary a line that marks the edge of a country or state:
The Rio Grande forms the *boundary* between the United States and Mexico.

frontier the far edge of a country, where it borders on another country:
As the train neared the *frontier*, guards came through to check our passports.

> antonyms: inside, interior, center

brighten

Verb. to gain more light:
We hoped the tunnel would *brighten* as we got closer to the end.

blaze to shine or burn brightly:
I threw dry wood on the fire to make it *blaze* so that I could see their faces better.

lighten The weary walkers were glad to see the sky *lighten* as the sun rose.

gleam to shine or glow:
The dirty lamp began to *gleam* as Aladdin rubbed it with an old rag.

> antonyms: darken, dim, dull

burden

Noun. something that is carried:
The pile of books seemed like a heavy *burden* for such a small child to carry.

load a burden:
It was a great relief to transfer the heavy *load* from my back into the truck.

weight something heavy:
The sleeping cat was an unmoving *weight* on my lap.

carefully

Adverb. paying close attention to avoid danger or risk:
The tourists stayed *carefully* away from the edge of the cliff.

cautiously using care:
The bicyclist *cautiously* avoided the potholes.

gingerly with great delicacy or care:
Gingerly, I pulled the cactus spine from my thumb.

warily with care and caution:
The mouse *warily* poked its nose out of the cupboard in case the cat was near.

> antonyms: carelessly, heedlessly, recklessly

celebrate

Verb. to show respect to a person or event with ceremonies or other activities:
We *celebrate* the birthday of George Washington because he was an important man in our country's history.

Spelling Thesaurus

honor to remember a person or event with respect:

These ceremonies *honor* the people from our town who fought in World War I.

commemorate to honor or maintain the memory of:

The mayor declared a holiday to *commemorate* the founding of the town.

> antonyms: ignore, overlook, neglect

chore

Noun. something that has to be done regularly:

Setting the table is a *chore* I have to do every evening before I watch television.

job a specific piece of work:

The chart shows which student has the *job* of cleaning the hamster cage every day.

task a piece of work to be done:

Cleaning the chalkboard is a *task* I enjoy.

duty an action or service assigned to someone:

It's my *duty* to check that the plants are watered every third day.

club

Noun. a group of people who meet for fun or a special purpose:

Jake and his friends decided to start a puzzle *club* to read and solve mysteries.

circle a group of people who have interests that they share and enjoy together:

Gerri is a member of a quilting *circle* that meets on the third Saturday of every month.

association a group of people joined together for a common purpose:

For many years Eli's family has belonged to an *association* of community volunteers.

create

Verb. to bring into being.

> *build*
> *compose*
> *design*
> *dream up*
> *fashion*
> *form*
> *generate*
> *invent*
> *originate*
> *plan*
> *produce*
> *shape*

antonyms: destroy, copy

Spelling Thesaurus

damp

Adjective. a little wet:
The benches were still *damp* from the morning rain.

moist slightly wet:
I cleaned the blackboard with a *moist* cloth.

humid having a lot of water vapor in the air:
The air outside the museum was hot and *humid*.

dank uncomfortably wet and chilly:
The cellar was dark and *dank* and smelled bad.

antonyms: dry, arid

deserve

Verb. to have a right to:
The students *deserve* extra recess time for their hard work this morning.

earn to win because of hard work or good behavior:
Chris will *earn* extra credit points if he completes his social studies assignment.

merit to be worthy of:
I hope the book report I just handed in will be good enough to *merit* a high grade.

discussion

Noun. the act of talking something over, often to exchange ideas:
Before doing the spelling exercises, we had a *discussion* about word endings.

talk an exchange of spoken words:
My uncle said he wanted to have a *talk* with me about our vacation plans.

conversation talk between two or more people:
They interrupted their *conversation* to give their tickets to the conductor.

chat a friendly, informal talk:
Margarita hoped to have a *chat* with her friends before the basketball game started.

drag

Verb. to move something along slowly or heavily:
The horse strained to *drag* the overloaded hay wagon.

haul to pull or move with effort:
The day we moved into the new house, it took three people to *haul* the file cabinet up the stairs.

tow to pull or drag behind:
I can hardly believe that this little truck will be able to *tow* the school bus out of the ditch.

Spelling Thesaurus

dull

Adjective. not interesting:
They walked out of the *dull* movie before it was over.

boring lacking in interest:
I almost fell asleep because the TV program was so *boring*.

tiresome causing boredom or weariness:
Mrs. Rodriguez said that she didn't want to hear any more of our *tiresome* excuses.

tedious long and tiring, boring:
Checking all the addresses was a *tedious* task.

> antonyms: interesting, exciting, fascinating

enjoyable

Adjective. giving joy or happiness:
The children spent an *enjoyable* afternoon at the beach.

pleasant giving a feeling of happiness:
It is *pleasant* to sit in the shade on a hot day.

agreeable nice, to one's liking:
The good weather made our trip to the beach most *agreeable*.

> antonyms: unpleasant, disagreeable, distressing

entertainment

Noun. something that interests and amuses:
After working all day, we went to a concert for *entertainment*.

fun enjoyment:
Just for *fun*, let's go down to the canal and watch the barges.

recreation something that is done for relaxation or amusement:
Sports are a kind of *recreation*.

especially

Adverb. mostly:
They *especially* wanted to see the Statue of Liberty when they visited New York.

particularly to a great degree, a lot:
The teacher was *particularly* pleased with our report on hurricanes.

chiefly above all, mainly:
The cat was *chiefly* interested in who was going to feed her.

primarily for the most part, most importantly:
The crossing guard is *primarily* responsible for making sure the children cross safely.

explore

Verb. to look through closely:
The class will begin to *explore* the history of space travel next week.

investigate to look into carefully in order to get information:
Each group will *investigate* a different animal that lives in the desert.

Spelling Thesaurus

study to try to learn about:
Next year we will *study* geometry and world history.
research to study carefully in order to find facts; to investigate:
My sister went to the public library in order to *research* our family tree.

faith

Noun. a feeling that something is true, or can be counted on:
The city of Montreal was unfamiliar to the travelers, but they had *faith* in the accuracy of their guidebook.
belief an acceptance of something as true:
Mrs. Ruiz has a strong *belief* that every one of her students can do excellent work.
trust a belief that something can be counted on:
My neighbor has *trust* in my ability to baby-sit her children.
confidence a feeling that something can be relied on:
I have *confidence* in my ability to finish the assignment before the deadline.

> antonyms: doubt, distrust, suspicions

fasten

Verb. to put two things together firmly:
We used a bolt to *fasten* the tire swing to the chain.
connect to join together:
The driver had to back up in order to *connect* the trailer to the car.
attach to connect one thing to another:
They used glue to *attach* the badges to the notebooks.
bind to tie or join together:
When we finish our stories, the teacher will *bind* them into a class book.

> antonyms: unfasten, detach, separate, disconnect

foam

Noun. a mass of tiny bubbles:
If you add vinegar to baking soda, the mixture will produce *foam*.
froth bubbles formed in or on a liquid:
The *froth* in the milkshake comes from the shaking.
lather bubbles formed by mixing soap and water:
Work up a good *lather* with shampoo to get your hair really clean.
suds soap bubbles:
I was up to my elbows in *suds* from the dishes when the phone rang.

Spelling Thesaurus

force

Verb. to make someone do something:

Don't *force* Yuka to go if she doesn't want to.

compel to force:

The storm will *compel* us to cancel the game.

coerce to make someone act in a given manner:

The bully tried to *coerce* the children to walk on the other side of the street.

require to demand in a way that can't be refused:

A police officer can *require* cars to stop even when the light is green.

frozen

Adjective, formed from the past participle of the verb freeze. made or become so cold that ice has formed in or on it:

No seeds could be planted in the hard, *frozen* ground.

icy made of or covered with ice:

The sidewalk was *icy* after the storm.

frosty cold enough for ice to form; freezing:

The *frosty* air made me wish I had gloves on.

> antonyms: hot, steaming, boiling

gigantic

Adjective. very big and powerful, like a giant.

> *colossal*
> *enormous*
> *huge*
> *immense*
> *mammoth*
> *monumental*
> *mountainous*
> *towering*
> *tremendous*
> *vast*

antonyms: tiny, minute, microscopic

goal

Noun. something that a person wants to get or become:

My *goal* is to be able to spell any word I hear.

objective a desired end result:

The *objective* of the game is to collect as many pieces as possible.

purpose the reason for which something exists or is done:

What is the *purpose* of the new machine?

aim the point toward which an action is directed:

His *aim* was to run a marathon in under three hours.

Spelling Thesaurus

grateful

Adjective. full of warm feelings for something that makes one happy or comfortable:
They were *grateful* to find shelter from the rain.

thankful feeling aware of receiving a favor or benefit:
The new students were *thankful* for the advice of their classmates.

appreciative showing or feeling thankfulness:
The *appreciative* audience stood up and cheered.

> antonyms: ungrateful, unsatisfied, rude

harmful

Adjective. causing loss or pain:
The older children made sure to keep *harmful* things out of the baby's reach.

hurtful causing pain:
Hassan apologized for the *hurtful* things he had said.

destructive causing or bringing injury or harm:
The *destructive* winds of the hurricane broke windows and knocked down trees.

> antonym: safe

hidden

Adjective, formed from the past participle of the verb **hide.** put or kept out of sight:
Sean searched for hours before he found the *hidden* lizard in the picture.

concealed kept out of sight:
Margo's fingers felt the *concealed* lock even though it was almost impossible to see.

secret known only to oneself or a few:
George and Margie looked for hours until they finally found the papers in a *secret* drawer in the old desk.

> antonyms: open, clear, obvious

hoist

Verb. to pull up:
The movers used a rope and a pulley to *hoist* the piano into the van.

raise to put in a higher position:
Olivia tried to *raise* the window in order to let some air into the stuffy room.

lift to move from a lower to a higher position:
Let's *lift* the lid so that we can see what's inside the treasure chest.

howl
Noun. a loud, wailing cry.

> bellow
> shriek
> scream
> shout
> screech
> wail
> yell
> yowl

antonyms: whisper, murmur

imagine
Verb. to picture something in one's mind:
The teacher asked the children to *imagine* what it would be like to live in another time in history.

suppose to think about something as if it is possible or really happening:
Suppose you had the chance to go to the Olympics.

guess to form an opinion without having enough knowledge or facts to be sure:
Harold couldn't *guess* the writer of that story.

informal
Adjective. not formal, without ceremony or following any rigid form:
The mayor agreed to an *informal* interview with the class.

casual not formal:
We were told to wear *casual* clothes to the party.

relaxed less strict, not rigid or tense:
The *relaxed* surroundings of the playroom helped the shy child get used to her new friends.

jewel
Noun. a valuable stone such as a diamond:
The ring had a glittering *jewel* set into a gold band.

gem a stone of great value:
The story was about a lost *gem* that belonged to a prince.

precious stone the most valuable kind of jewel, usually a diamond, ruby, emerald, or sapphire:
A *precious stone* can be cut and polished so that it glitters.

treasure something of great value, such as gold or a jewel:
The hidden *treasure* will be found as soon as we can figure out the code used on this map.

Spelling Thesaurus

journey

Noun. a long trip:
They wrote postcards from every stop on their *journey.*

trip the act of going from one place to another:
The class will take a *trip* to the state park.

expedition a long trip made for a specific reason:
The scientists will collect mosses on their *expedition* to the northern plains.

trek a long trip, especially when slow or difficult:
We were on the road for days, and sometimes it seemed as if our *trek* would never end.

excursion a short trip made for a specific reason:
The bus left in the morning for the *excursion* to the zoo.

known

*Verb, past participle of **know.***
to have been certain of the facts or truth of:
I have *known* that story since I was a little child.

understood to have known very well:
We have *understood* our responsibility from the first day we started this job.

recognized to have accepted that something is true:
Doctors have always *recognized* the importance of eating fresh vegetables.

labor

Noun. hard work:
After the cement was poured, the workers could rest from their *labor.*

work the use of a person's energy or ability to do something:
We have a lot of *work* to do on our science project.

toil hard or exhausting work:
The *toil* of digging up the ground makes starting a garden a difficult job.

effort hard work:
When the rain started, they were glad they had put the *effort* into finishing the roof.

leader

Noun. a person who shows the way:
The scout *leader* showed the troop how to follow the animal tracks to the stream.

guide a person who shows the way:
The *guide* led the children out of the forest.

director a person who supervises or guides other people:

The *director* of the tour pointed out the sights in the city.

loyalty

Noun. strong and lasting faithfulness and support:
My sister showed her *loyalty* by going to all my soccer games.

devotion a strong affection or great faithfulness:
The volunteer's *devotion* to the cause was shown by his tireless work.

steadfastness firm and devoted loyalty:
We proved our *steadfastness* by cheering even when our team was losing.

lure

Verb. to attract strongly:
We hoped the seeds on the floor would *lure* the gerbil out from behind the bookcase.

attract to cause to come near:
If you don't want flies, you shouldn't leave out food that will *attract* them.

tempt to appeal strongly to:
The offer of a free sample was enough to *tempt* many people into the store.

draw to cause to move toward, to attract:
The clowns made lots of noise to *draw* a crowd.

antonym: repel

manufacture

Verb. to make or process something, especially using machinery:
We visited a big building where they *manufacture* bicycles.

produce to make or create something:
The workers in the garment factory *produce* a complete shirt every fifteen minutes.

assemble to make something by putting parts together:
Workers in the Michigan plant *assemble* car parts that were produced in Canada.

mission

Noun. a special job:
The astronauts trained for their *mission* to the space station.

assignment a specific task that is given out:
Each student was given an *assignment* to complete during vacation.

duty something that a person is supposed to do:
It's the teacher's *duty* to explain the fire drill procedure.

mistake

Noun. something that is not correctly done:
I corrected the *mistake* I made on the test.

Spelling Thesaurus

error something that is wrong:
The students found only one spelling *error* in their article.
blunder a careless or stupid mistake:
It was a serious *blunder* to forget the time of the game.
fault a weakness or mistake:
The lack of light was a *fault* in the design of the workroom.

modern
Adjective. having to do with the present day or with recent time.

> *contemporary*
> *current*
> *fresh*
> *new*
> *novel*
> *present*
> *recent*
> *up-to-date*
> *up-to-the-minute*

antonyms: old, old-fashioned, antique, antiquated, out-of-date, outdated, obsolete

narrow
Adjective. having only a small amount of space between one side and the other:

The deer jumped easily over the *narrow* stream.
thin not thick, having little space between one side and the other:
I was full, so I only took a *thin* slice of cake.
slender not big around:
The *slender* snake slipped into the tiny gap between the rocks.
slim not thick; skinny:
The *slim* boy was just able to squeeze between the two stacks of boxes in the crowded storeroom.

antonyms: wide, broad

naughty
Adjective. behaving badly:
Sneaking cookies can be a *naughty* thing to do.
disobedient refusing or failing to carry out someone's wishes or orders:
The baby-sitter said not to climb on the table, but the *disobedient* child did it anyway.
mischievous playful in a way that causes harm or trouble:
That *mischievous* puppy is chewing on my slipper again.

antonyms: good, obedient

notice
Verb. to become aware of:
The teacher will *notice* if we put in extra effort.
observe to look at with attention:

Observe the scene carefully so you can remember the details later.

mark to give attention to:

Mark my words; you'll be sorry if you don't.

heed pay attention to:

The child did not *heed* the warning and fell on the slippery ice.

obey

Verb. to carry out wishes, orders, or instructions:

Most drivers *obey* the traffic laws.

follow to act according to wishes, orders, or instructions:

If you *follow* the directions, you'll do it right.

comply to act in agreement with a rule or request:

The people who *comply* with the order to form a line will be dismissed first.

> antonyms: ignore, defy, disobey

outfit

Noun. a set of clothes:

I got a new *outfit* for my birthday.

clothing things worn to cover the body:

He had on too much *clothing* for such a hot day.

ensemble a coordinated outfit or costume:

A bright green cap matched the shirt and pants and completed the eye-catching *ensemble.*

attire set of clothes:

The actors changed into street *attire* before leaving the theater.

peer

Verb. to look hard or closely so as to see something clearly:

I tried to *peer* through the grime on the window to see who was inside.

look to use one's eyes, to see:

Look at the pictures and choose the one that you like best.

gaze to look long and unusually attentively at:

They stopped to *gaze* at the toys displayed in the window.

stare to look very hard at:

Their aunt told them it was rude to *stare* at people.

pier

Noun. a structure built out over the water used as a landing place for boats and ships:

There are always adults and children fishing off the end of the *pier.*

wharf a structure built along a shore as a landing place for boats and ships:

The merchant's house was close to the *wharf* where his ships unloaded.

Spelling Thesaurus

dock a platform where boats and ships are tied up:
We crossed the gangplank from the *dock* to the deck of the ship.

prehistoric

Adjective. belonging to a time before people started writing history:
Woolly mammoths lived in *prehistoric* times but do not exist today.

primitive of or having to do with an early or original state:
The archaeologist found pieces of *primitive* pottery.

ancient of or having to do with times very long ago:
The ring of stones was the only sign of an *ancient* fort on top of the hill behind the farm.

> antonyms: contemporary, current, modern, new

prevent

Verb. to keep something from happening or someone from doing something:
The barricade was meant to *prevent* people from falling in the hole.

stop to keep something from moving or acting:
They tried to *stop* the skateboard from rolling into the storm drain.

hinder to hold back:
Don't let me *hinder* you from catching your bus.

thwart to prevent someone or something from succeeding:

The hero tried to *thwart* the plans of the evil king.

> antonyms: allow, encourage, let, permit

protest

Noun. an objection against something:
The letter was written as a *protest* against the new rules.

objection an expression of not liking or approving:
They made an *objection* to the mayor about the plan to close the library.

complaint a statement that something is wrong:
The toy company took our *complaint* seriously.

provide

Verb. to give what is needed or wanted:
One cup of cottage cheese will *provide* a high amount of protein and calcium.

supply to give something needed or wanted:
Each family will *supply* room and board for an exchange student.

furnish to supply or provide:
The cafeteria will *furnish* all the meals for the weekend activities.

deliver to carry or take to a destination:
The entertainment company says it can *deliver* everything we need for our graduation party.

Spelling Thesaurus

offer to present to be accepted or turned down:
That bus company claims to *offer* the lowest fares.

prowl
Verb. to move or roam quietly or secretly.

> *creep*
> *glide*
> *lurk*
> *slink*
> *skulk*
> *sneak*
> *steal*

antonyms: barge, strut, swagger, clump, parade, march, stride

raise
Verb. to pick up or move to a higher place:
Raise your hand if you have any questions.
lift to pick up:
Can they *lift* the table by themselves?
boost to push or shove up:
Give me a *boost* so I can reach the window ledge.

heave to lift, raise, pull, or throw, usually with effort:
The farm workers will *heave* the crates of carrots onto the truck.

antonyms: lower, bring down, take down, drop

recall
Verb. to bring back to mind:
I know we've met, but I can't *recall* your name.
remember to bring an image or idea from the past to mind:
Do you *remember* the words to the song?
recollect to bring something back to mind:
After exchanging news, the old friends began to *recollect* the adventures of their childhood.

antonym: forget

receive
Verb. to take or get:
I hope to *receive* a letter from my pen pal soon.
accept to take something that is given:
Our neighbor asked us to *accept* the gift with her thanks.
acquire to get or gain as one's own:
They hope to *acquire* more books for the library.
get to come to have or own:
That swimmer will *get* a ribbon at the end of the race.

Spelling Thesaurus

obtain to get through effort:
They wrote to the director to *obtain* permission to visit the Space Center.

antonyms: give, discard, abandon, donate, distribute

remain

Verb. not to go away:
I washed the shirt many times, but the stains and splotches *remain.*

stay not to leave:
Will you leave the party early or *stay* until it ends?

last to go on:
We were sure our friendship would *last* forever.

endure to remain:
Even after all these years, the friendships I made in kindergarten *endure.*

continue to keep on happening, being, or doing:
The festival will *continue* for three more days.

antonyms: stop, cease, finish, vanish

return

Verb. to come or go back:
The visitor promised to *return* soon.

recur to happen or appear again:
The pain in my knee might *recur* if I don't let it heal.

revisit to come to the same place again:
They plan to *revisit* the place where they first played together.

antonyms: leave, depart, go away

severe

Adjective. very strict or harsh:
The punishment for the crime was *severe.*

strict following or enforcing rules in a careful, exact way:
He was known as a *strict* teacher.

stern serious and strict:
At first he seemed *stern,* but later we realized how kind he was.

grim stern, frightening, and harsh:
They feared to go before the *grim* judge.

antonyms: easygoing, kind, mild

shear

Verb. to cut with scissors or clippers:
We watched the farmer *shear* the wool from the sheep.

clip to cut:
The barber can *clip* just a little off your hair to make it even.

prune to cut off or cut out parts, usually of plants:
They *prune* the new growth from the vines each autumn.

trim to cut away or remove parts to make something neat:
I *trim* the edges of each article before putting it in the scrapbook.

crop to cut or bite off the top part of something:

They keep the goat in the yard to *crop* the grass.

sort

Verb. to separate according to kind or size:
We were told to *sort* the clothes by color.

classify to arrange in groups:
The instructor told us to *classify* the animals by what they ate.

categorize to group or classify things:
The librarian said to *categorize* the magazines by topic.

file to put away in an arranged order:
His job was to *file* the papers in alphabetical order.

special

Adjective. different from others in a certain way; not ordinary.

choice
distinguished
exceptional
extraordinary
noteworthy
outstanding
rare
remarkable
superior
uncommon
unique

antonyms: ordinary, common, usual, unremarkable

strength

Noun. the quality of being strong:
They weren't sure they had the *strength* to move the file cabinet.

energy the strength or eagerness to work or do things:
We always have more *energy* early in the morning.

power the ability to do something:
My sister has the *power* to throw a ball all the way across the gym.

vigor active power or force:
The neighborhood group opposed the plan for a new mall with *vigor*.

force the power to move or stop something:
The *force* of a tornado's winds can lift a car into the air.

antonyms: weakness, feebleness

subject

Noun. something thought, written, or talked about:
What was the *subject* of the visitor's lecture?

topic what a speech, discussion, or piece of writing is about:
The *topic* of the article should appear in the first paragraph.

problem a question to be thought about and answered:
We eagerly tackled the *problem* of how to organize the art supplies.

issue a subject that is being discussed or considered:
They felt that the central *issue* was who would get to go on the trip.

Spelling Thesaurus

tardy

Adjective. arriving or happening after the appointed time:
She left early, but she was still *tardy.*

late coming after the usual time:
Our uncle was *late,* so we started lunch without him.

overdue delayed beyond the appointed time:
Their books were *overdue* and the fine was ten cents a day.

> antonyms: early, on time, prompt

tease

Verb. to annoy or make fun of in a playful way:
It's not a good idea to *tease* a porcupine.

annoy to bother or disturb:
Will it *annoy* you if I turn on the radio?

ridicule to make fun of:
The shortstop feared that his teammates would *ridicule* him for dropping the ball.

mimic to imitate, especially in order to make fun of:
I promised not to *mimic* my little brother any more.

taunt to challenge or insult:
The fans sometimes *taunt* the referee.

trophy

Noun. a cup, small statue, or other prize given to someone for winning a contest or doing something outstanding:
Jack won a *trophy* for making the best chili.

prize something that is won in a contest or game:
The *prize* for winning the race was a blue ribbon.

award something that is given for merit or excellence:
The fifth grade class won an *award* for their mural.

medal a flat coin-shaped piece of metal, often attached to a ribbon, usually given as a reward for an achievement:
Each member of the winning Olympic softball team received a gold *medal.*

cup an ornament in the shape of a cup, offered as a prize:
The team members' names were engraved on the *cup* that they won.

twin

Adjective. being identical or very much alike:
In the science fiction story, the planet had *twin* moons.

matching being similar or equal to another:
The singer and the drummer wore *matching* costumes.

identical exactly alike:
The *identical* cars were parked side by side.

> antonyms: single, different

type

Noun. a group of things that are alike or have the same qualities: What *type* of animal would you like as a pet?

kind a group of things that are the same in some way: There is only one *kind* of paper on the shelf.

sort a group of people or things that have something in common: They were the *sort* of people who always make you feel welcome.

class a related group of people or things: Mammals are one *class* of animals, and reptiles are another.

category a group or class of things: We had to choose a *category* for each spelling word.

upset

Noun. an unexpected result in a contest, competition, or election: The mayor lost the election in an *upset*.

defeat a loss in a contest or competition: The team had faced *defeat* before.

thrashing a severe defeat or loss, often unexpected: The sportscaster announced that the home team took a *thrashing* in the final game of the series.

useful

Adjective. having a good use or purpose: A first aid kit is a *useful* thing to have on a trip.

helpful giving help: The people at the store offered *helpful* information.

valuable having great use or importance: Baby-sitting has been a *valuable* experience.

beneficial having a good effect: A vacation will be *beneficial* to our health.

vault

Noun. a room or compartment that is safe for keeping valuables: Be sure to put all the documents in the hotel *vault* as soon as you get there.

safe a strong metal box or other container used to store money, jewelry, and other valuables: The *safe* was built into the wall and hidden behind a picture.

safe-deposit box a metal box for storing valuables inside a bank vault: After each of their children was born Mr. and Mrs. Swenson put the birth certificate in the family's *safe-deposit box*.

Spelling Thesaurus

verse

Noun. words written in a particular rhythmic pattern and often in rhyme:
Martha designs birthday cards and writes a *verse* in each one.

poetry words chosen and arranged to create a feeling and meaning through sound and rhythm:
The program consisted of *poetry* and music.

rhyme verse or poetry having sounds at the ends of lines that are alike or the same:
Mattie wrote a funny *rhyme* that the town newspaper printed.

W

waste

Noun. things that are thrown away:
The *waste* from some kitchens after a party could feed an entire family.

rubbish useless things:
I cleaned the *rubbish* out of the attic.

garbage food and other things that are thrown out:
Twice a week the truck comes by to pick up the *garbage*.

trash unwanted things that are thrown away:
Put the *trash* in the can under the sink.

scrap worn or used material that can be used again in some way:
We used the *scrap* from the sewing class to make a quilt.

whine

Verb. to cry in a soft, high complaining voice:
They heard the puppy *whine* from behind the closed door.

wail to make a mournful cry:
The cats always *wail* when they're hungry or want attention.

whimper to cry with weak, broken sounds:
The child might *whimper* in fear when the dog begins to bark.

wonderful

Adjective. very good; fine.

> *delightful*
> *enjoyable*
> *exciting*
> *fascinating*
> *favorable*
> *gratifying*
> *joyful*
> *marvelous*
> *pleasant*
> *pleasing*
> *pleasurable*
> *refreshing*
> *satisfying*
> *splendid*
> *terrific*

antonyms: unpleasant, disagreeable

Spelling Thesaurus

worn

Adjective, formed from the past participle of the verb wear.
damaged by use or wear:
I put on my *worn* jeans when I work in the garden.

shabby worn out and faded:
The musician's coat was *shabby* but clean and neatly patched.

frayed separated into loose threads:
Fold the *frayed* hem of the skirt under and sew it down.

threadbare worn out so much that the threads show through:
My favorite shirt is too *threadbare* to wear to school.

ragged worn out and torn:
A *ragged* shirt was all we found in the abandoned house.

Spelling Thesaurus

How to Use the Spelling Dictionary

A **dictionary** helps you use a word correctly. You will see **guide words** at the top of each page. The guide word on the left shows the first word on that page. The one on the right shows the last word on that page.

The word you look up is a **main entry** word. All entry words are in alphabetical order.
If the word is a homograph, you will usually find separate entries.

The **part of speech** of each meaning is given.

An **example sentence** helps you know how to use each meaning of the word.

A **definition** tells what the entry word means. If there is more than one meaning, each meaning will be numbered.

refuse¹ Anything thrown away as useless or worthless; trash or rubbish. The street was littered with *refuse* after the parade. **re•fuse** (ref′ ūs′) *noun*.
refuse² **1.** To say no to. She tried to *refuse* my offer of help. **2.** To decline to do. The horse might *refuse* to jump. **refuse** (ri fūz′) *verb*, **refused, refusing**.

Other **forms** of the entry word are given to show how to add an ending if you need to.

A **respelling** shows you how to pronounce the word. Look at the pronunciation key on each right-hand page in this Dictionary, or look at the table of Common Spelling Patterns on page 159.

Spelling Dictionary

Spelling Dictionary

-able 1. Capable of. **2.** Tending to. A glass vase is *breakable*. **-a•ble** (ə bəl) *suffix*.

aboard On or in a ship or train. When I took the train to New York, the conductor shouted, "All *aboard* !" *Adverb*.
—On or into for passage. Go *aboard* the ship before it departs. *Preposition*. **a•board** (ə bôrd′) *adverb* ; *preposition*.

acid rain Rain that can harm plants and other parts of the environment because it contains chemical pollution. **ac•id rain** (as′id rān) *noun*.

across To or on the other side. She got *across* in a sailboat. *Adverb*.
—To or on the other side of. Let's race *across* the street. *Preposition*. **a•cross** (ə krôs′) *adverb; preposition*.

action 1. Something that is done; an act. Giving someone else your seat on the bus is a kind *action*. **2.** A way of working or moving. This washing machine has a gentle *action*. **ac•tion** (ak′ shən) *noun, plural* **actions**.

active 1. Moving around or doing something much of the time. We have a very *active* kitten. **2.** Capable of acting. An *active* volcano can erupt at any time. **ac•tive** (ak′ tiv) *adjective;* **actively** *adverb*.

adventure 1. An exciting experience. Our trip to Alaska was quite an *adventure*. **2.** A dangerous undertaking. The trip into space was a daring *adventure*. **ad•ven•ture** (ad ven′ chər) *noun, plural* **adventures**.

affair 1. Concern. This is your *affair*. **2.** Event. The dance is going to be a formal *affair*. **3. affairs** Matters of business or government. The *affairs* of government kept her busy. **af•fair** (ə fâr′) *noun, plural* **affairs**.

agent 1. A person who acts for or in place of another. I bought my house through a real estate *agent*. **2.** A force that causes change. Gasoline is a flammable *agent*. **a•gent** (ā′ jənt) *noun, plural* **agents**.

agile 1. Able to move and react quickly and easily. A cat is an *agile* animal. **2.** Able to think quickly. Astronauts need *agile* minds. **ag•ile** (aj′əl) *adjective*.

agree 1. To say that one is willing; give permission. She *agreed* to let him use her baseball glove. **2.** To have the same opinion or feeling. My friends all *agree* that it was a good movie. **3.** To come to an understanding. The class *agreed* that they would send flowers to their teacher. **a•gree** (ə grē′) *verb*, **agreed, agreeing**.

aim The act of pointing something toward a target. The basketball player took *aim* at the basket. *Noun*.
—To aspire. The young actress will *aim* for stardom. *Verb*. **aim** (ām) *noun, plural* **aims**; *verb*, **aimed, aiming**.

airline A system for scheduled transport of passengers and freight by air. The *airline* had a nonstop flight to California. **air•line** (âr′ līn′) *noun, plural* **airlines**.

-al Action, process.
—Like, similar. **-al** (əl) *noun suffix; adjective suffix*.

Alabama A state in the southeastern United States. The capital of Alabama is Montgomery. The abbreviation for Alabama is AL. **Al•a•bam•a** (al′ə bam′ə) *noun*.

Alaska A state in the extreme northwestern part of North America. The capital of Alaska is Juneau. The abbreviation for Alaska is AK. **A•las•ka** (ə las′kə) *noun*.

Albany The capital of New York State. **Al•ban•y** (ôl′bə nē) *noun*.

at; āpe, fär, câre; end; mē, it, īce; pîerce; hot, ōld: sông, fôrk; oil; out; up; ūse; rūle; pùll; tûrn; chin; sing; shop; thin; **th**is; **hw** in **wh**ite; **zh** in treasure. The symbol ə stands for the unstressed vowel sound in **a**bout, tak**e**n, penc**i**l, lem**o**n, and circ**u**s.

Spelling Dictionary

alert A warning signal. Follow instructions when you hear the *alert. Noun.*
—To warn. *Verb.*
—Quick to act. The boy was *alert* when he was walking home at night. *Adjective.*
a•lert (ə lûrt′) *noun, plural* **alerts**; *verb*, **alerted, alerting**; *adjective.* **alertly** *adverb.*

allow 1. To let do or happen. Will you *allow* me to go to the dance? 2. To assign a suitable amount. The hostess will *allow* for two servings per guest. **al•low** (ə lou′) *verb*, **allowed, allowing.**

allowance 1. A set amount of money given at regular times. I get an *allowance* each week. 2. An amount granted in exchange for something. They got an *allowance* of five hundred dollars for trading in their old car. 3. Take into consideration. You should make *allowance* for his inexperience. **al•low•ance** (ə lou′əns) *noun, plural* **allowances.**

all right 1. Good enough. The book was not as good as I had hoped, but it was *all right.* 2. Not hurt or ill. I hope everyone is *all right. Adjective.*
—1. Well enough. James does *all right* in school. 2. Yes. *All right,* I'll go along. 3. For certain. That's the answer, *all right. Adverb.* **all right** (ôl rīt′) *adjective, adverb.*

alphabet The system of letters used to stand for the different sounds of a language. There are twenty-six letters in our *alphabet.* **al•pha•bet** (al′fə bet′) *noun, plural* **alphabets.**

amateur 1. A person who does something for the pleasures of doing it, not for pay. For many years, only *amateurs* in sports were allowed in the Olympic Games. 2. A person who does something without much experience or skill. I haven't been acting for long, so I still feel like an *amateur. Noun.*
—Done by or made up of amateurs. I will run the mile in the *amateur* track meet. *Adjective.* **am•a•teur** (am′ə chər *or* am′ə tər) *noun, plural* **amateurs;** *adjective.*

amaze 1. To surprise greatly. Did the results of the experiment *amaze* you? 2. To fill with wonder. This trick will *amaze* everyone. **a•maze** (ə māz′) *verb,* **amazed, amazing.**

ambush 1. A surprise attack made by people who are in a hidden place. In the jungle the troops were always afraid of an *ambush* by the enemy. 2. A hidden place from which people can make a surprise attack. The bandits waited in *ambush* to hold up the stagecoach. **am•bush** (am′bush) *noun, plural* **ambushes.**

amendment A formal change made according to official procedures. In 1920, women were given the right to vote by an *amendment* to the United States Constitution. **a•mend•ment** (ə mend′mənt) *noun, plural* **amendments.**

America North, Central, and South America considered as a whole. **A•mer•i•ca** (ə mer′i kə) *noun.*

amuse 1. To keep interested or busy in a way that gives pleasure. This toy will *amuse* the baby. 2. To make someone laugh. A good comedian can *amuse* anyone. **a•muse** (ə mūz′) *verb,* **amused, amusing.**

amusement 1. Something that provides entertainment. A puppet show provided the *amusement* at the party. 2. Something that helps pass the time in an entertaining way. I read mystery stories for *amusement.* **a•muse•ment** (ə mūz′mənt) *noun, plural* **amusements.**

ancient 1. Having had an existence for many years. In Egypt there are many *ancient* tombs. 2. Prehistoric, old; relating to a period of time long ago. The Egyptian tombs are from *ancient* times. **an•cient** (ān′shənt) *adjective.*

announce To make something known in an official or formal way. The principal will *announce* the names of the students on the honor roll later this afternoon. **an•nounce** (ə nouns′) *verb,* **announced, announcing.**

announcement 1. A public statement. Did you hear the *announcement* of the new school rules? 2. A printed notice. The wedding *announcement* came in the mail. **an•nounce•ment** (ə nouns′mənt) *noun, plural* **announcements.**

appear 1. To come into sight. Orion will *appear* in the night sky. **2.** To come before the public. The actor will *appear* in a new television series. **ap•pear** (ə pîr′) *verb, appeared, appearing.*

appoint To name or select. The mayor will *appoint* a new police chief. **ap•point** (ə point′) *verb.*

appointment 1. The act of naming or selecting for a position, office, or duty. The *appointment* of the new judge was announced in the newspaper. **2.** A position or office to which one is appointed. The doctor was offered an *appointment* on the hospitial staff. **3.** An agreement to meet or see someone at a certain time and place. I have an *appointment* at ten o'clock. **ap•point•ment** (ə point′mənt) *noun, plural* **appointments.**

apron A garment worn on the front of the body to protect the clothing. **a•pron** (ā′prən) *noun, plural* **aprons.**

arc 1. A curved line between two points on a circle. **2.** Any line curving in this way. The rainbow formed an *arc* in the sky. **arc** (ärk) *noun, plural* **arcs.**

arch 1. A curved structure over an open space such as a doorway. **2.** The lower part of the foot that forms an upward curve between the heel and the toes. *Noun.*
—To form into an arch; curve. *Verb.* **arch** (ärch) *noun, plural* **arches;** *verb,* **arched, arching.**

arctic 1. Near the North Pole or relating to the area around it. **2.** Very cold. **arc•tic** (ärk′tik *or* är′tik) *adjective.*

argument 1. An angry quarrel. The *argument* between the two became loud. **2.** A set of reasons for or against something. Each group presented its *argument.* **3.** Controversy. The *argument* over the borders continued. **ar•gu•ment** (är′gyə mənt) *noun, plural* **arguments.**

Arizona One of the southwestern states of the United States. The capital of Arizona is Phoenix. The abbreviation for Arizona is AZ. **Ar•i•zo•na** (ar′ə zō′nə) *noun.*

Arkansas One of the south central states of the United States. The capital of Arkansas is Little Rock. The abbreviation for Arkansas is AR. **Ar•kan•sas** (är′kən sô′) *noun.*

assignment 1. A task that is given. The student tried hard to finish the *assignment.* **2.** An appointment. The soldier received his new *assignment.* **as•sign•ment** (ə sīn′mənt) *noun, plural* **assignments.**

assistance The act of assisting; help; aid. We will need some *assistance* with carrying in the packages. **as•sist•ance** (ə sis′təns) *noun.*

assure 1. To give confidence to. Sally *assured* her father that she would pass the test. **2.** To cause to be certain. Their hard work *assured* the success of the project. **as•sure** (ə shùr′) *verb,* **assured, assuring.**

astronaut A member of the crew of a spacecraft. **as•tro•naut** (as′trə nôt′) *noun, plural* **astronauts.**

athlete A person who is trained in sports or other exercises that take strength, skill, and speed. That baseball player is a good *athlete.* **ath•lete** (ath′lēt) *noun, plural* **athletes.**

astronaut

atmosphere 1. A gaseous mass enveloping a celestial body. **2.** The whole mass of air surrounding Earth. The space shuttle passed through the *atmosphere* on its return to Earth. **at•mo•sphere** (at′mə sfir′) *noun, plural* **atmospheres.**

attach To join one thing to another. The boy *attached* the basket to his bicycle. —Bound by feelings of affection. The children were *attached* to the puppy. **at•tach** (ə tach′) *verb,* **attached, attaching;** *adjective.*

attention 1. The act of careful listening. Pay *attention* to the teacher. **2.** Care. The nurse

at; āpe, fär, câre; end; mē, it, īce; pîerce; hot, ōld; sông, fôrk; oil; out; up; ūse; rüle; pùll; tûrn; chin; sing; shop; thin; this; hw in white; zh in treasure. The symbol ə stands for the unstressed vowel sound in about, taken, pencil, lemon, and circus.

Spelling Dictionary

gave me skillful *attention.* **3.** A military position of readiness. The soldier stood at *attention.* **at•ten•tion** (ə ten′shən) *noun.*

attic A room or space in a house just below the roof. **at•tic** (at′ik) *noun, plural* **attics**.

August The eighth month of the year. August has thirty-one days. **Au•gust** (ô′gəst) *noun.*

Austin The capital city of Texas. **Aus•tin** (ô′stən) *noun.*

author 1. A creator of written work. E.B. White is the *author* of several books. **2.** A person who begins or initiates. Mr. Patton is the *author* of the new education plan. **au•thor** (ô′thər) *noun, plural* **authors**.

autumn The season between summer and winter. **au•tumn** (ô′təm) *noun.*

average A number found by adding a group of addends and dividing their sum by the number of addends in the group. *Noun.* To find the average of. *Verb.* Usual, typical, ordinary. The *average* house cat weighs about five pounds. *Adjective.* **av•er•age** (av′ər ij *or* av′rij) *noun, plural* **averages**; *verb,* **averaged, averaging;** *adjective.*

avoid To keep away from. We took a back road to *avoid* the heavy highway traffic. **a•void** (ə void′) *verb,* **avoided, avoiding.**

awhile 1. For a while. **2.** A little time. Please stop *awhile* before continuing your journey. **a•while** (ə hwīl′ or ə wīl′) *adverb.*

B

background 1. The part of a picture or scene that seems to be in the distance. The sun was setting in the *background* of the photograph. **2.** Past events or facts that help to explain some later event or situation. My history class is studying the *background* of the American Revolution. **back•ground** (bak′ground′) *noun, plural* **backgrounds.**

bacon Salted, smoked meat from the back and sides of a hog. **ba•con** (bā′kən) *noun.*

Baltimore A seaport city in Maryland. **Bal•ti•more** (bôl′tə mōr) *noun.*

bandage A piece of material used to cover a wound. *Noun.*
—To cover a wound with a piece of material. *Verb.* **ban•dage** (ban′dij) *noun, plural* **bandages**; *verb,* **bandaged, bandaging.**

banner A flag or other piece of cloth with a design or words on it. The knights carried a bright, colorful *banner.* **ban•ner** (ban′ər) *noun, plural* **banners**.

bargain 1. Something offered for sale or bought at a low price. **2.** An agreement. We made a *bargain* that I would wash the dishes if Pat would dry them. *Noun.*
—To talk over the price of a sale or the terms of an agreement. *Verb.* **bar•gain** (bär′gin) *noun, plural* **bargains**; *verb,* **bargained, bargaining.**

barge A large, flat-bottomed boat used to carry freight on canals and rivers. *Noun.*
—**1.** To move or enter clumsily or rudely. Do you always *barge* into a room like that? **2.** To carry by barge. *Verb.* **barge** (bärj) *noun, plural* **barges**; *verb,* **barged, barging.**

barnyard A fenced area around a barn. **barn•yard** (bärn′yärd′) *noun, plural* **barnyards**.

barrel

barrel 1. A round container with curved sides made of boards held together with hoops. **2.** Informal for much; a lot. We had a *barrel* of fun. *Noun.*
—To travel at a high speed. When the train goes through, it will *barrel* past our house. *Verb.* **bar•rel** (bar′əl) *noun, plural* **barrels**, *verb.*

basement The lowest story of a building, usually below ground. **base•ment** (bās′mənt) *noun, plural* **basements**.

basic Fundamental; essential. Learn the *basic* skills before you try to skydive. **bas•ic** (bā′sik) *adjective.*

bass¹ 1. A male singing voice with the lowest range, below baritone. **2.** A musical instrument that has a similar range. **bass** (bās) *noun, plural* **basses**.

Spelling Dictionary

bass² Any of various freshwater or saltwater food and game fish of North America. **bass** (bas) *noun, plural* **bass** or **basses.**

beautiful **1.** Possessing beauty. We traveled to Switzerland to see the *beautiful* mountain scenery. **beau•ti•ful** (bū′tə fəl) *adjective.*

became Past tense of **become.** The train will *become* hot if the air conditioning breaks. **be•came** (bi kām′) *verb.*

beggar A person who lives by begging. **beg•gar** (beg′ər) *noun, plural* **beggars.**

behave To act correctly. He promised that he would *behave* when visiting his father's office. **be•have** (bi hāv′) *verb.*

behavior A way of behaving or acting. The class studied the *behavior* of bats. **be•hav•ior** (bi hāv′yər) *noun, plural* **behaviors.**

believe **1.** To accept as true or real. Can you *believe* that ridiculous story? **2.** To possess a strong religious faith. **be•lieve** (bi lēv′, bē lēv′) *verb,* **believed, believing.**

bench A long seat for several people, usually made of wood or stone. **bench** (bench) *noun, plural* **benches.**

bet **1.** An agreement between two people involving the probability of a certain outcome or result. **2.** The money or thing risked. *Noun.*
—To promise something of value to another if you are wrong. I *bet* my week's allowance on the race. *Verb.* **bet** (bet) *noun, plural* **bets;** *verb,* **bet** or **betted, betting.**

beware To be on guard. *Beware* of deep water. **be•ware** (bi wâr′) *verb.*

blaze¹ **1.** A bright, intense flame or fire. The *blaze* destroyed a block of buildings. **2.** A bright, intense light or glow. We shielded our eyes from the *blaze* of the sun. **3.** A brilliant or striking display. The parade was a *blaze* of color. *Noun.*
—**1.** To burn brightly. Torches *blazed* through the night. **2.** To shine brilliantly; be bright. The city streets *blazed* with light. *Verb.* **blaze** (blāz) *noun, plural* **blazes;** *verb,* **blazed, blazing.**

blaze² **1.** A light-colored marking on the face of an animal, such as a horse or a cow. **2.** A mark made on a tree to show a trail or boundary, as by chipping off a piece of bark. *Noun.*
—To mark with blazes. The hikers will *blaze* a trail through the forest. *Verb.* **blaze** (blāz) *noun, plural* **blazes;** *verb,* **blazed, blazing.**

blossom The flower of a plant. *Noun.*
—**1.** To bloom. The trees are *blossoming.* **2.** To develop successfully. Karen's writing skills should *blossom* when she starts her new course. *Verb.* **blos•som** (blos′əm) *noun, plural* **blossoms;** *verb*

bolt **1.** A pin or rod used for holding things together, usually with a head at one end and thread for a nut to be attached on the other end. **2.** A sliding bar for fastening a door. I closed the door and slid the *bolt* shut. **3.** A flash of lightning. *Noun.*
—**1.** To fasten or secure with a bolt. **2.** To spring or move suddenly: The child *bolted* out the door. *Verb.* **bolt** (bōlt) *noun, plural* **bolts;** *verb,* **bolted, bolting.**

boost **1.** An upward lift. **2.** An increased amount. **3.** An act of encouragement. *Noun.*
—**1.** To push from below. I will *boost* you over the fence. **2.** To increase in amount. The summer drought will *boost* the price of corn. *Verb.* **boost** (büst) *noun, plural* **boosts;** *verb,* **boosted, boosting.**

border An outer part or edge. This skirt has a pretty red *border.* *Noun.*
—**1.** To put an edge on. I'll *border* the sleeves of your dress with lace. **2.** To touch or lie near an edge. Mexico *borders* the United States. *Verb.* **bor•der** (bôr′dər) *noun, plural* **borders;** *verb.*

bore¹ Someone or something that is very dull. This television show is a real *bore.* **bore** (bôr) *noun, plural* **bores.**

bore² To make a hole in. We had to *bore* a hole in the wall. **bore** (bôr) *verb* **bored, boring.**

---

at; āpe, fär, câre; end; mē, it, īce; pîerce; hot, ōld: sông, fôrk; oil; out; up; ūse; rüle; pùll; tûrn; chin; sing; shop; thin; **this**; hw in white; zh in treasure. The symbol ə stands for the unstressed vowel sound in about, taken, pencil, lemon, and circus.

Spelling Dictionary

bough A large branch of a tree. The *bough* on the apple tree was full of flowers. **bough** (bou) *noun, plural* **boughs**.

boundary A line that marks the edge of a country, state, or other area; border. The Rio Grande forms the *boundary* between Mexico and the United States. **bound•a•ry** (bound ′ə rē or boun′drē) *noun, plural* **boundaries.**

boycott To join with others in refusing to buy from or deal with a person, nation, or business. We will *boycott* the store down the street to show support for the workers on strike. *Verb.*
—a planned joining with others in refusing to buy from or deal with a person, nation, or business. *Noun.* **boy•cott** (boi′kot) *verb,* **boycotted, boycotting;** *noun, plural* **boycotts.**

brake Something used to stop or slow the movement of a wheel. Michael stopped his bicycle by pressing the *brake. Noun.*
To operate the brake on a vehicle. **brake** (brāk) *noun, plural* **brakes;** *verb.*

break 1. The act of breaking. **2.** A gap in an electrical circuit. **3.** A planned interruption. There was a station *break* for commercials. *Noun.*
—**1.** To make into pieces by force. **2.** To harm or damage. The baby will *break* the typewriter if he bangs on it. *Verb.* **break** (brāk) *noun, plural* **breaks;** *verb* **broke, broken, breaking.**

breeze A gentle wind. **breeze** (brēz) *noun, plural* **breezes.**

bridge A structure built for passing from one side to the other. I walked across the *bridge* to the other shore of the river. **bridge** (brij) *noun, plural* **bridges.**

brighten To make bright or brighter. Adding bleach will *brighten* the laundry. **bright•en** (brīt′ən) *verb.*

broad 1. Wide. I like to travel on *broad* highways. **2.** Clear; full. In summer in Alaska, it can be *broad* daylight at 9:00 P.M. **3.** Extensive. There was a *broad* choice of food at the restaurant. **broad** (brôd)

adjective; **broadly** *adverb;* **broaden** *verb,* **broadness** *noun.*

broken Past participle of **break; broke.**
1. Damaged or injured. **2.** Failed to keep. He's *broken* his promise. **3.** Gone beyond. She's *broken* the track's speed record for the mile. *Verb.*
—**1.** Shattered in pieces. **2.** Damaged. **3.** Having breaks. A *broken* line of trees marked the estate's boundary. **4.** Not kept. A *broken* promise is hard to forgive. *Adjective.* **bro•ken** (brō′kən) *verb; adjective.*

broom A long stick with a brush at one end, used for sweeping. **broom** (brüm or brûm) *noun, plural* **brooms.**

bruise 1. An injury that doesn't break the skin but does discolor it. **2.** An injury to the surface of a fruit or vegetable. *Noun.*
—**1.** To give a bruise. **2.** To hurt the feelings of. Her cruel words *bruised* my feelings. *Verb.* **bruise** (brüz) *noun, plural* **bruises;** *verb* **bruised, bruising.**

brushes Plural of **brush,** which is a tool used for scrubbing, smoothing, sweeping, or painting. *Noun.*
—To scrub, smooth, sweep or paint with a brush. Dave *brushes* his dog's hair. *Verb.* **brush** (brush) *noun, plural* **brushes;** *verb,* **brushed, brushing.**

bubble 1. A tiny, round body of gas trapped in a liquid. There are *bubbles* in soda water. **2.** A thin film of liquid filled with gas. *Noun.*
—**1.** To form bubbles. **2.** To be filled with excitement or anticipation. The little girl *bubbles* with excitement before visiting her grandmother. *Verb.* **bub•ble** (bub′əl) *noun, plural* **bubbles;** *verb,* **bubbled, bubbling.**

budge To move just a little. I couldn't *budge* the huge rock. **budge** (buj) *verb,* **budged, budging.**

bulletin A brief notice from an official source. The weekly *bulletin* announces the important happenings in school. **bul•le•tin** (bùl′i tin) *noun, plural* **bulletins.**

bulletin

Spelling Dictionary

burden 1. Something carried. The donkey carried a heavy *burden.* **2.** Something hard to bear. The *burden* of shame was so heavy that the family moved out of town. *Noun.*
—To put a burden on. Don't *burden* me with your troubles. *Verb.* **bur•den** (bûr′dən) *noun, plural* **burdens**; *verb,* **burdened, burdening**.

bureau 1. A low chest of drawers used in a bedroom. Laura put her perfume on the *bureau.* **2.** A business office providing services to the public. You must take your driver's test at the Motor Vehicles *Bureau.* **bu•reau** (byùr′ō) *noun, plural* **bureaus**.

California One of the Pacific states of the United States. The capital of California is Sacramento. The abbreviation is CA. **Cal•i•for•ni•a** (kal′ə fôrn′yə or kal′ə fôr′nē ə) *noun.*

camel A long-necked mammal used as a beast of burden in Asia and Africa because it can travel long distances without water. **cam•el** (kam′əl) *noun, plural* **camels**.

canoe A long, narrow boat, pointed at both ends and moved by paddles. The campers traveled downstream by *canoe. Noun.*
—To go in a canoe. *Verb.* **ca•noe** (kə nü′) *noun plural* **canoes**; *verb,* **canoed, canoeing.**

canyon A deep valley with high, steep sides. **can•yon** (kan′yən) *noun, plural* **canyons**.

capital 1. A capital letter. **2.** A capital city. **3.** An amount of wealth or goods, especially as in business. That corporation has a large amount of *capital. Noun.*
—**1.** Belonging to the series of uppercase or larger letters: A, B, C, etc. **2.** First in importance. Every state has a *capital* city. *Adjective.* **cap•i•tal** (kap′i təl) *noun, plural* **capitals**; *adjective.*

capitol The building in which a state legislature meets. **cap•i•tol** (kap′i təl) *noun.*

captain 1. The commander of a body of troops or of a military establishment. The *captain* ordered his troops to march forward. **2.** A dominant figure. *Noun.*
—To be captain of. Robert *captained* the soccer team to victory. *Verb.* **cap•tain** (kap′tən) *noun, plural* **captains**; *verb.*

career A profession followed as a permanent occupation. Her *career* as a physician has been a success. **ca•reer** (kə rîr′) *noun.*

careful Using care. Alfredo is *careful* whenever he uses sharp tools. **care•ful** (kâr′fəl) *adjective.*

carefully 1. Using great caution. **2.** Done in a thorough or exact way. Joshua *carefully* fastened the wings to the model plane. **care•ful•ly** (kâr′fə lē) *adverb.*

cartilage A strong, flexible material that forms parts of the body of humans and other animals that have a backbone. *Cartilage* is not as stiff or as hard as bone. **car•ti•lage** (kär′tə lij) *noun.*

carton A cardboard container. Bring me a *carton* of milk from the store. **car•ton** (kär′tən) *noun, plural* **cartons**.

carve 1. To cut into small pieces. Everyone likes to *carve* the turkey. **2.** To design by cutting. The artist can *carve* a statue out of stone. **carve** (kärv) *verb,* **carved, carving.**

case 1. Any special situation for a person or thing. This is a *case* for the police. **2.** An instance of disease. You have a bad *case* of measles. **3.** Matter for a court of law to decide. **4.** A box or container. Please put the tools back in their *case.* **case** (kās) *noun, plural* **cases**.

cash Money in the form of coins and bills. I don't carry much *cash* with me. *Noun.*
—To get or give money for. The bank will *cash* your check. *Verb.* **cash** (kash) *noun; verb,* **cashed, cashing.**

at; āpe, fär, câre; end; mē, it, īce; pîerce; hot, ōld; sông, fôrk; oil; out; up; ūse; rüle; pùll; tûrn; chin; sing; shop; thin; <u>th</u>is; hw in white; zh in treasure. The symbol ə stands for the unstressed vowel sound in about, taken, pencil, lemon, and circus.

Spelling Dictionary

caution A warning about something. Use *caution* on slippery roads. **cau•tion** (kô′shən) *noun, plural* **cautions**.

celebrate 1. To observe in a special way. We *celebrate* Thanksgiving with a huge meal. **2.** To perform rites publicly. The parents will *celebrate* their son's graduation. **cel•e•brate** (sel′ə brāt′) *verb,* **celebration, celebrator** *noun.*

cellar a room or group of rooms built underground. **cel•lar** (sel′ər) *noun, plural* **cellars.**

census An official count of the people living in a country or district. A census is taken to find out how many people there are. **cen•sus** (sen′səs) *noun, plural* **censuses.**

central 1. Being near the center. My school is in the *central* part of town. **2.** Being the principal part of something. Tom Sawyer is the *central* character in the book. **cen•tral** (sen′trəl) *adjective.*

century A period of 100 years. **cen•tu•ry** (sen′chə rē) *noun, plural* **centuries**.

chalkboard A smooth, hard surface made to be written on with chalk. **chalk•board** (chôk′bôrd′) *noun, plural* **chalkboards**.

chance 1. Fate; the way things happen. They met by *chance*. **2.** A risk. Sonny will take a *chance* and not set his alarm clock. **chance** (chans) *noun plural* **chances**.

channel 1. The deepest part of a river. **2.** Body of water joining two larger bodies of water. **3.** A band of frequencies that carries the programs of a television or radio station. What *channel* is carrying the World Series? *Noun.*
—**1.** To form a channel in. **2.** To direct into a particular course. She helped me *channel* my talent toward a career. *Verb.* **chan•nel** (chan′əl) *noun, plural* **channels**; *verb,* **channeled, channeling**

chart 1. A sheet that shows information as a list or graphs. Our class made a *chart* showing all the students' birthdays. **2.** A map. The sailors used a detailed *chart* to follow their course. *Noun.*
—**1.** To make a map or chart of. The explorers *charted* the coastline. **2.** To lay out a plan. We need to *chart* a system for getting our work done. *Verb.* **chart** (chärt) *noun, plural* **charts**; *verb.*

cheap 1. Available below the going price or the real value. The chair was purchased for a *cheap* price at the auction. **2.** Gained with little effort. **cheap** (chēp) *adjective,* **cheapen** *verb,* **cheaply** *adverb,* **cheapness** *noun.*

cheer 1. A shout of happiness, encouragement, or praise. We greeted our team with *cheers*. **2.** Good spirits. Everyone is full of *cheer* during the holidays. *Noun.* **1.** To give hope to. Try to *cheer* him up. **2.** To urge by shouting approval. *Verb.* **cheer** (chîr) *noun, plural* **cheers**; *verb,* **cheerful** *adjective.*

Chicago A city in northeast Illinois on Lake Michigan. **Chi•ca•go** (shi kä′gō) *noun.*

childhood The state of being a child. Susan remembered her *childhood* as a happy time of life. **child•hood** (chīld′hùd′) *noun, plural* **childhoods**.

chore 1. A small job or task. Drying the dishes is one of my nightly *chores*. **2.** Something to do that is difficult or unpleasant. I find writing letters a difficult *chore*. **chore** (chôr) *noun, plural* **chores**.

chose Past tense of **choose**. Kenneth will *choose* the blue ball because it's his favorite color. **chose** (chōz) *verb.*

chosen Past participle of **choose**. Michael was *chosen* by the music teacher to lead the chorus. **cho•sen** (chō′zən) *verb.*

cinnamon A spice made from the bark of a laurel tree of the East Indies. My father puts *cinnamon* in his apple pies. **cin•na•mon** (sin′ə mən) *noun.*

civic 1. Having to do with a city. Keeping our streets and parks clean is a matter of *civic* pride. **2.** Having to do with the responsibilities or privileges of a citizen or citizenship. It is a person's *civic* duty to vote. **civ•ic** (siv′ik) *adjective.*

civil 1. Relating to citizens. Voting is our *civil* duty. **2.** Relating to the state as a government organization. The courts are *civil* bodies.

3. Polite but not friendly. Apologizing was the only *civil* thing to do. **civ•il** (siv′əl) *adjective.*

classify 1. To arrange in groups. The librarian will *classify* the books according to the authors who wrote them. **2.** To assign to a class. Would you *classify* this stone as a pebble or a rock? **clas•si•fy** (klas′ə fī′) *verb,* **classified, classifying.**

clerk 1. A person who keeps records. He serves as the town *clerk.* **2.** A salesperson in a store. The *clerk* rang up the sale on the cash register. *Noun.*
—To act or work as a clerk. *Verb.* **clerk** (klûrk) *noun, plural* **clerks;** *verb.*

Cleveland A city in northeast Ohio. **Cleve•land** (klēv′lənd) *noun.*

climate 1. The weather conditions in a particular place. The *climate* in Vermont is difficult to predict. **2.** The mood of a certain situation. The survey tried to find out the *climate* of public opinion. **cli•mate** (klī′mit) *noun, plural* **climates.**

clover

clover A low plant with leaves composed of three leaflets and with white or purple flowers; a source of nectar for bees and food for cattle. **clo•ver** (klō′vər) *noun, plural* **clovers.**

club 1. A heavy stick used as a weapon. **2.** A group of people with similar interests. The hiking *club* began its winter camping season. *Noun.*
—To beat with a club. *Verb.* **club** (klub) *noun, plural* **clubs;** *verb* **clubbed, clubbing.**

clutch A device in a machine that connects or disconnects parts. In order to shift gears, Rickey had to depress the *clutch. Noun.*
—To grasp tightly. *Verb.*

—Acting in a critical situation. The *clutch* hitter hit a home run to win the game. *Adjective.* **clutch** (kluch) *noun, plural* **clutches;** *verb; adjective.*

coach 1. A large, four-wheeled closed carriage drawn by horses, with seats inside for passengers and a raised seat outside for the driver. **2.** A railroad passenger car. **3.** A teacher or trainer, as of an athlete or athletic team, singer, actor, or dancer. **coach** (kōch) *noun, plural* **coaches.**

coarse 1. Not fine. We bought *coarse* salt to make ice cream. **2.** Thick and rough. The *coarse* wool of the sweater made my skin itch. **3.** Crude; vulgar. His *coarse* manners made us uncomfortable. **coarse** (kôrs) *adjective;* **coarsely** *adverb;* **coarseness** *noun.*

coast 1. The land near the sea; seashore. California is on the *coast. Noun.*
—**1.** To sail along the shore of. **2.** To slide along without effort or power. Robert can *coast* down the hill on his skateboard. *Verb.* **coast** (kōst) *noun, plural* **coasts;** *verb.* **coastal** *adjective.*

code 1. A collection of laws or rules. Our school's dress *code* requires students to dress neatly. **2.** A system of symbols used to represent secret meanings. *Noun.*
—To put into the symbols of a code. *Verb.* **code** (kōd) *noun, plural* **codes;** *verb,* **coded, coding.**

coffee A drink made from the roasted beans of a tropical tree. **cof•fee** (kô′fē) *noun, plural* **coffees.**

collar A band or strap worn around the neck. All dogs are required to wear a *collar. Noun.*
— To put a collar on. *Verb.* **col•lar** (kol′ər) *noun, plural* **collars;** *verb,* **collared.**

collection 1. A group of objects that belong together. I have a nice *collection* of seashells. **2.** Any gathering. A *collection* of people

at; āpe, fär, câre; end; mē, it, īce; pîerce; hot, ōld: sông, fôrk; oil; out; up; ūse; rüle; pùll; tûrn; chin; sing; shop; thin; <u>th</u>is; hw in white; zh in treasure. The symbol ə stands for the unstressed vowel sound in about, taken, pencil, lemon, and circus.

Spelling Dictionary

stood around the statue. **3.** A gathering of money. A *collection* was taken for the needy family. **col•lec•tion** (kə lek′shən) *noun,* *plural* **collections**.

Colorado One of the western states of the United States. The capital of Colorado is Denver. The abbreviation for Colorado is CO. **Col•o•ra•do** (kol′ə rad′ō *or* kol′ə rä′dō) *noun.*

column 1. A supporting post; pillar. The building had five huge *columns*. **2.** Anything looking like a post. A *column* of water shot up in the air. **3.** One of two or more sections of typed lines side by side on a page and separated by blank space. **4.** An article that appears regularly

column

in a newspaper or magazine. She writes a *column* for the newspaper. **5.** An arrangement of items one above another. Put the higher numbers at the top of the *column.* **col•umn** (kol′əm) *noun, plural* **columns.**

command 1. An order given. **2.** The ability to use or control. She has an excellent *command* of the German language. *Noun.* —To give an order. The trainer *commanded* the dog to sit still. *Verb.* **com•mand** (kə mand′) *noun, plural* **commands***; verb.*

committee A group of people chosen to do certain work. The *committee* decorated the gym for the dance. **com•mit•tee** (kə mit′ē) *noun, plural* **committees***.*

compare 1. To represent as similar or equal. **2.** To examine for likeness or differences. We will *compare* our answers. **com•pare** (kəm pâr′) *verb,* **compared, comparing.**

concentration 1. Close attention. The mayor's *concentration* was focused on the problem. **2.** Strength. The high *concentration* of some medicines can make them toxic. **con•cen•tra•tion** (kon′sən trā′shən) *noun, plural* **concentrations***.*

condemn 1. To express strong opposition to; disapprove of. Many doctors *condemn* smoking. **2.** To declare to be no longer safe or fit for use. The city will *condemn* the old building. **con•demn** (kən dem′) *verb,* **condemned, condemning.**

condense 1. To make or become less in size or volume. Milk *condenses* when the water in it is boiled away. **2.** To change from a gas to a liquid form. Steam *condenses* to water when cooled. **con•dense** (kən dens′) *verb,* **condensed, condensing.**

congressional Having to do with a congress. **con•gres•sion•al** (kən gresh′ə nəl) *adjective.*

Connecticut One of the states of the northeast United States. The capital of Connecticut is Hartford. The abbreviation for Connecticut is CT. **Con•nect•i•cut** (kə net′i kət) *noun.*

constellation A group of stars. A constellation forms a pattern in the sky that looks like a picture. **con•stel•la•tion** (kon′stə lā′shən) *noun, plural* **constellations.**

consume 1. To use up or destroy. A car *consumes* gasoline. **2.** To eat or drink up. I usually *consume* three meals a day. **con•sume** (kən süm′) *verb,* **consumed, consuming.**

consumer A person who buys and uses up things. **con•sum•er** (kən sü′mər) *noun, plural* **consumers.**

content[1] Happy; satisfied. She is *content* with her job. **con•tent** (kən tent′) *adjective.*

content[2] Subject matter. I read the *content* of the letter. **con•tent** (kon′ tent) *noun.*

contest A struggle to win. A spelling *contest* will be held tomorrow. *Noun.* —To argue against. I'm going to *contest* the issue with my cousin. *Verb.* **con•test** (kon′test′ *for noun;* kən test′ *for verb*) *noun, plural* **contests***; verb.*

conviction 1. The state of being found guilty of a crime. **2.** A strong belief. The candidate speaks with *conviction* about the issues. **con•vic•tion** (kən vik′shən) *noun, plural* **convictions***.*

convoy Protection that goes along with ships, people, or goods. A *convoy* of police follows the mayor wherever she goes. *Noun.*
—To go along with for protection. Each submarine will *convoy* a fleet of ships. *Verb.* **con•voy** (kon′voi′*for noun and verb;* kən voi′*for verb*) *noun, plural* **convoys**; *verb.*

correction The act of making something right. The *correction* of my spelling errors took ten minutes. **cor•rec•tion** (kə rek′shən) *noun, plural* **corrections**.

couch A piece of furniture big enough for two or more people to sit on at the same time. **couch** (kouch) *noun, plural* **couches**.

could've Shortened form of "could have." **could•'ve** (kùd′əv) *contraction.*

council 1. A group of people who meet to give advice and discuss questions. 2. A group of elected people who make laws for and manage a town. **coun•cil** (koun′səl) *noun plural* **councils**.

councilor A member of a council, especially of the council of a city or town. **coun•ci•lor** (koun′sə lər) *noun, plural* **councilors**.

crawl 1. Very slow movement. The traffic slowed to a *crawl*. 2. A rapid swimming stroke. *Noun.*
—To move slowly and close to the ground. Soon the baby will be old enough to *crawl*. *Verb.* **crawl** (krôl) *noun, plural* **crawls**; *verb.*

cream The yellowish part of milk that contains butterfat. **cream** (krēm) *noun, plural* **creams**.

create 1. To cause to come into existence. The scientist *created* a robot to dive into the ocean. 2. To be the cause of. Lack of rain *creates* drought. **cre•ate** (krē āt′) *verb,* **created, creating.**

creation 1. The act of causing something to exist or happen. *Creation* of the motion picture took many months. 2. Anything that has been made. A sculpture, a painting, or a book is a *creation*. **cre•a•tion** (krē ā′shən) *noun, plural* **creations.**

creep 1. A creeping movement. 2. *Usually plural,* a feeling of horror. The movie gave me the *creeps*. *Noun.*
—To move with the body close to the ground, as on hands and knees. The baby will *creep* toward his toy. *Verb.* **creep** (krēp) *noun, plural* **creeps**; *verb* **crept, creeping.**

crime 1. Anything that is against the law. Robbery is a *crime*. 2. Anything that seems wrong or foolish. It seems a *crime* to waste food. **crime** (krīm) *noun, plural* **crimes**.

cruel Causing pain and grief. **cru•el** (krü′əl) *adjective.*

crumb A small fragment of bread or other baked goods. There were *crumbs* on the kitchen table. **crumb** (krum) *noun, plural* **crumbs**.

crystal 1. A clear mineral that looks like glass. 2. A clear cover over a watch or clock. Be sure not to scratch the *crystal* on your watch. 3. Glassware. *Noun.*
—Made of or resembling crystal. I have a pair of *crystal* earrings. *Adjective.* **crys•tal** (kris′təl) *noun, plural* **crystals**; *adjective.*

cupboard A cabinet or closet with shelves for storing things. **cup•board** (kub′ərd) *noun, plural* **cupboards**.

curtain 1. A hanging screen, usually cloth, that can be drawn back or up. Sally pulled back the *curtain* to let in the sunlight. 2. The movable screen separating the stage from the auditorium. **cur•tain** (kûr′tin) *noun, plural* **curtains**.

cushion A soft pad; pillow. The *cushion* on your chair has nearly worn out. *Noun.*
—1. To place on a cushion. 2. To lessen the effect of something. You can *cushion* a fall by rolling when you hit the ground. *Verb.* **cush•ion** (kùsh′ən) *noun; verb.*

cycle 1. A series of events that happen one after another in the same order, over and over again. Spring, summer, autumn, and winter are the *cycle* of the four seasons of the year. 2. A bicycle, tricycle, or motorcycle. *Noun.*
—To ride a bicycle, tricycle, or motorcycle.

at; āpe, fär, câre; end; mē, it, īce; pîerce; hot, ōld: sông, fôrk; oil; out; up; ūse; rüle; pùll; tûrn; chin; sing; shop; thin; this; hw in white; zh in treasure. The symbol ə stands for the unstressed vowel sound in about, taken, pencil, lemon, and circus.

Spelling Dictionary

Verb. **cy•cle** (sī′kəl) *noun, plural* **cycles**; *verb*, **cycled, cycling.**

cyclist A person who rides a bicycle, tricycle, or motorcycle. **cy•clist** (sī′klist) *noun, plural* **cyclists**.

cyclone A storm that is characterized by very powerful winds. **cy•clone** (sī′klōn) *noun, plural* **cyclones.**

dairy 1. A place where milk is kept and made into cheese or butter. 2. A farm that produces milk. **dair•y** (dâr′ē) *noun, plural* **dairies.**

daisy

daisy A flower with white, pink, or yellow petals around a yellow center. **dai•sy** (dā′zē) *noun, plural* **daisies.**

damp Slightly wet. Wipe the table with a *damp* rag. **damp** (damp) *adjective;* **dampness** *noun.*

darkness 1. A condition without light. The complete *darkness* of the night was a little frightening. 2. Evil. The old king's reign was an era of *darkness.* **dark•ness** (därk′nis) *noun; verb,* **darken.**

daughter 1. A female child. A girl or woman is the *daughter* of her mother and father.

daugh•ter (dô′tər) *noun, plural* **daughters.**

decay The gradual loss of strength or quality. *Noun.*
—1. To decline from a sound or prosperous condition. The bridge will *decay* if it is not repaired. 2. To decompose; rot. The fruit turned moldy and began to *decay. Verb.* **de•cay** (di kā′) *noun, plural* **decays;** *verb.*

December The twelfth month of the year. December has thirty-one days. **De•cem•ber** (di sem′bər) *noun, plural* **Decembers.**

decorate 1. To make more attractive by adding something beautiful. Help me *decorate* the room for the party. 2. To award an honor to. The army *decorated* the soldier for bravery. **dec•o•rate** (dek′ə rāt′) *verb.*

decoration 1. The act of making more beautiful; decorating. The *decoration* of the gym for the dance took all day. 2. Something that is used to decorate; ornament. 3. A badge or medal. **dec•o•ra•tion** (dek′ə rā′shən) *noun, plural* **decorations.**

degree 1. A stage or step in a process or series. People become good piano players one *degree* at a time. 2. Amount or extent. A high *degree* of skill is needed to weave a rug. 3. A unit for measuring temperatures, angles, or arcs. Our normal body temperature is 98.6 *degrees* Fahrenheit. **de•gree** (di grē′) *noun, plural* **degrees.**

Delaware One of the Middle Atlantic states of the United States. The capital of Delaware is Dover. The abbreviation of Delaware is DE. **Del•a•ware** (del′ə wâr′) *noun.*

delay 1. To put off to a future time. The umpire *delayed* the game because of the rain. 2. To act slowly. *Verb.*
—1. The act of delaying. 2. The time in which something is delayed. The *delay* caused by the heavy traffic was frustrating. *Noun.* **de•lay** (di lā′) *verb; noun, plural* **delays.**

delicious Pleasing to the taste. This cake is *delicious.* **de•li•cious** (di lish′əs) *adjective; adverb,* **deliciously.**

delight Extreme joy or happiness. The winner showed *delight* with her prize. *Noun.* —To please greatly. *Verb.* **de•light** (di līt′) *noun, plural* **delights;** *verb.*

deserve **1.** To have the right to. You *deserve* more money than you're being paid. **2.** To be worthy of. The student *deserves* praise for the science project. **de•serve** (di zûrv′) *verb,* **deserved, deserving.**

despite In spite of; regardless of. *Despite* his lack of formal training, my brother is an excellent pianist. **de•spite** (di spīt′) *preposition.*

Detroit A city in southeast Michigan on the Detroit River. **De•troit** (di troit′) *noun.*

development **1.** The act or process of developing. **2.** An event or happening. A new *development* in the story was broadcast every hour. **3.** A group of houses or other buildings on a large area of land. The houses in a *development* often look alike. **de•vel•op•ment** (di vel′əp mənt) *noun, plural* **developments.**

diagnose To identify a disease. Did the doctor *diagnose* your illness? **di•ag•nose** (dī′əg nōs′) *verb,* **diagnosed, diagnosing.**

digestion The process of breaking down food into a form that can be absorbed and used by the body. **di•ges•tion** (di jes′chən *or* dī jes′chən) *noun, plural* **digestions.**

direction **1.** The guidance of action. Teachers work under the *direction* of the principal. **2.** An order or instruction given by an authority. Follow the doctor's *directions.* **3.** The course along which something lies. The sailboat was heading in a southerly *direction.* **di•rec•tion** (di rek′shən or dī rek′shən) *noun, plural* **directions;** *adjective,* **directionless.**

dis- **1.** The opposite of. **2.** Not. **dis-** (dis) *prefix.*

disappear **1.** To pass from view suddenly. The magician made the coins *disappear.* **2.** To cease to be. **dis•ap•pear** (dis′ə pîr′) *verb.* **disappearance** *noun.*

disappoint To fail to live up to the hopes of. You will *disappoint* the children if you do not keep the promise you made to them. **dis•ap•point** (dis′ə point′*verb.*

disapprove To have a strong feeling against. I *disapprove* of selfish people. **dis•ap•prove** (dis′ə prüv′) *verb.*

discover To locate or find out for the first time. Did Edison really *discover* electricity? **dis•cov•er** (dis kuv′ər) *verb.*

discussion Talking something over; consideration of a question. The class had a long *discussion* on how to spend their money. **dis•cus•sion** (dis kush′ən) *noun, plural* **discussions.**

dishonest Showing deceit or lack of fair play. A student who cheats on a test is *dishonest.* **dis•hon•est** (dis on′ist) *adjective;* **dishonestly** *adverb.*

dispute A difference of opinion. There is a *dispute* between the two children. *Noun.* —**1.** To participate in an argument. **2.** To fight over. The two countries *disputed* the boundary. *Verb.* **dis•pute** (di spūt′) *noun, plural* **disputes;** *verb,* **disputed, disputing.**

dissolve **1.** To mix thoroughly and evenly with a liquid. *Dissolve* the powder in milk to make the instant pudding. **2.** To bring to an end. The club members voted to *dissolve* the dance committe after the dance. **dis•solve** (di zolv′) *verb,* **dissolved, dissolving.**

distance **1.** The amount of space between two things or points. The *distance* from my house to the school is two blocks. **2.** A point or place that is far away. The driver saw a large truck in the *distance.* **dis•tance** (dis′təns) *noun, plural* **distances.**

disturb **1.** To interrupt. Do not *disturb* the baby's sleep. **2.** To throw into confusion. The cat *disturbed* the papers on the desk. **dis•turb** (di stûrb′) *verb; noun,* **disturber.**

ditch A long, narrow hole dug in the ground. **ditch** (dich) *noun, plural* **ditches.**

at; āpe, fär, câre; end; mē, it, īce; pîerce; hot, ōld: sông, fôrk; oil; out; up; ūse; rüle; pùll; tûrn; chin; sing; shop; thin; this; hw in white; zh in treasure. The symbol ə stands for the unstressed vowel sound in about, taken, pencil, lemon, and circus.

dizzy 1. Having the feeling of spinning and being about to fall. I felt too *dizzy* to walk. **2.** Causing dizziness. The amusement ride climbed to a *dizzy* height. **diz•zy** (diz′ē) *adjective,* **dizzier, dizziest;** *adverb,* **dizzily.**

doubt 1. The condition of being unsure. We were in *doubt* as to the best gift. **2.** Difficulty in believing. His warm smile helped ease my *doubt. Noun.*
—**1.** To be unsure of. I *doubt* her word after she's lied to us so many times. **2.** To consider unlikely. I *doubt* that it will snow before December. *Verb.* **doubt** (dout) *noun, plural* **doubts;** *verb; adjective,* **doubtful.**

dough A thick mixture of flour, liquid, and other ingredients used to make biscuits, bread, and cookies. **dough** (dō) *noun, plural* **doughs.**

drag 1. To pull along the ground. We had to *drag* the dog away from the bushes. **2.** To go slowly. Time seems to *drag* when you're bored. *Verb.* **drag** (drag) *verb,* **dragged, dragging.**

drain 1. To draw off gradually. My father *drained* the water from the swimming pool. **2.** To empty by drinking. *Verb.*
—**1.** A means of draining. During the storm the sewer *drain* overflowed. **2.** A gradual using up. *Noun.* **drain** (drān) *verb; noun, plural* **drains.**

drawer A sliding shelf or box. Antonio put his socks in the top *drawer.* **draw•er** (drôr) *noun, plural* **drawers.**

dreadful 1. Causing fear. **2.** Disagreeable; unpleasant. The boy showed *dreadful* manners in the cafeteria. **dread•ful** (dred′fəl) *adjective;* **dreadfully** *adverb; noun,* **dreadfulness.**

dream 1. A series of thoughts, feelings, and apparent sights that a person has while asleep. **2.** A hope or ambition to do or succeed at something. My *dream* is to become a scientist. *Noun.*
—**1.** To see, feel, or think in a dream. I often *dream* about riding a horse. **2.** To imagine. I didn't take an umbrella because I never *dreamed* it would rain. *Verb.* **dream** (drēm) *noun, plural* **dreams;** *verb,* **dreamed** *or* **dreamt, dreaming.**

drowsy Sleepy. **drow•sy** (drou′zē) *adjective;* **drowsily** *adverb.*

drum 1. Musical instrument that is hollow and covered at the top and at the bottom with material that is stretched tight. **2.** A container that is shaped like a drum. *Noun.*
—**1.** To beat or play on a drum. **2.** To make a sound like a drum. *Verb.* **drum** (drum) *noun, plural* **drums;** *verb,* **drummed, drumming.**

due 1. Owed or owing. The rent for the apartment is *due* on the first day of each month. **2.** Expected or supposed to arrive or be ready. **3.** Appropriate; proper. I addressed the principal with *due* respect. *Adjective.*
—**1.** Something that is owed. **2. dues.** A fee that a person pays to a club for being a member. *Noun.*
—Straight; directly. The explorers walked *due* west. *Adverb.* **due** (dü or dū) *adjective; noun, plural* **dues;** *adverb.*

dull 1. Lacking sharpness. **2.** Slow in action; boring. The movie on TV last night was *dull.* **3.** Lacking a shine. **4.** Not clear or vivid, for example, in color or sound. **dull** (dul) *adjective.*

during 1. Throughout the time of. The trees and grass are green *during* the summer. **2.** At some time in the course of. We were awakened by a telephone call *during* the night. **dur•ing** (dùr′ing or dyùr′ing) *preposition.*

duty 1. Conduct expected of a person. It is my *duty* to feed the cat daily. **2.** Behavior required by a person's occupation. She carried out her *duty* as a teacher. **3.** A tax. They paid *duty* on all foreign purchases. **du•ty** (dü′tē, dū′tē) *noun, plural* **duties.**

east 1. The direction in which the sun appears to rise. **2.** The eastern part of a country, always capitalized. The Appalachian Mountains are in the *East. Noun.*
—Referring to the direction in which the sun appears to rise. We planted bushes along the

east side of the house. *Adjective.*
—To or toward the east. Our house faces
east. Adverb. **east** (ēst) *noun; adjective;
adverb.*

echo The repeating of sound. An echo is caused
when sound waves bounce off a surface.
—**1.** To send back the sound of something.
2. To be heard again. **3.** To repeat or imitate
closely. The students *echo* the words of their
teachers. *Verb.* **echo** (ek′ō) *noun, plural*
echoes; *verb.*

education 1. The process of acquiring
knowledge. A college *education* usually takes
four years. **2.** The field of study that deals
with teaching methods and problems.
I took a course in elementary *education.*
ed•u•ca•tion (ej′ə kā′shən) *noun, plural*
educations; *adjective* **educational.**

educator A person who is an expert in the field
of education. **ed•u•ca•tor**
(ej′ə kā tər) *noun, plural* **educators.**

election The act of choosing by voting.
election (i lek′shən) *noun, plural* **elections.**

emergency 1. A crisis. **2** A situation that needs
immediate action. He can always be relied
on in an *emergency.* **e•mer•gen•cy**
(i mûr′jən sē) *noun, plural* **emergencies.**

en- also **em- 1.** To put or go into or onto.
2. To cause to become. **3.** To give. **4.** To cover
thoroughly. **en-, em-** (en, em) *prefix.*

endurance The ability to continue. You need
endurance to succeed in long-distance
swimming. **en•dur•ance** (en dùr′əns or
en dyùr′əns) *noun.*

engineer 1. A person who is trained in a branch
of engineering. The *engineer* was in charge of
building the bridge. **2.** A person who controls
an engine. Casey Jones was a famous
engineer. **en•gi•neer** (en′jə nîr′) *noun,
plural* **engineers.**

English 1. A language spoken in the United
Kingdom, the United States, Canada, Australia,
New Zealand, and in many other parts of the
world. **2.** English language, literature, and
writing as a subject of study. **3.** The people of
England. *Noun.*
—Relating to England, the English people, or

the English language. *Adjective.* **En•glish**
(ing′glish) *noun; adjective.*

enjoyable Giving pleasure. Flying is an
enjoyable experience for me. **en•joy•a•ble**
(en joi′ə bəl) *adjective.*

entertainment 1. Something that interests
and amuses. The clowns provided excellent
entertainment. **2.** The act of entertaining.
The *entertainment* of guests is the job
of a host or hostess. **en•ter•tain•ment**
(en′tər tān′mənt) *noun, plural*
entertainments.

entrance[1] **1.** The act of
entering. The movie star
made a grand *entrance.*
2. The place of entering.
The *entrance* to the house
was brightly lighted.
en•trance (en′trəns) *noun,
plural* **entrances.**

entrance[2] To fill with delight.
The play should *entrance* the
children. **en•trance**
(en trans′) *verb.*

entrance

equipment Anything that is provided for a
particular purpose or use; supplies. The coach
brought in the *equipment* for the team.
e•quip•ment (i kwip′mənt) *noun.*

-er also **-ier** or **-yer.** A person or thing that does
something. **-er** (ər) *suffix.*

erosion A wearing, washing, or eating away.
Erosion usually happens gradually over a long
time. **e•ro•sion** (i rō′zhən) *noun.*

especially 1. Mainly; chiefly. We came over
especially to see you. **2.** More than usually; to
a special degree. The music was *especially*
exciting tonight. **es•pe•cial•ly**
(e spesh′ə lē) *adverb.*

establishment 1. The act of establishing.
2. Something established. A department
store, a school, a business, and a household

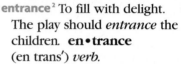

at; āpe, fär, câre; end; mē, it, īce; pîerce; hot,
ōld: sông, fôrk; oil; out; up; ūse; rüle; pùll; tûrn;
ch in; sing; sh op; th in; th is; hw in wh ite; zh in
treasure. The symbol ə stands for the unstressed
vowel sound in about, taken, pencil, lemon,
and circus.

Spelling Dictionary

are *establishments*. **es•tab•lish•ment** (e stab′lish mənt) *noun, plural* **establishments.**

evening The last part of the day and early part of the night. Last *evening* there was a gorgeous sunset. **eve•ning** (ēv′ning) *noun, plural* **evenings**.

eventful Full of events. **event•ful** (i vent′fəl) *adjective*.

everywhere 1. In or to every place. **ev•ery•where** (ev′rē hwâr′ *or* ev′rē wâr′) *adverb*.

excite 1. To stir up feeling in. **2.** To cause to be felt. **3.** To increase activity in. **4.** To raise to a higher energy level. The ideas that *excite* people are often not new. **ex•cite** (ek sīt′) *verb*.

exercise 1. Activity that trains or improves the body or the mind. Walking is good *exercise*. **2.** Use or practice. **3.** A ceremony or program. We had a graduation *exercise* today. *Noun.* —**1.** To put or go through exercises. **2.** To make use of. You should *exercise* your rights as a citizen by voting. *Verb.* **ex•er•cise** (ek′sər sīz′) *noun, plural* **exercises.**

exhaust 1. To make very weak or tired. **2.** To use up completely. The campers *exhausted* their supply of water. *Verb.* —The steam or gases that escape from an engine. *Noun.* **ex•haust** (eg zôst′) *verb; noun, plural* **exhausts.**

expect 1. To look or wait for something that will probably happen. I *expect* her to arrive tonight. **2.** To consider reasonable, necessary, or an obligation. We *expect* club members to attend all meetings. **ex•pect** (ek spekt′) *verb; adjective,* **expectable.**

explain 1. To make clear. Can you *explain* this problem to me? **2.** To give the reason for or cause of. Please *explain* your absence. **ex•plain** (ek splān′) *verb*.

explanation 1. The act or process of making something plain or clear. **2.** A reason or meaning. My parents wanted an *explanation* for why the vase was broken. **ex•pla•na•tion** (ek′splə nā ′shən) *noun, plural* **explanations.**

explore 1. To travel and look into little-known places. Soon we will *explore* the planets. **2.** To look into closely. I had to *explore* my bedroom before I could find my watch. **ex•plore** (ek splôr′) *verb*.

explosion 1. A noisy blowing up. The *explosion* destroyed the building. **2.** A violent outburst of feelings. **3.** A sudden increase. The population *explosion* has caused many people to go hungry. **ex•plo•sion** (ek splô′zhən) *noun, plural* **explosions.**

expression 1. The act of stating, especially in words. The *expression* of his ideas was well received. **2.** A show of feeling by look, voice, or action. His tight jaw was a clear *expression* of anger. **ex•pres•sion** (ek spresh′ən) *noun, plural* **expressions**.

eyebrow The hair growing on the ridge over the eye, or the ridge itself. Joe raised his *eyebrows* in surprise. **eye•brow** (ī′brou′) *noun, plural* **eyebrows**.

fable A short story that is intended to teach a lesson, often using animals who speak and act like humans. **fa•ble** (fā′bəl) *noun, plural* **fables**.

fail To lose strength. **2.** To be deficient. The young man *failed* in his attempt to break the world record. **fail** (fāl) *verb*.

failure 1. The lack of success. It is difficult to admit *failure*. **2.** An inability to perform normally. The plane couldn't take off because of engine *failure*. **3.** A falling short. Crop *failure* this year cost farmers millions of dollars. **fail•ure** (fāl′yər) *noun, plural* **failures**.

faith 1. Unquestioning belief. My *faith* in you is enormous. **2.** A great deal of reliance and trust. **faith** (fāth) *noun*.

Spelling Dictionary

falcon A bird with pointed wings and a long tail. **fal•con** (fôl′kən or fal′kən) *noun, plural* **falcons.**

falcon

false 1. Not true or correct; wrong. To say that the earth is larger than the sun is *false.* **2.** Not real; artificial. The actor wore a *false* beard. **false** (fôls) *adjective,* **falser, falsest.**

famous Very well known. Thomas Edison was a *famous* inventor. **fa•mous** (fā′məs) *adjective.*

farther More distant. *Adjective.*
—At a greater distance. The sailboat drifted *farther* from shore. *Adverb.* **far•ther** (fär′thər) *adjective; adverb.*

fasten 1. To attach firmly. Let me *fasten* the clip to your dress. **2.** To fix firmly in place. The sign tells us to *fasten* our seat belts. **fas•ten** (fas′ən) *verb.*

fault 1. Something that is wrong with and spoils something else. **2.** Responsibility for a mistake. **fault** (fôlt) *noun.*

fawn 1. A young deer. The young *fawn* stayed with its mother. **2.** Light grayish brown. **fawn** (fôn) *noun, plural* **fawns.**

February The second month of the year. February has twenty-eight days; twenty-nine in leap years. **Feb•ru•ar•y** (feb′rü er′ē or feb′ū er′ē) *noun, plural* **Februaries.**

federal 1. Formed by an agreement between states or provinces to join together as one nation. The United States has a *federal* government. **2.** Having to do with the central government of the United States. **fed•er•al** (fed′ər əl) *adjective.*

fertilize 1. To make fertile. The manure will *fertilize* the land. **2.** To put fertilizer on. **fer•ti•lize** (fûr′tə līz′) *verb* **fertilized, fertilizing.**

fertilizer A substance that is added to soil to make it better for the growing of crops. Manure and certain chemicals are used as *fertilizers.* **fer•ti•liz•er** (fûr′tə li′zər) *noun, plural* **fertilizers.**

few A small number. Only a *few* of the children will play the game. *Noun.*
—Not many persons or things. *Pronoun.*
—Not many; a limited number. The boy caught a *few* fish at the lake. *Adjective.* **few** (fū) *noun; pronoun; adjective.*

field trip A visit made by students and teachers for purposes of firsthand observation. The class went on a *field trip* to the zoo. **field trip** (fēld trip) *noun, plural* **field trips.**

fierce 1. Likely to make violent attacks; dangerous; savage. Bears are shy animals but they can become *fierce* if they are threatened. **2.** Very strong or violent; raging. **fierce** (fîrs) *adjective,* **fiercer, fiercest.**

figure 1. A symbol that stands for a number. What is the first *figure* in the column? **2.** An amount given in figures. Offer him a better *figure* for the car. **3.** A form or outline; shape. **4.** A person. Washington is a well-known *figure* in American history. *Noun.*
—**1.** To think or estimate. She'd *figure* it was possible. **2.** To find out by using numbers; calculate. *Verb.* **fig•ure** (fig′yər) *noun, plural* **figures**; *verb.*

file[1] (from Early French *fil,* meaning "thread") To arrange in order. *Verb.*
—**1.** A folder, drawer, cabinet, or other container in which papers, cards, or records are arranged in order. Put this folder back in the *file.* **2.** A set of papers, cards, or records arranged in order. Please get out the *file* on your expenses. **3.** A row of persons, animals, or things arranged one behind the other. Let's arrange ourselves in single *file. Noun.* **4.** *Computers.* A collection of information, program instructions, or words stored on a

at; āpe, fär, câre; end; mē, it, īce; pîerce; hot, ōld; sông, fôrk; oil; out; up; ūse; rüle; pùll; tûrn; chin; sing; shop; thin; this; hw in white; zh in treasure. The symbol ə stands for the unstressed vowel sound in about, taken, pencil, lemon, and circus.

Spelling Dictionary

computer disk. Each *file* has a name that identifies it. **file** (fīl) *verb*, **filed, filing**; *noun, plural* **files**.

file² (from Old English *fē ol*, meaning "file") A tool used for smoothing rough surfaces. She smoothed the rough metal surface with a *file. Noun.*
—To cut, smooth, or grind with a file. I *filed* my fingernails. *Verb.* **file** (fīl) *noun, plural* **files**; *verb,* **filed, filing.**

fireplace 1. An opening in a room, with a chimney leading up from it, used for building fires. **2.** An outdoor structure of brick or stone in which fires are built. **fire•place** (fīr′plās′) *noun, plural* **fireplaces.**

fist A hand tightly closed with fingers doubled into the palm. The boy shook his *fist* at the television. **fist** (fist) *noun, plural* **fists.**

flashlight A small portable electric light, powered by batteries. **flash•light** (flash′līt′) *noun, plural* **flashlights**.

flashlight

flavor 1. A particular taste. The salt adds *flavor* to the dish. **2.** A special quality. I love to read books with a *flavor* of the wild. *Noun.*
—To give flavor or taste to. The onions *flavor* the stew. *Verb.* **fla•vor** (flā′vər) *noun, plural* **flavors**; *verb.*

flea Any of a large group of wingless insects that feed on the blood of mammals and birds. **flea** (flē) *noun, plural* **fleas**.

flight 1. The act of passing through the air. I watched the *flight* of the ducks heading south. **2.** The distance traveled by a bird or a plane. We had a comfortable *flight.* **3.** A set of stairs from one floor to another. **flight** (flīt) *noun, plural* **flights**.

Florida The southernmost Atlantic state of the United States. The capital of Florida is Tallahassee. The abbreviation for Florida is FL. **Flor•i•da** (flôr′i də *or* flor′i də) *noun.*

foam 1. A frothy mass of fine bubbles formed in or on the surface of a liquid. **2.** A material in a lightweight form. We used packing *foam* to ship the breakable object. *Noun.*
—To produce foam. The rushing stream *foamed* over the rocks. *Verb.* **foam** (fōm) *noun; verb,* **foamed, foaming.**

fold A layer of something doubled over. There were moths in a *fold* of the blanket. *Noun.*
—**1.** To double over. Will you please *fold* the napkins? **2.** To bend close to the body. Kurt *folds* his arms when he's angry. **3.** To wrap. You can *fold* the fish in a sheet of newspaper. *Verb.* **fold** (fōld) *noun, plural* **folds**; *verb.*

folktale A traditional story that has been handed down through the ages. The story of Cinderella is a *folktale.* **folk•tale** (fōk′tāl′) *noun, plural* **folktales.**

follow 1. To go or come after. *Follow* me down this path. **2.** To act according to; obey. You must *follow* the doctor's orders. **3.** To go along. *Follow* this road until it ends. **4.** To listen or observe closely. The listeners *followed* the story with interest. **fol•low** (fol′ō) *verb.*

fond 1. Having a liking for. I am *fond* of cats. **2.** Liking or loving. He gave her a *fond* hello. **fond** (fond) *adjective.*

fool A person with no sense. Don't make a *fool* of yourself. *Noun.*
—**1.** To play or joke. I like to *fool* around with my friends after school. **2.** To trick. His sweet smile can *fool* anyone. *Verb.* **fool** (fül) *noun, plural* **fools**; *verb.*

footlights The row of lights along the front edge of a stage in a theater. The *footlights* gave the actor's face an eerie look. **foot•lights** (fut′līts′) *plural noun.*

force 1. Power or strength. The wind hit with such *force* that trees were blown over. **2.** The power to influence. **3.** A group of people working together. The police *force* in our town is excellent. **4.** Something that produces change in a body. The *force* of gravity keeps us from floating in the air. *Noun.*

—**1.** To make a person act against his or her will. **2.** To gain by struggle. I'll *force* my way in if I must. **3.** To make with unnatural effort. She couldn't even *force* a smile. *Verb.* **force** (fôrs) *noun, plural* **forces**; *verb.*

foreign 1. Belonging outside a place or country. Mexico is a *foreign* country to Americans. **2.** Not usually found in an area. Lions are *foreign* to North America. **for•eign** (fôr′ən) *adjective.*

form 1. The shape of something. **2.** A paper with blank spaces to fill in. **3.** Kind or type. Heat is a *form* of energy. **4.** General structure. The house is triangular in *form. Noun.*
—**1.** To give shape to. Parents help us *form* our ideas. **2.** To take a certain shape or arrangement. Please *form* a line behind the door. *Verb.* **form** (fôrm) *noun, plural* **forms**; *verb.*

formula 1. An explanation of how to prepare a medicine, food, or other mixture. A formula says how much of each ingredient to use. **2.** A rule expressed in symbols or numbers. The *formula* for finding the area of a rectangle is A = lw. **3.** A way of naming a chemical compound that uses a symbol for each element in a molecule of the compound. The chemical *formula* for water is H_2O. **for•mu•la** (fôr′myə lə) *noun, plural* **formulas.**

forward 1. To help along. My older brother helped to *forward* my education. **2.** To send on. Please *forward* my mail. *Verb.*
—**1.** Near the front. The *forward* part of a car usually holds the engine. **2.** Far ahead. Her ideas were *forward* for their time. *Adj.*
—**1.** Toward what is in front or ahead. March *forward* in line. **2.** Into view; forth. New facts were brought *forward. Adverb.* **for•ward** (fôr′wərd) *verb; adjective; adverb.*

foul 1. Very unpleasant or dirty. There was a foul odor in the air when the sewer pipes broke. **2.** Cloudy, rainy, or stormy. *Foul* weather delayed the ship. **3.** Very bad; evil. The villain in the story had committed all sorts of *foul* deeds. **4.** Breaking the rules. An umpire or referee applies the rules and prevents any *foul* play. **5.** Outside the foul

line in a baseball game. The batter hit a *foul* ball. *Adjective.*
—**1.** A breaking of rules. The basketball player committed a *foul* by knocking down another player. **2.** A baseball that is hit outside the foul line. That ball was a *foul! Noun.*
—**1.** To make dirty. The factory will *foul* the lake by pumping waste in it. **2.** To tangle or become tangled. The child will *foul* the fishing line in the bushes on the shore. **3.** To hit a foul ball in baseball. The batter most likely will *foul* the ball to the right of first base. **foul** (foul) *adjective,* **fouler, foulest;** *noun, plural* **fouls;** *verb,* **fouled, fouling.**

Fourth of July A holiday that celebrates the birthday of the United States. Also called **Independence Day.**

fowl One of a number of birds that are used for food. Chickens, turkeys, and ducks are fowl. **fowl** (foul) *noun, plural* **fowl** or **fowls.**

freeze 1. A state of weather marked by low temperatures. The *freeze* last winter nearly destroyed the orange crop in Florida. **2.** The act of fixing at a certain level. The price *freeze* will be lifted in June. *Noun.*
—**1.** To turn into ice. The lake should *freeze* in this weather. **2.** To become very cold. **3.** To become suddenly motionless. **4.** To fix at a certain level. The supermarket will *freeze* prices for the rest of this year. *Verb.* **freeze** (frēz) *noun; verb,* **froze, frozen, freezing.**

frequency 1. A happening again and again; the number of times something happens or takes place over a period of time. The *frequency* of the storms this spring caused the pond to overflow. **2.** The number of cycles per second of a radio wave or other kind of waves or radiation. **fre•quen•cy** (frē′kwən sē) *noun, plural* **frequencies.**

at; āpe, fär, câre; end; mē, it, īce; pîerce; hot, ōld; sông, fôrk; oil; out; up; ūse; rüle; pùll; tûrn; chin; sing; shop; thin; **th**is; hw in white; zh in treasure. The symbol ə stands for the unstressed vowel sound in about, taken, pencil, lemon, and circus.

Spelling Dictionary

frontier 1. A border between two countries. We crossed the *frontier* between Canada and the United States. **2.** A region of a country that contains its latest settlement. America's *frontier* kept moving westward. **3.** The outer limits of achievement. Outer space is America's last *frontier.* **fron•tier** (frun tîr′, fron tîr′) *noun, plural* **frontiers,** *adjective.*

frozen Past participle of **freeze 1.** Turned into ice. The water has *frozen* solid. **2.** Became very cold. My nose has *frozen.* **3.** Became motionless. The dancers remained *frozen* in position. **4.** Become fixed at a certain level. The price of lettuce has been *frozen. Verb.* **—1.** Hardened by cold. **2.** Very cold. **3.** Too frightened to move. *Adjective.* **fro•zen** (frō zən) *verb; adjective.*

fudge 1. A soft, creamy candy that can contain nuts. **2.** Foolish nonsense. **fudge** (fuj) *noun, plural* **fudges.**

-ful 1. Full of. **2.** Displaying the qualities of. **3.** Enough to fill. **-ful** (fəl) *suffix.*

furious 1. Extremely angry. The coach was *furious* with the goalie. **2.** Unusually active. A hurricane always brings *furious* winds. **fu•ri•ous** (fyür′ē əs) *adjective.*

fury 1. Violent anger; rage. **2.** Violent or fierce action. The *fury* of the storm raged all night. **fu•ry** (fyür′ē) *noun, plural* **furies.**

gasoline A liquid made from petroleum used mainly as a motor fuel. **gas•o•line** (gas′ə lēn′or gas′ə lēn′) *noun, plural* **gasolines.**

gem 1. A jewel cut and polished for beauty. The king had a large *gem* in his crown. **2.** A thing valued for being perfect of its kind. **gem** (jem) *noun, plural* **gems.**

generation 1. A group of persons born around the same time. My parents call me and my friends the younger *generation.* **2.** One step in the line of descent from a common

ancestor. A grandparent, parent, and child make up three *generations.* **3.** The act or process of generating; production. **gen•er•a•tion** (jen′ə rā′ shən) *noun, plural* **generations.**

Georgia One of the southeastern states of the United States. The capital of Georgia is Atlanta. The abbreviation for Georgia is GA. **Geor•gia** (jôr′jə) *noun.*

gigantic Extremely big in size. The television came in a *gigantic* box. **gi•gan•tic** (jī gan′tik) *adjective;* **gigantically** *adverb.*

glisten To sparkle. Her eyes *glisten* in the light. **glis•ten** (glis′ən) *verb.*

gnat A small, flying insect. We were annoyed by the *gnats* on our camping trip. **gnat** (nat) *noun, plural* **gnats.**

gnaw To bite or nibble persistently. Spot *gnawed* on the bone. **gnaw** (nô) *verb.*

goal 1. The terminal point of a race. **2.** The end toward which effort is directed. Nita's *goal* is to be a doctor. **3.** An area in which players in various games attempt to score a point. **goal** (gōl) *noun, plural* **goals.**

goldfish A small yellow or orange fish usually kept in aquariums. **gold•fish** (gōld′fish′) *noun, plural* **goldfishes.**

gopher A burrowing rodent with large cheek pouches. Gophers burrow underground. They are found throughout North America. **go•pher** (gō′fər) *noun, plural* **gophers.**

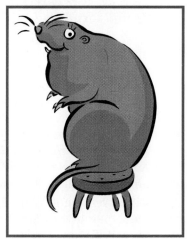

gopher

government 1. The act of governing or ruling. The *government* of the dictator was challenged by the people. **2.** The institutions and laws that govern a political unit. The *government* of Germany is a democracy. **gov•ern•ment**

(guv′ərn mənt or guv′ər mənt) *noun, plural* **governments**.

graceful Showing grace or ease of movement in form or action. Fred Astaire was a *graceful* dancer. **grace•ful** (grās′fəl) *adjective*.

grant 1. Something that is granted; a gift. The college student received a *grant* from the Rotary Club. **2.** A parcel of land granted by a government. Many large universities began with land *grants* from the U.S. government. *Noun*.
—**1.** To consent or allow. Since you finished your chores on time, Mother will *grant* your request. **2.** To give possession of formally. The king *granted* the castle to his knight. *Verb*. **grant** (grant) *noun*, **grants**; *verb*.

grateful Appreciative of something received. The farmers were *grateful* for the rain. **grate•ful** (grāt′fəl) *adjective*.

gravitation The force or pull that draws all the bodies in the universe toward one another. **grav•i•ta•tion** (grav′i tā′shən) *noun*.

gravy The thickened and seasoned juices of cooked meat. **gra•vy** (grā′vē) *noun, plural* **gravies.**

greet 1. To welcome in a friendly way upon meeting. **2.** To meet or react to. The factory workers should *greet* the pay raise with cheers. **greet** (grēt) *verb*.

grind 1. To make into a powder or small pieces by rubbing or crushing. We watched the butcher *grind* the meat. **2.** To wear down, sharpen, or polish by rubbing. The doctor will *grind* a new lens for my glasses.
—The act of grinding. The *grind* of the engines was overwhelmingly loud. *Noun*. **grind** (grīnd) *verb*, **ground**; *noun*.

grip 1. A firm, strong hold. She had a good *grip* on the rope. **2.** Mental grasp. I feel that I have a good *grip* on the math formulas. *Noun*.
—**1.** Grasp firmly. **2.** To hold the interest strongly. A good story will always *grip* my interest. *Verb*. **grip** (grip) *noun, plural* **grips**; *verb*, **gripped**, **gripping.**

grown Past participle of **grow**. Having developed or matured. *Verb*.

—Having reached full growth. The little boy tried to act like a *grown* man. *Adjective*. **grown** (grōn) *verb; adjective*.

guide 1. One who shows the way or leads. A *guide* took us through the museum. **2.** Something such as a book that provides guiding information. *Noun*.
—To act as a guide. I'll *guide* you through the house. *Verb*. **guide** (gīd) *noun, plural* **guides**; *verb*, **guided**, **guiding.**

hamburger 1. A cooked patty of ground beef. **2.** A sandwich containing such a patty. Reginald likes lettuce on his *hamburger.* **ham•bur•ger** (ham′bûr′gər) *noun, plural* **hamburgers**.

hamper[1] To get in the way of action or progress. Cars will *hamper* efforts to clean the streets. **ham•per** (ham′pər) *verb*.

hamper[2] A large basket or container with a cover. There is a *hamper* for the dirty laundry. **ham•per** (ham′pər) *noun, plural* **hampers**.

handful 1. An amount equal to that which fits in a hand. You may have a *handful* of buttons to play with. **hand•ful** (hand′fùl′) *noun, plural* **handfuls** or **handsful.**

harmful Causing injury. Smoking is *harmful* to your health. **harm•ful** (härm′fəl) *adjective*, **harmfully** *adverb*, **harmfulness** *noun*.

harness Straps to attach a horse or other animal to a wagon or plow. The farmer loosened the *harness. Noun*.
—**1.** To put a harness on. The farmer *harnessed* the horses. **2.** To control and make use of. We are beginning to *harness*

at; āpe, fär, câre; end; mē, it, īce; pîerce; hot, ōld: sông, fôrk; oil; out; up; ūse; rüle; pùll; tûrn; chin; sing; shop; thin; **th**is; hw in white; zh in treasure. The symbol ə stands for the unstressed vowel sound in about, taken, pencil, lemon, and circus.

Spelling Dictionary

energy from the sun. *Verb.* **har•ness**
(här′nəs) *noun, plural* **harnesses;** *verb.*

hasn't Shortened form of "has not." It *hasn't*
bothered me a bit. **has•n't** (haz′ənt)
contraction.

haven't Shortened form of "have not." I *haven't*
been to a dance yet. **have•n't** (hav′ənt)
contraction.

Hawaii Islands in the Pacific, the 50th state of
the United States. The capital of Hawaii is
Honolulu. The abbreviation for Hawaii is HI.
Ha•wai•i (hə wī′ē) *noun.*

hawk A bird of prey with sharp, curved claws
and a strong, hooked bill. Some varieties of
hawk are nearly extinct. *Noun.*
—**1.** To hunt using a trained hawk. She
enjoys *hawking* as a sport. **2.** To advertise
or peddle goods. In the market the peddlers
hawk their wares. **hawk** (hôk) *noun,*
plural **hawks;** *verb,* **hawkish** *adjective.*

heal To make well. We are learning more and
more about how to *heal* ourselves. **heal**
(hēl) *verb.*

hectare A unit of area in the metric system. It
is equal to 10,000 square meters, or about
2 1/2 acres. **hec•tare** (hek′târ) *noun,*
plural **hectares.**

heel[1] **1.** The back part of a person's foot. Sally's
new shoes rub up uncomfortably against her
heels. **2.** Anything resembling a heel. I have
to have the *heels* on these shoes fixed. **heel**
(hēl) *noun, plural* **heels.**

heel[2] **1.** To lean over to one side. Look at that
sailboat *heel!* **2.** To follow closely. Dogs can
learn to *heel* quite easily. **heel** (hēl) *verb,*
heeled, heeling.

height **1.** The distance from top to bottom.
The *height* of the statue is 11 feet. **2.** How tall
a person is. Molly's *height* makes her a good
basketball player. **3.** The highest point. She
reached the *height* of success at a young age.
height (hīt) *noun, plural* **heights.**

herself **1.** A form of *she* to make a statement
stronger. She insisted on coming *herself.*
2. Her normal, healthy self. She was *herself*
again after a good sleep. **her•self** (hûr self′)
pronoun.

hidden A past participle of **hide.** The dog has
hidden its bone. **hid•den** (hid′ən) *verb.*

hinge A joint on which a door swings back and
forth. It's time to put oil in the rusty *hinges.*
Noun.
—To hang or turn as if on a hinge. The large
door slowly *hinged* open. *Verb.* **hinge** (hinj)
noun, plural **hinges;** *verb,* **hinged, hinging.**

hoarse **1.** Harsh and grating in sound. The car
made a *hoarse* noise when the brakes were
applied. **2.** Having a rough, husky voice. After
yelling at the game, the cheerleader was
hoarse. **hoarse** (hôrs) *adjective.*

hoist **1.** A lift. I need a *hoist* to get over this
wall. **2.** A lifting device for heavy loads. We
used a *hoist* to move the refrigerator. *Noun.*
—To lift or pull up. A heavy chain was used to
hoist the boxes. *Verb.* **hoist** (hoist) *noun,*
plural **hoists;** *verb.*

homesick Longing for home and family. Most of
us are *homesick* when we first leave home.
home•sick (hōm′sik′) *adjective.*

honest **1.** Fair; to be trusted. That grocer gives
each customer an *honest* deal. **2.** Real;
authentic. The dresser is an *honest* and
definite antique. **3.** Sincere. Mother believes it
is important to be *honest* when you tell your
story. **hon•est** (on′ist) *adjective;* **honestly**
adverb.

hose **1.** Stockings or socks. Jim made a stuffed
animal out of the old *hose.* **2.** A flexible
rubber tube for carrying fluids. *Noun.*
—To water with a hose. The store owner likes
to *hose* down the sidewalk in front of her
shop to keep it clean. *Verb.* **hose** (hōz)
noun, plural **hoses;** *verb,* **hosed, hosing.**

hospital A place where the sick or injured are
taken for medical care. Kenneth went to the
hospital after he fell from his bicycle.
hos•pi•tal (hos′pi′təl) *noun, plural*
hospitals.

housework The work of keeping a home in
order. My entire family is responsible for
sharing the *housework.* **house•work**
(hous′wûrk′) *noun.*

howl **1.** A long, loud cry of sadness, pain, or
anger. We were awakened by the dog's *howl.*

2. A yell or shout. He let out a *howl* of laughter when he saw my outfit. *Noun.* —**1.** To let out a long, loud cry of sadness, pain, or anger. **2.** To yell or shout. *Verb.* **howl** (houl) *noun, plural* **howls;** *verb.*

how's Shortened form of "how is." **how's** (houz) *contraction.*

-ible Variant of **-able.** See **-able. ible** (ə bəl) *adjective suffix.*

ice-skating The act of skating on ice. George enjoys *ice-skating* with his friends in the winter. **ice-skat•ing** (īs′skāt′ing) *noun.*

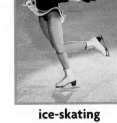
ice-skating

Idaho One of the northwestern states of the United States. The capital of Idaho is Boise. The abbreviation for Idaho is ID. **I•da•ho** (ī′də hō′) *noun.*

identify 1. To establish the identity of. The woman *identified* her keys. **2.** To become as one with another. I *identify* with my friends. **i•den•ti•fy** (ī den′tə fī′) *verb,* **identified, identifying; identifiable** *adjective;* **identifiably** *adverb,* **identifier** *noun.*

ignorance A lack of knowledge; being ignorant. My *ignorance* of current affairs meant that I couldn't join the debate team this year. **ig•no•rance** (ig′nər əns) *noun.*

Illinois One of the north central states of the United States. The capital of Illinois is Springfield. The abbreviation for Illinois is IL. **Il•li•nois** (il′ə noi′) *noun.*

imagination The ability to form pictures, images, or concepts in the mind. Edison had a fabulous *imagination.* **i•mag•i•na•tion** (i maj′ə nā′shən) *noun, plural* **imaginations.**

imagine 1. To form a picture or concept in your mind. **2.** To suppose or guess. I *imagine* it's time to go. **i•mag•ine** (i maj′in) *verb.*

immigrant A person who comes to live in a country in which he or she was not born. My grandparents were *immigrants* to the United States from Italy. **im•mi•grant** (im′i grənt) *noun, plural* **immigrants.**

immune 1. Protected from a disease. The doctor gave me a vaccination that made me *immune* to measles. **2.** Safe from undergoing something; not subject. No one is *immune* from criticism. **im•mune;** (i mūn′) *adjective.*

importance The state of being important or significant. Athletes know the *importance* of exercise. **im•por•tance** (im pôr′ təns) *noun.*

impossible 1. Not able to be; not possible. It is *impossible* for people to fly by flapping their arms. **im•pos•si•ble** (im pos′ə bəl) *adjective,* **impossibly** *adverb.*

in- or **im-** or **il-** or **ir- 1.** Not. *Inappropriate* means not appropriate. **2.** In or into; within. *Inborn* means born within a person. She has an *inborn* talent for art. *Prefix.* **in-, im-, il-, ir-** (in,im,il,ir) *prefix.*

include 1. To have as part of the whole; contain. The invitation list doesn't *include* her name. **2.** To put in a class. The tools *include* a hammer, a saw, and a wrench. **in•clude** (in klüd′) *verb* **included, including.**

indeed Definitely; without any question. Yes, *indeed,* I want to go on vacation. **in•deed** (in dēd′) *adverb.*

Indiana One of the north central states of the United States. The capital of Indiana is Indianapolis. The abbreviation for Indiana is IN. **In•di•an•a** (in′dē an′ə) *noun.*

indicate 1. To direct attention to. The captain *indicated* the exit was at the rear of the ship. **2.** To show. The map *indicated* that the lake was in the western part of the state. **in•di•cate** (in′di kāt′) *verb,* **indicated, indicating.**

at; āpe, fär, câre; end; mē, it, īce; pîerce; hot, ōld: sông, fôrk; oil; out; up; ūse; rüle; pùll; tûrn; chin; sing; shop; thin; **this;** hw in white; zh in treasure. The symbol ə stands for the unstressed vowel sound in about, taken, pencil, lemon, and circus.

Spelling Dictionary

informal 1. Not formal; casual. We wore *informal* clothes to the party. **2.** Without ceremony. The proceedings were conducted in an *informal* way. **in•for•mal** (in fôr′məl) *adjective,* **informally** *adverb.*

information 1. The communication of knowledge. You can get more *information* by writing to the company. **2.** Facts about something. The phone book contains *information* about dialing. **in•for•ma•tion** (in′fər ma′tion) *noun;* **informational** *adjective.*

injure To cause harm to; damage or hurt. I *injured* myself when I fell off my bicycle. **in•jure** (in′jər) *verb,* **injured, injuring.**

inscription 1. Something inscribed. There was an *inscription* on the tombstone. **2.** A brief, usually informal dedication, as in a book. **in•scrip•tion** (in skrip′shən) *noun, plural* **inscriptions.**

insect Any class of small animals with bodies divided into three parts and having three pairs of legs and one or two pairs of wings. **in•sect** (in′sekt) *noun, plural* **insects.**

insect

insight An instance of understanding the true nature of a thing. After listening to the speaker, I had an *insight* about what he was trying to explain to the class. **in•sight** (in′sīt′) *noun, plural* **insights.**

instruction 1. The act of teaching. His *instruction* was very helpful. **2.** *plural* An outline of steps to follow. The swing set came with helpful assembly *instructions.* **in•struc•tion** (in struk′shən) *noun, plural* **instructions,** *adjective,* **instructional.**

invent 1. To think up. He'll *invent* an excuse for anything. **2.** To create for the first time. Bell *invented* the telephone. **in•vent** (in vent′) *verb; noun,* **invention, inventor.**

invention 1. An original device. Television is a wonderful *invention.* **2.** A made-up story.

Bob's excuse was sheer *invention.* **in•ven•tion** (in ven′chən) *noun, plural* **inventions.**

invitation 1. The act of requesting someone to come to some place or to do something. I appreciate the *invitation* to go bowling, but I am busy this Saturday. **2.** A written request that someone be present at an event. **in•vi•ta•tion** (in′vi tā′shən) *noun, plural* **invitations.**

-ion 1. The act of. Discussion means the act of discussing. **2.** The condition of being. *Confusion* means the state of being confused. **-ion** *noun suffix.*

Iowa One of the midwestern states of the United States. The capital of Iowa is Des Moines. The abbreviation for Iowa is IA. **I•o•wa** (ī′ə wə) *noun.*

itself 1. A form of *it* used to make a statement stronger. The house *itself* isn't worth very much. **2.** A form used instead of *it.* The cat fell but caught *itself.* **it•self** (it self′) *pronoun.*

-ize 1. To cause to be like. *Naturalize* means to make a citizen of someone who was born in another country. **2.** To arrange or cause to be formed into. *Itemize* means to form a group of items into a list. **3.** To subject to an action. *Terrorize* means to subject to terror. **-ize** (īz) *verb suffix.*

January The first month of the year. January has thirty-one days. **Jan•u•ar•y** (jan′yū er′ē) *noun.*

jealous 1. Fearful of losing someone's love to another person. A young child will often be *jealous* of a new baby in the family. **2.** Having envy of a person, or what a person has or can do. I used to be *jealous* of my friend's ability to play football well. **jeal•ous** (jel′əs) *adjective.*

jewel 1. A precious stone. **2.** A person who is precious. My granddaughter is a *jewel. Noun.*

Spelling Dictionary

—To adorn with jewels. We watched her *jewel* the vest. *Verb.* **jew•el** (jü′əl) *noun; plural* **jewels**; *verb,* **jeweled, jeweling.**

jogger A person who jogs. Since my father became a *jogger,* he has become healthier. **jog•ger** (jog′ər) *noun, plural* **joggers.**

journalist A writer who works for a newspaper or magazine or TV news department. My friend's father is an award-winning *journalist.* **jour•nal•ist** (jûr′nə list) *noun, plural* **journalists.**

journey A trip from one place to another. The *journey* lasted two days. *Noun.* —To go on a journey. We *journeyed* through the western part of the United States. *Verb.* **jour•ney** (jûr′nē) *noun, plural* **journeys**; *verb,* **journeyed, journeying.**

jury **1.** A group of persons sworn to give a verdict on some matter submitted to them. The *jury* found him guilty. **2.** A committee for judging and awarding prizes at a contest or exhibition. The *jury* selected the first prize winner. **ju•ry** (jùr′ē) *noun, plural* **juries.**

Kansas One of the midwestern states of the United States. The capital of Kansas is Topeka. The abbreviation for Kansas is KS. **Kan•sas** (kan′zəs) *noun.*

Kentucky One of the south central states of the United States. The capital of Kentucky is Frankfort. The abbreviation for Kentucky is KY. **Ken•tuck•y** (kən tuk′ē) *noun.*

kettle A container for boiling liquids or cooking foods. **ket•tle** (ket′əl) *noun, plural* **kettles.**

knack A special ability or skill for doing something easily. My cousin has a *knack* for repairing cars. **knack** (nak) *noun.*

knead **1.** To work and press into a mass with the hands. She will *knead* the dough. **2.** To form or shape. I like to *knead* clay into the shape of a ball. **knead** (nēd) *verb.*

kneel To put one's knees on the ground. The knights and ladies *kneeled* before the royal couple. **kneel** (nēl) *verb,* **knelt** or **kneeled; kneeling.**

knife **1.** A cutting instrument made of a thin, flat metal blade attached to a handle. He cut the tomatoes with a very sharp *knife.* **2.** Any cutting edge or blade. The *knife* on the machine was getting rusty. **knife** (nīf) *noun, plural* **knives.**

knight

knight **1.** A warrior of medieval times. King Arthur had many faithful *knights.* **2.** A chess piece. In chess, a *knight* is usually in the shape of a horse's head. *Noun.* —To make a knight of. The king and queen *knighted* two soldiers for their courage and loyalty. *Verb.* **knight** (nīt) *noun, plural* **knights**; *verb,* **knighted, knighting.**

knowledge **1.** An understanding that is gained through experience or study. I have enough *knowledge* of football to be able to follow a game. **2.** The fact of knowing. The *knowledge* that the car could slide on the icy road made the driver more careful. **know•ledge** (nol′ij) *noun.*

known Past participle of **know; knew 1.** Had clearly in mind, as in studies. Before today's class, Sheila hadn't *known* much about the Civil War. **2.** Been acquainted with. I have *known* Cindy for years. *Verb.* —Familiar to everyone. It's a *known* fact that oil and water don't mix. *Adjective.* **known** (nōn) *verb; adjective.*

at; āpe, fär, câre; end; mē, it, īce; pîerce; hot, ōld: sông, fôrk; oil; out; up; ūse; rüle; pùll; tûrn; chin; sing; shop; thin; this; hw in white; zh in treasure. The symbol ə stands for the unstressed vowel sound in about, taken, pencil, lemon, and circus.

Spelling Dictionary

labor 1. Hard work. Your salary will depend on the amount of *labor* you do. **2.** Workers as a group. *Labor* is in favor of safer working conditions. *Noun.*
—**1.** To work hard. We had to *labor* long into the night. **2.** To move with difficulty. The teams of dogs will have to *labor* to pull sleds through such deep snow. *Verb.* **la•bor** (lā′bər) *noun, plural* **labors**; *verb.*

Labor Day A holiday in the United States that honors working people. Labor Day is celebrated on the first Monday in September.

lantern Usually a light that can be carried around and that has a safety covering. The camper used a *lantern* to light the path. **lan•tern** (lan′tərn) *noun, plural* **lanterns**.

launch¹ 1. To start in motion; send off. The scientists will *launch* a rocket. **2.** To start something. The company *launched* its store by having a big sale. *Verb.*
—The act or process of launching. The *launch* of the rocket began with the countdown. *Noun.* **launch** (lônch) *verb,* **launched, launching**; *noun, plural* **launches.**

launch² **An open motorboat. The lifeguard boarded the *launch* in the water. **launch (lônch) *noun, plural* **launches.**

lawn An area of grass that is kept mowed. **lawn** (lôn) *noun, plural* **lawns.**

lawyer A person who is trained in law and who advises and acts for other people in legal matters. **law•yer** (lô′yər) *noun, plural* **lawyers.**

lazy 1. Unwilling to work. My brother is *lazy* because he won't look for a job. **2.** Slow-moving. We took a boat ride down a *lazy* river. **la•zy** (lā′zē) *adjective,* **lazier, laziest**.

leader 1. One who goes ahead and shows others the way. The scout *leader* guided us through the woods. **2.** A person in charge or in control. Vera is the *leader* of the school

band. **lead•er** (lē′dər) *noun, plural* **leaders**.

leather Animal skin that has been treated. The rider wore pants made of *leather. Noun.*
—Made of leather. *Leather* gloves are warmer than cotton ones. *Adjective.* **leath•er** (leth′ər) *noun, plural* **leathers**; *adjective.*

lecture 1. A talk given to an audience. **2.** A scolding. I got a *lecture* from my parents for breaking the window. *Noun.*
—**1.** To give a lecture. **2.** To scold. The coach *lectured* us for not exercising every day. *Verb.* **lec•ture** (lek′chər) *noun, plural* **lectures**; *verb,* **lectured, lecturing.**

led Past tense and past participle of **lead 1.** To have guided by going on ahead, teaching, or showing. **2.** To have spent or gone through. We *led* a quiet life this summer. **3.** To have been first in something, as in athletics. Our team *led* the division. **led** (led) *verb.*

ledge 1. A narrow shelf. The window *ledge* is too narrow for a potted plant. **2.** A ridge of rock. A bobcat stood on the *ledge* just above us. **ledge** (lej) *noun, plural* **ledges**.

legal 1. having to do with law. Go to a lawyer for *legal* advice. **2.** Allowed by or according to the law or the rules; lawful. They're the *legal* owners of the farm. **le•gal** (lē′gəl) *adjective.*

lend To let someone use something with the understanding that it will be returned. Will you *lend* me your umbrella? **lend** (lend) *verb,* **lent.**

-less 1. Without; not having. *Hopeless* means without hope. **2.** That cannot be. *Countless* means that cannot be counted. **-less** (ləs) *adjective suffix.*

lettuce A plant with large green or reddish leaves. *Lettuce* is eaten in a salad. **let•tuce** (let′is) *noun, plural* **lettuces.**

likelihood The condition or quality of being expected. In all *likelihood*, the student will pass the exam. **like•li•hood** (līk′lē hůd′) *noun.*

limb 1. A leg, arm, or wing. Growing pains make my *limbs* hurt. **2.** One of the large branches of a tree. **limb** (lim) *noun, plural* **limbs**.

lion A large, meat-eating cat of Africa and Asia. The male *lion* has a shaggy mane. **li•on** (līʹən) *noun, plural* **lions**.

lion

lizard A reptile with a long, scaly body, long tail, and usually four legs. The *lizard* dashed away under a rock. **liz•ard** (lizʹərd) *noun, plural* **lizards**.

loaf¹ A rounded mass of bread or other food. I just bought a fresh *loaf* of bread at the bakery. **loaf** (lōf) *noun, plural* **loaves**.

loaf² To do nothing. On Sunday I like to *loaf*. **loaf** (lōf) *verb*.

lock 1. A fastening for a door or box that is opened by a key. 2. An enclosure in a canal. The boat floated into the *lock. Noun.*
—1. To fasten with a lock. Don't forget to *lock* the front door before you leave. 2. To link together and make fast. Let's *lock* arms as we walk. 3. To grip in a firm hold. Don't *lock* your arm around my neck so tightly. *Verb.* **lock** (lok) *noun, plural* **locks**; *verb*.

lodge 1. A place to live in, especially a small house. My grandmother lives in a *lodge* up the hill. 2. A branch of an organization. My father's *lodge* meets on Tuesday nights. 3. The den of a wild animal, such as a beaver. *Noun.*
—1. To live in a rented place for a period of time. Let's *lodge* in that cabin by the stream. 2. To get caught and stay in a place. Your kite might *lodge* itself in the branches of that tree. 3. To bring before an authority. We're going to *lodge* a complaint with the mayor. *Verb.* **lodge** (loj) *noun, plural* **lodges**; *verb*.

Los Angeles A city in southwest California. **Los An•ge•les** (lôs anʹjə ləs) *noun*.

lose 1. To be unable to find; misplace. Did you *lose* your keys? 2. To fail to maintain. Don't *lose* your patience. 3. To be defeated. We'll never *lose* another game. 4. To get rid of. I've been trying to *lose* some weight. **lose** (lüz) *verb*.

lotion A special liquid used on the skin. Lotion heals, soothes, softens, or cleans the skin. **lo•tion** (lōʹ shən) *noun, plural* **lotions**.

Louisiana One of the south central states of the United States, the capital of Louisiana is Baton Rouge. The abbreviation for Louisiana is LA. **Lou•i•si•an•a** (lü ēʹzē anʹə or lüʹə zē anʹə) *noun.*

love 1. Strong affection arising from kinship or personal ties. The newlyweds were in *love* with each other. 2. A strong liking for something. Her essay described her *love* of music. *Noun.*
—1. To cherish. I *love* my sister's doll collection. 2. To feel strong affection. 3. To take pleasure in. *Verb.* **love** (luv) *noun, plural* **loves**; *verb*.

loyalist A person who is loyal. Though everyone began to doubt the government, my father remained a *loyalist*. **loy•al•ist** (loiʹə list) *noun, plural* **loyalists**.

loyalty Strong and lasting affection and support. Galahad showed great *loyalty* to King Arthur. **loy•al•ty** (loiʹəl tē) *noun, plural* **loyalties.**

luggage A traveler's containers for carrying personal belongings. I checked in my *luggage* at the airport. **lug•gage** (lugʹij) *noun*.

lure 1. An inducement to pleasure or gain. The salary was a big *lure* to the job. 2. A decoy for attracting animals to capture, such as an artificial bait used for catching fish. *Noun.*
—To tempt with a promise of pleasure. The sound of music *lured* us to the park. *Verb.* **lure** (lůr) *noun, plural* **lures**; *verb*, **lured, luring.**

-ly¹ 1. In a certain way or manner. *Perfectly* means in a perfect way. 2. To a certain degree or extent. *Highly* means to a high degree. **-ly** (lē) *adjective suffix.*

-ly² 1. Like. *Friendly* means like a friend. 2. Happening at a certain period of time.

at; āpe, fär, câre; end; mē, it, īce; pîerce; hot, ōld; sông, fôrk; oil; out; up; ūse; rüle; pùll; tûrn; chin; sing; shop; thin; <u>th</u>is; hw in white; zh in treasure. The symbol ə stands for the unstressed vowel sound in about, taken, pencil, lemon, and circus.

Spelling Dictionary

Weekly means happening every week. **-ly** (lē) *adverb suffix.*

mail To send by mail. I will *mail* the letter to you today. *Verb.*
—**1.** Letters and other postal matter conveyed under public authority through the post office. The *mail* arrived late this morning. *Noun.*
2. *Computers: E-mail.* A form of communication that can be sent and received on a computer. *Noun.* **mail** (māl) *verb, noun.*

mailbox A box to hold letters. There is a *mailbox* down the street. **mail•box** (māl′boks) *noun, plural* **mailboxes**.

main Greatest in size or importance; chief. What is her *main* idea? **main** (mān) *adjective.*

Maine One of the northeastern states of the United States. The capital of Maine is Augusta. The abbreviation for Maine is ME. **Maine** (mān) *noun.*

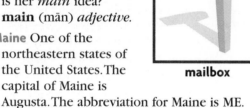

mailbox

male A male individual. My cat is a *male*. *Noun.*
—Having to do with the sex that can father young. The *male* offspring of the finch are usually golden in color. *Adjective.* **male** (māl) *noun, plural* **males**; *adjective.*

manage **1.** To direct with authority. She *manages* her business quite well. **2.** To get along. Can you *manage* by yourself? **3.** To handle. Can you *manage* an electric saw? **man•age** (man′ij) *verb,* **managed, managing.**

mane **1.** The long hair that grows around the neck of some mammals. The lion's *mane* was

orange. **2.** Long hair on a person's head. Her *mane* of hair was lovely. **mane** (mān) *noun, plural* **manes**.

manufacture The making of products by hand or machine. The *manufacture* of this company is sweatshirts. *Noun.*
—To make into a product for use. Some companies *manufacture* excellent radios. *Verb.* **man•u•fac•ture** (man′yə fak′chər) *noun; verb,* **manufactured, manufacturing**.

margin **1.** The edge of a page outside the printed text. Don't write in the *margin*. **2.** An extra amount. Leave a *margin* of 15 minutes when driving to the airport. **mar•gin** (mär′jin) *noun, plural* **margins**.

Maryland An eastern state of the United States. The capital of Maryland is Annapolis. The abbreviation for Maryland is MD. **Mar•y•land** (mer′ə lənd) *noun.*

Massachusetts One of the northeastern states of the United States. The capital of Massachusetts is Boston. The abbreviation for Massachusetts is MA. **Mas•sa•chu•setts** (mas′ə chü′səts) *noun.*

master **1.** A person who controls someone or something. The dogs came when their *master* called them. **2.** A person especially skilled. That author is a *master* of the mystery novel. *Noun.*
—**1.** To get control of. I finally *mastered* my fear of heights. **2.** To become skilled at. Troy will *master* the game of tennis. *Verb.*
—**1.** Being a master or expert. The work on the new house was done by a *master* carpenter. **2.** Most important; main. The city council made a *master* plan for street repairs. **3.** Controlling the operation of other machines, as with a master key or clock. *Adjective.* **mas•ter** (mas′tər) *noun, plural* **masters**; *verb.*

matter **1.** Anything that takes up space and has weight. All things are made of *matter*. **2.** Something that is the subject of interest. This is a serious *matter*. *Noun.*
—To be important. It does *matter* a great deal to me. *Verb.* **mat•ter** (mat′ər) *noun, plural* **matters**; *verb.*

mature To become fully grown or developed. *Verb.* —**1.** Fully thought out. The situation called for a *mature* decision. **2.** Fully grown, ripe, or developed. When a puppy becomes *mature*, it is called a dog. **3.** Having reached a final state. The *mature* tree provides extensive shade. *Adjective.* **ma•ture** (mə chùr′ *or* mə tùr′ *or* mə tyùr′) *verb,* **matured, maturing;** *adjective,* **maturer, maturest.**

mayor An elected official who heads a city. **ma•yor** (mā′ər) *noun, plural* **mayors.**

measure 1. To find or show the size, weight, or amount of something. The doctor *measured* me and found that I had grown two inches in a year. **2.** To have as a measurement. The painting *measured* three feet high. *Verb.* —**1.** The size, weight, or amount of something. Without a ruler, I could only guess at the *measure* of the piece of wood. **2.** A unit, standard, or system of measurement. Inches and meters are *measures* of length. *Noun.* **meas•ure** (mezh′ər) *verb,* **measured, measuring;** *noun, plural* **measures.**

medal A flat, inscribed piece of metal given as an award for an outstanding deed. She wore the *medal* on a chain around her neck. **med•al** (med′əl) *noun, plural* **medals.**

median The middle number in a series of numbers arranged in order from smallest to largest. If the series has an even number of elements, the *median* equals the average of the two middle numbers. **me•di•an** (mē′dē ən) *noun, plural* **medians.**

medicine 1. A substance used in treating disease. I have to take my *medicine* to get well. **2.** The science of healing. The field of *medicine* is growing every day. **med•i•cine** (med′ə sin) *noun, plural* **medicines.**

Memorial Day A holiday in the United States honoring Americans who have died while fighting in wars. *Memorial Day* is observed on the last Monday in May.

merry-go-round A revolving circular platform equipped with wooden animals, especially horses, and often having seats. It is ridden for amusement. Also, **carousel. mer•ry-go-round** (mer′ē gō round′), *noun, plural* **merry-go-rounds.**

message A communication in writing, speech, or by signal. A *message* was sent to all subscribers. **2.** A lesson contained in a story, play, or speech. Did you understand the *message* of his speech? **mes•sage** (mes′ij) *noun, plural* **messages.**

Miami A city in southwest Florida. **Mi•am•i** (mī a′mē) *noun.*

Michigan One of the north central states in the United States. The capital of Michigan is Lansing. The abbreviation for Michigan is MI. **Mich•i•gan** (mish′i gən) *noun.*

might've Shortened form of "might have." I *might've* been able to catch the train if I hadn't stopped for tea. **might•'ve** (mīt′əv) *contraction.*

Minnesota One of the midwestern states of the United States. The capital of Minnesota is St. Paul. The abbreviation for Minnesota is MN. **Min•ne•so•ta** (min′ə sō′tə) *noun.*

minute¹ 1. A unit of time equal to 1/60 of an hour; 60 seconds. **2.** A short period of time; moment. Can I speak to you for a *minute*? **3. minutes.** A written record of what was said and done at a meeting or conference. **mi•nute** (min′it) *noun, plural* **minutes.**

minute² 1. Very small; tiny. A *minute* particle of dirt blew into my eye. **2.** Paying close attention to details. The detective made a *minute* examination of the room for clues. **mi•nute** (mī nūt′, mī nūt′) *adjective.*

mis- 1. Wrong or bad. *Misfortune* means bad fortune. **2.** In a bad or wrong way. *Mispronounce* means to pronounce in the wrong way. **mis-** (mis) *prefix.*

mission 1. A special job or task. The astronauts went on a *mission* to the moon. **2.** A group

at; āpe, fär, câre; end; mē, it, īce; pîerce; hot, ōld: sông, fôrk; oil; out; up; ūse; rüle; pùll; tûrn; chin; sing; shop; thin; **th**is; hw in white; zh in treasure. The symbol ə stands for the unstressed vowel sound in about, taken, pencil, lemon, and circus.

Spelling Dictionary

of persons sent to perform a task. Four rangers formed a rescue *mission* to search for the lost child. **mis•sion** (mish′ən) *noun, plural* **missions**.

Mississippi One of the south central states of the United States. The capital of Mississippi is Jackson. The abbreviation for Mississippi is MS. **Mis•sis•sip•pi** (mis′ə sip′ē) *noun*.

Missouri One of the midwestern states of the United States. The capital of Missouri is Jefferson City. The abbreviation for Missouri is MO. **Mis•sour•i** (mi zùr′ē, mi zùr′ə) *noun*.

mistake 1. A misunderstanding. I ate your dessert by *mistake*. **2.** An error or a wrong action. It was my *mistake* that the door wasn't locked. *Noun.*
—**1.** To misunderstand what is seen or heard. It's easy to *mistake* what you overhear. **2.** To judge incorrectly. Don't *mistake* the difficulty of this task. **3.** To identify incorrectly. You might *mistake* me for my twin sister. *Verb.* **mis•take** (mis tāk′) *noun, plural* **mistakes**; *verb* **mistook, mistaken, mistaking.**

model 1. A pattern for work to be done. The U.S. Constitution is used as a *model* by many new governments. **2.** A small copy of something. I made an airplane *model*. **3.** A style or design. This is the latest *model*. **4.** One who shows clothes by wearing them. My sister works as a *model* at the department store. *Noun.*
—**1.** To make a model of. George *modeled* a horse out of clay. **2.** To show by wearing. She will *model* the clothes. *Verb.* **mod•el** (mod′əl) *noun, plural* **models**; *verb.*

modern Up-to-date; characteristic of the present day. She wears only the most *modern* clothes. **mod•ern** (mod′ərn) *adjective.*

Montana One of the western states of the United States. The capital of Montana is Helena. The abbreviation for Montana is MT. **Mon•tan•a** (mon tan′ə) *noun.*

mood 1. A conscious state of mind. Her *mood* is always cheerful. **2.** Dominant emotion. The child was in a bad *mood*. **3.** A verb form that shows whether the action expressed is to be thought of as a fact, a possibility, or a command. The exercise in English class was to identify the *mood* of each verb. **mood** (müd) *noun, plural* **moods**.

motion picture A series of pictures on a film. They are projected onto a screen at such a high speed that it appears to the viewer that the people and things in the picture are moving. A motion picture is also called a movie. **mo•tion pic•ture** (mō′shən pik′chər) *noun, plural* **motion pictures**.

motor An engine that makes a machine work. The *motor* of a fan makes the fan blades turn. *Noun.*
—To travel by automobile. I like to *motor* around town. *Verb.*
—Run by a motor. I wish I had a *motor* scooter. *Adjective.* **mo•tor** (mō′tər) *noun, plural* **motors**; *verb; adjective.*

mount¹ 1. A high hill. They placed their flag on the top of the *mount*. **2.** Something upon which a person or thing is displayed. The *mount* for the picture was a piece of cardboard. **mount** (mount) *noun, plural* **mounts**.

mount² 1. To go up; climb. I can't *mount* the stairs with all these boxes. **2.** To get up on. If you hold on to the saddle, you can easily *mount* your horse. **3.** To increase. The cost of beef is expected to *mount*. **4.** To display by fastening in proper position on a support. We can *mount* your picture on this piece of cardboard. **mount** (mount) *verb.*

mountain 1. A rise in the earth's surface higher than a hill. **2.** A great amount or huge number. The movie star received a *mountain* of mail daily. **moun•tain** (moun′tən) *noun, plural* **mountains**.

mountain

mountaineer 1. A person who lives in the mountains. The *mountaineer's* shack was stocked with food for the winter. **2.** A person

who climbs mountains for sport.
moun•tain•eer (moun′tə nîr′) *noun,
plural* **mountaineers.**

mouthpiece The part of a musical instrument,
telephone, or other object that is put between
or near the lips. I spoke into the *mouthpiece*
of the telephone. **mouth•piece**
(mouth′pēs′) *noun, plural* **mouthpieces.**

movement 1. Motion; any change of position.
I could see no *movement* in the dark.
2. The efforts of a group of people working
together toward a common goal. The feminist
movement has achieved many of its goals.
move•ment (müv′mənt) *noun, plural*
movements.

muscle 1. A tissue in the body that is made of
strong fibers. *Muscles* can be tightened or
relaxed to make the body move. **2.** Strength.
We'll need some more *muscle* if we're going
to move that piano. **mus•cle** (mus′əl)
noun, plural **muscles.**

musical 1. Having to do with or producing
music. What *musical* instruments do you
play? **2.** Sounding beautiful, like music.
What a *musical* voice she has! **3.** Fond of or
skilled in music. She is a truly *musical*
person. **4.** Set to music. I enjoyed the
musical production of my favorite story.
mu•si•cal (myü′zi kəl) *adjective.*

mustn't Shortened form of "must not." I
mustn't spend too much money today.
must•n't (mus′ənt) *contraction.*

must've Shortened form of "must have."
I *must've* left it back in the car. **must•'ve**
(must′əv) *contraction.*

narrow A passage between two bodies of
water. The deer jumped across the *narrow* to
get away from the fire. *Noun.*
—To lessen in width. The workers *narrowed*
the sidewalk. *Verb.*
—**1.** Of slender width. This alley is too
narrow to drive through. **2.** Limited in
space. In York there is a street so *narrow*

that the rooftops nearly touch. **3.** Not open
to other opinions. The candidate has a
narrow view on that issue. *Adjective.*
nar•row (nar′ō) *noun, plural* **narrows;**
verb; adjective.

Nashville The capital city of Tennessee.
Nash•ville (nash′vil) *noun.*

national 1. Having to do with a land united
under one government. The *national*
government of the United States is headed
by the president. **2.** Characteristic of or
having to do with the people who make up
a nation. The *national* costume is very
colorful. *Adjective.*
—A citizen of a country. Only *nationals* may
vote in some elections. *Noun.* **na•tion•al**
(nash′ə nəl) *adjective; noun, plural*
nationals.

nature 1. All that is not made by humans.
Mountains, oceans, prairies, and woods are
part of *nature.* **2.** The forces at work
throughout the universe. The hurricane was
a display of *nature* at its fiercest. **3.** The
instincts or inborn tendencies that direct
behavior. Her *nature* is to be generous.
na•ture (nā′chər) *noun, plural* **natures.**

naughty Behaving badly; disobedient. Our new
puppy is very *naughty.* **naugh•ty** (nô′tē)
adjective.

navy 1. A fleet of ships. The United States
has one of the most powerful *navies* in the
world. **2.** *Often capitalized.* A nation's armed
forces for sea warfare. My big sister has
joined the *Navy.* **3.** A dark blue color.
na•vy (nā′vē) *noun, plural* **navies.**

Nebraska One of the midwestern states of the
United States. The capital of Nebraska is
Lincoln. The abbreviation for Nebraska is NE.
Ne•bras•ka (nə bras′kə) *noun.*

needn't Shortened form of "need not."
You *needn't* worry. **need•n't** (nēd′ənt)
contraction.

at; āpe, fär, câre; end; mē, it, īce; pîerce; hot,
ōld; sông, fôrk; oil; out; up; ūse; rüle; pùll; tûrn;
chin; sing; shop; thin; this; hw in white; zh in
treasure. The symbol ə stands for the unstressed
vowel sound in about, taken, pencil, lemon,
and circus.

Spelling Dictionary

neither 1. Not either. The word neither is used before the first of two or more negative choices or possibilities connected by *nor*. When I was sick I could *neither* eat nor drink. **2.** Nor. My parents don't want to see the movie; *neither* do I . *Conjunction.*
—Not one or the other; not either. *Neither* team played well in the game. *Adjective.*
—Not the one nor the other. I tried on two coats, but *neither* fit me. *Pronoun.*
nei•ther (nē′<u>th</u>ər *or* nī′<u>th</u>ər) *conjunction; adjective; pronoun.*

nephew The son of one's brother or sister. **neph•ew** (nef′ū) *noun, plural* **nephews.**

Nevada One of the western states of the United States. The capital of Nevada is Carson City. The abbreviation for Nevada is NV. **Ne•vad•a** (nə vad′ə *or* nə vä′də) *noun.*

New Hampshire One of the northeastern states of the United States. The capital of New Hampshire is Concord. The abbreviation for New Hampshire is NH. **New Hamp•shire** (nü *or* nū hamp′shər) *noun.*

New Jersey One of the middle Atlantic states of the United States. The capital of New Jersey is Trenton. The abbreviation for New Jersey is NJ. **New Jer•sey** (nü *or* nū jûr′zē) *noun.*

New Mexico One of the southwestern states of the United States. The capital of New Mexico is Santa Fe. The abbreviation for New Mexico is NM. **New Mex•i•co** (nü *or* nū mek′si kō′) *noun.*

New Orleans A city in southeast Lousiana. **New Or•le•ans** (nü ôr′lē ənz *or* nū ôr lēnz′) *noun.*

newspaper A daily or weekly publication telling the news and containing articles, stories, and advertisements. **news•pa•per** (nüz′pā′pər, nūz′pā′pər) *noun, plural* **newspapers.**

New York One of the middle Atlantic states of the United States. The capital of New York is Albany. The abbreviation for New York is NY. **New York** (nü *or* nū yôrk′) *noun.*

nightgown A loose item of clothing worn to bed. I need a warmer *nightgown* for this

winter. **night•gown** (nīt′goun′) *noun, plural* **nightgowns.**

nighttime The period of darkness from sunset to sunrise. At *nighttime* there is little activity on Main Street. **night•time** (nīt′tīm′) *noun;* **nighttime** *adjective.*

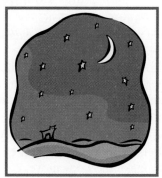

nighttime

nitrogen A gas that has no color or smell. *Nitrogen* makes up almost four-fifths of the air on earth. **ni•tro•gen** (nī′trə jən) *noun.*

nobody Not anybody. *Nobody* could find the lost notebook. **no•bod•y** (nō′bod′ē) *pronoun.*

noisy 1. Making noise. The students were *noisy* in the classroom. **2.** Full of noise; loud. The *noisy* audience quieted down when the curtain rose. **nois•y** (noi′zē) *adjective;* **noisier, noisiest, noisily;** *adverb;* **noisiness;** *noun.*

no one Nobody. *No one* in the room recognized the name. **no one** (nō′wən) *pronoun.*

normal A state considered usual. This year's rainfall is above *normal. Noun.*
—**1.** Conforming to accepted behavior or standards. Such behavior is *normal.*
2. Relating to average development. We were happy to hear that the baby is *normal* in every way. *Adjective.* **nor•mal** (nôr′məl) *noun; adjective.*

north 1. The direction toward the North Pole. From our town, we had to drive to the *north* to get to Seattle. **2.** *Capitalized:* The northern part of a country. I've always

enjoyed living in the *North. Noun.*
—Referring to the direction toward the North Pole. The *north* wind is usually very cold. *Adjective.*
—To or toward the north. Go *north* if you want to do any skiing. *Adverb.* **north** (nôrth) *noun; adjective; adverb.*

North Carolina One of the southeastern states of the United States. The capital of North Carolina is Raleigh. The abbreviation for North Carolina is NC. **North Car•o•li•na** (nôrth kar′ə lī′nə) *noun.*

North Dakota One of the midwestern states of the United States. The capital of North Dakota is Bismarck. The abbreviation for North Dakota is ND. **North Da•ko•ta** (nôrth də kōt′ə) *noun.*

northeast 1. The direction midway between north and east. **2.** *Capitalized:* The northeastern part of a country. The *Northeast* usually has cold winters. *Noun.*
—Referring to the direction midway between north and east. Do you live in the *northeast* section of town? *Adjective.*
—To or toward the northeast. We headed *northeast. Adverb.* **north•east** (nôrth ēst′) *noun; adjective; adverb.*

northwest 1. The direction midway between north and west. **2.** *Capitalized:* The northwestern part of a country. The vast forests of the *Northwest* stretch for miles. *Noun.*
—Referring to the direction midway between north and west. He said the cabin was *northwest* of here. *Adjective.*
—To or toward the northwest. We knew we needed to be driving *northwest. Adverb.* **north•west** (nôrth west′) *noun; adjective; adverb.*

nothing Zero. Ten minus ten leaves *nothing. Noun.*
—Not anything. I have *nothing* to bring. *Pronoun.* **noth•ing** (nuth′ing) *noun; pronoun.*

notice 1. A warning or announcement. I gave my *notice* that I would leave this job in two weeks. **2.** A written or printed announcement. There was a *notice* of her wedding in the newspaper. **3.** The condition of being seen or observed. Her entrance escaped my *notice. Noun.*
—To give attention to or see. Did you *notice* the sign in the window? *Verb.* **no•tice** (nō′tis) *noun, plural* **notices;** *verb,* **noticed, noticing;** *adjective,* **noticeable;** *adverb,* **noticeably.**

November The eleventh month of the year. November has thirty days. **No•vem•ber** (nō vem′bər) *noun.*

numerator The number above or to the left of the line in a fraction. In the fraction 1/2, 1 is the *numerator* and 2 is the denominator. **nu•mer•a•tor** (nü′mər rā′tər *or* nū′mə rā′tər) *noun, plural* **numerators.**

nutrient Something that is needed by people, animals, or plants for life and growth. The protein in meat is a *nutrient* for people and many animals. **nu•tri•ent** (nü′trē ənt *or* nū′trē ənt) *noun, plural* **nutrients.**

oak A tree with hard wood and nuts called acorns. **oak** (ōk) *noun, plural* **oaks.**

obey To do what one is told to do. The dog was trained to *obey* its owner. **o•bey** (ō bā′) *verb.*

observatory A place or building that has telescopes for observing and studying the sun, moon, planets, and stars. We watched the eclipse from the *observatory.* **ob•serv•a•to•ry** (əb zûr′və tôr′ē) *noun, plural* **observatories.**

October The tenth month of the year. October has thirty-one days. **Oc•to•ber** (ok tō′bər) *noun.*

at; āpe, fär, câre; end; mē, it, īce; pîerce; hot, ōld; sông, fôrk; oil; out; up; ūse; rüle; pu̇ll; tûrn; chin; sing; shop; thin; **this**; hw in white; zh in treasure. The symbol ə stands for the unstressed vowel sound in about, taken, pencil, lemon, and circus.

Spelling Dictionary

o'er A shortened form of "over," used long ago in poetry and other forms of writing. **o'er** (ō'ər) *contraction.*

office 1. A place where the work of a business or profession is done. **2.** All the people who work in such a place. The *office* gave a huge party for the boss. **3.** A position of authority, trust, or responsibility. Who is running for the *office* of mayor? **of•fice** (ô'fis) *noun, plural* **offices.**

official A person who holds a certain office or position. The President and Vice President are the two highest *officials* in the executive branch of the United States government. *Noun.*
—**1.** Of or having to do with an office or position of authority. Taking notes at each meeting is one of the *official* duties of the club secretary. **2.** Coming from or approved by an authority to do a specific job. The governor made an *official* statement to the press. **3.** Having the authority to do a specific job. Our neighbor was the *official* referee at the basketball game. **4.** Formal and proper. There was an *official* ball for the Queen. *Adjective.* **of•fi•cial** (ə fish'əl) *noun, plural* **officials;** *adjective.*

Ohio One of the north central states of the United States. The capital of Ohio is Columbus. The abbreviation for Ohio is OH. **O•hi•o** (ō hī'ō) *noun.*

Oklahoma One of the southwestern states of the United States. The capital of Oklahoma is Oklahoma City. The abbreviation for Oklahoma is OK. **O•kla•ho•ma** (ō'klə hō'mə) *noun.*

operation 1. The act or way of working or directing. The *operation* of the business took up a lot of the owner's time. **2.** The condition of being at work. The machine is in *operation.* **3.** Treatment that is performed on the body of a sick or hurt person or animal by surgery. I had an *operation* to remove my tonsils. **op•er•a•tion** (op'ə rā'shən) *noun, plural* **operations.**

opposite A person or thing that is completely different from another. Wet is the *opposite* of dry. *Noun.*

—**1.** As different as possible. Hot is *opposite* to cold. **2.** Across from one another. I sat at one end of the table, and Selim sat at the *opposite* end. *Adjective.* **op•po•site** (op'ə zit) *noun, plural* **opposites;** *adjective; adverb,* **oppositely.**

orbit 1. The path that a planet or other heavenly body follows as it moves in a circle around another heavenly body. **2.** One complete trip of a spacecraft along a path. The scientists sent a satellite into *orbit* around Earth. *Noun.*
—To move in an orbit around a heavenly body. The earth *orbits* the sun. *Verb.* **or•bit** (ôr'bit) *noun, plural* **orbits;** *verb,* **orbited, orbiting.**

orchard A place where fruit trees grow. The apple *orchard* is lovely in the spring. **or•chard** (ôr'chərd) *noun, plural* **orchards.**

Oregon One of the Pacific states of the United States. The capital of Oregon is Salem. The abbreviation for Oregon is OR. **O•re•gon** (ôr'i gən, *or* ôr'i gon') *noun.*

outdoors 1. The open air. The *outdoors* gives me a sense of peace and tranquility. **2.** The world away from human dwellings. The campers enjoyed the *outdoors. Noun.*
—**1.** Outside a house or shelter. Laura went *outdoors* to get some fresh air. **2.** In or into the open. We ate *outdoors. Adverb.* **out•doors** (out'dôrz') *noun; adverb.*

outfit 1. Clothing; equipment for a special purpose. I bought a lovely *outfit* for my skiing trip. **2.** A group of persons working together. Harry and I were in the same military *outfit. Noun.*
—To provide with an outfit. The store *outfitted* the campers. *Verb.* **out•fit** (out'fit') *noun, plural* **outfits.**

overthrow To cause to lose power; defeat, as by force or a struggle. After years of suffering, the people will *overthrow* the dictator. *Verb.*
—The loss of power; defeat. The *overthrow* of the tyrant was celebrated by huge crowds. *Noun.* **o•ver•throw** (ō'vər thrō' *for verb;*

Spelling Dictionary

ō'vər thrō'*for noun*) *verb,* **overthrew, overthrown.**

oxen *Plural of* **ox. 1.** Type of domestic cattle used for food and for pulling heavy loads. My grandfather has *oxen* on his farm. **2.** Any of a group of mammals with horns and hoofs. Buffaloes, bison, and yaks are *oxen.* **ox•en** (ok'sən) *noun, plural.*

ox

oxygen A gas that has no color or smell and that most of life needs to live. *Oxygen* makes up about one fifth of the air. **ox•y•gen** (ok'si jən) *noun.*

pace 1. Stride; a step in walking. The walker set a strong *pace* to win the race. **2.** Rate of progress. The group worked at a good quick *pace. Noun.*
—**1.** To walk with slow, steady steps. The expectant father *paced* the floor in the hospital's waiting room. **2.** To measure by paces. The treasure hunter *paced* off five feet from the tree and began to dig. *Verb.* **pace** (pās) *noun; plural* **paces**; *verb,* **paced, pacing.**

package 1. A group of things wrapped up together. We put our *package* of newspapers out on recycling day. **2.** A box or case in which something is wrapped. *Noun.*
—To put in a package. *Package* the food in these containers. *Verb.* **pack•age** (pak'ij) *noun, plural* **packages**; *verb.*

pain 1. Physical suffering associated with illness. **2.** Mental distress. My grandmother's death caused me much *pain. Noun.*
—To make suffer; to cause distress. My sprained ankle still *pained* me. *Verb.* **pain** (pān) *noun, plural* **pains**; *verb.*

painful Feeling or giving pain. The treatment was especially *painful* for the young patient. *Adjective.* **pain•ful** (pān'fəl) *adjective;* **painfully** *adverb;* **painfulness** *noun.*

palm¹ The inside surface of the hand between the wrist and the fingers. *Noun.*
—**1.** To hold or hide in the hand. The magician *palmed* the cards so we would think they had disappeared. **2.** To get rid of by fooling someone. The crook *palmed* off the cheap stone as a diamond. *Verb.* **palm** (päm) *noun, plural* **palms**; *verb,* **palmed, palming.**

palm² Any of a number of trees, shrubs, or vines with fanning leaves that grow in warm climates. **palm** (päm) *noun, plural* **palms**.

pane A sheet of glass framed in a window or door. Raindrops were falling on the window *pane.* **pane** (pān) *noun, plural* **panes**.

pants A garment for the part of the body below the waist. Pants are designed so that they cover each leg separately. **pants** (pants) *noun.*

paragraph A distinct part of a piece of writing, begun on an indented line and usually containing one specific point. You must rewrite the first *paragraph* of your composition. **par•a•graph** (par'ə graf') *noun, plural* **paragraphs**.

pardon 1. The act of forgiving. I beg your *pardon* if I hurt you. **2.** A legal document releasing a person from punishment.

at; āpe, fär, câre; end; mē, it, īce; pîerce; hot, ōld: sông, fôrk; oil; out; up; ūse; rüle; pùll; tûrn; chin; sing; shop; thin; **th**is; **hw** in **wh**ite; **zh** in treasure. The symbol ə stands for the unstressed vowel sound in about, taken, pencil, lemon, and circus.

Spelling Dictionary

The prisoner received a *pardon* from the governor. *Noun.*
—To forgive. I hope you will *pardon* my tardiness. *Verb.* **par•don** (pär′dən) *noun, plural* **pardons;** *verb.*

partial 1. Not complete; not total. We have a *partial* list of club members. **2.** Showing more favor than is fair to one side, person, or group. The umpire should not be *partial* to the home team. **par•tial** (pär′shəl) *adjective.*

particular 1. Having to do with the separate parts of a whole thing. We only focused on fixing one *particular* part of the machine. **2.** To do with one person or thing only. This artist's *particular* talent is drawing plants. **3.** Unusual in some way; special. She raced for first place with *particular* energy. **4.** Paying great attention to details. She followed the directions for the model with *particular* attention. **par•tic•u•lar** (pər tik′yə lər) *adjective.*

past 1. Time gone by. History is a study of the *past*. **2.** The verb form that shows a happening in the past. The *past* of do is did. *Noun.*
—Gone by; ended; over. Summer is *past. Adjective.*
—Beyond in time or space. The bus goes *past* my house. *Preposition.* **past** (past) *noun, plural* **pasts;** *adjective; preposition.*

paste 1. A smooth food product made usually by grinding. The sauce contains tomato *paste*. **2.** A mixture of starch and water used to stick things together. Use *paste* to stick the pictures in the album. *Noun.*
—To fasten together with paste. We decided to *paste* the photographs into an album. *Verb.* **paste** (pāst) *noun, plural* **pastes;** *verb,* **pasted, pasting.**

patient A person under medical care. Sarah was a *patient* in the hospital. *Noun.*
—Willing to put up with pain, waiting, or trouble. The teacher was very *patient* with the beginners. *Adjective.* **pa•tient** (pā′shənt) *noun, plural* **patients;** *adjective.*

pause A brief stop. There was a *pause* in the conversation. *Noun.*
—To stop briefly. Let's *pause* a minute to think. *Verb.* **pause** (pôz) *noun, plural* **pauses;** *verb,* **paused, pausing.**

peace 1. Freedom from war. **2.** Freedom from worry or disagreement. I'm at *peace* with the world. **3.** A lack of noise or disorder; quiet or calm. I love the *peace* and quiet of the country. **peace** (pēs) *noun.*

peaceful 1. Quiet and calm. It's soothing to gaze at the *peaceful* river. **2.** Without force or violence. We want to lead a *peaceful* life with our neighbors. **peace•ful** (pēs′fəl) *adjective.*

peanut butter A thick spread made of ground, roasted peanuts. David thinks *peanut butter* makes the best sandwiches. **pea•nut but•ter** (pē′nut but′ər) *noun.*

peer[1] 1. An equal. The defendant was judged by a jury of his *peers*. **2.** A nobleman. He took pride in being a *peer.* **peer** (pîr) *noun, plural* **peers.**

peer[2] To look sharply or curiously. Michael *peered* out the window at the rain. **peer** (pîr) *verb.*

Pennsylvania One of the eastern states of the United States. The capital of Pennsylvania is Harrisburg. The abbreviation for Pennsylvania is PA. **Penn•syl•van•ia** (pen′səl vā′nyə) *noun.*

pepper 1. A seasoning with a sharp taste. The soup has too much *pepper* in it. **2.** Any of the tropical plants whose berries are ground to make this seasoning. **3.** The fruit of a plant that can be eaten raw or cooked. Some *peppers* are sweet, and others are hot. *Noun.*
—To season with pepper. The cook salted and *peppered* the fried eggs. *Verb.* **pep•per** (pep′ər) *noun, plural* **peppers;** *verb.*

perfect 1. To make without fault. I went to Mexico to *perfect* my Spanish. **2.** To make complete. I *perfected* the recipe by adding just a touch of nutmeg. *Verb.*
—**1.** Without fault; excellent. This *perfect* apple doesn't have one bruise or bad spot. **2.** Total; complete. The launch was a *perfect* success. *Adjective.* **per•fect** (pər fekt′ *for verb,* pur′fikt *for adjective*) *verb; adjective.*

performance 1. The giving of a play or concert. The students gave an excellent *performance* of their play. **2.** The doing of an action. I admired the lawyer's *performance* in court. **per•form•ance** (pər fôr′məns) *noun, plural* **performances**.

perhaps Possibly but not for sure. *Perhaps* we will see you after school today. **per•haps** (pər haps′) *adverb*.

phase 1. A stage of development. Most babies go through a *phase* when they try to put everything in their mouths. **2.** A part or side; aspect. Advertising, accounting, and selling are some of the *phases* of many businesses. **3.** The appearance and shape of the moon or a planet as it is seen at a particular time, which depends on how much of its lighted side can be seen from Earth. **phase** (fāz) *noun, plural* **phases.**

Philadelphia A city in southeast Pennsylvania on the Delaware River. **Phil•a•del•phi•a** (fil′ə del′fē ə) *noun*.

Phoenix A city in Arizona, in the central part. **Phoe•nix** (fē′niks) *noun*.

phone

phone A telephone. *Noun.*
—To call by telephone. Will you please *phone* me this afternoon? *Verb.* **phone** (fōn) *noun, plural* **phones**; *verb.*

physical 1. Relating to the body, not the mind or spirit. As we grow many *physical* changes take place in our bodies. **2.** Relating to the laws of matter and energy. In science class, we study some of the *physical* forces of nature. **phys•i•cal** (fiz′i kəl) *adjective; adverb,* **physically.**

physician A doctor. **phy•si•cian** (fə zish′ ən) *noun, plural* **physicians.**

physique A person's body. My father's *physique* is big and muscular. **phy•sique** (fi zēk′) *noun, plural* **physiques**.

picture 1. An image produced by painting, drawing, or photography. **2.** A description in words. She gave us a good *picture* of the scene. **3.** A motion picture; movie. We enjoyed the *picture* about the whales. *Noun.* —**1.** To make a picture of by painting, drawing, or photographing. The artist *pictured* a bird sitting on the bench. **2.** To imagine. *Picture* me in a general's uniform. *Verb.* **pic•ture** (pik′chər) *noun, plural* **pictures**; *verb.*

pier 1. A structure extending out into the water, used as a landing place for boats. We walked down to the end of the *pier.* **2.** A support for a bridge. Modern bridges have steel *piers* to support them. **3.** A breakwater; a wharf projecting into the water. Surfers usually stay far from the *pier.* **pier** (pîr) *noun, plural* **piers**.

pigeon A bird with a thick body and short legs. *Pigeons* are found in nearly every city in the world. **pi•geon** (pij′ən) *noun, plural* **pigeons**.

pine[1] A cone-bearing evergreen tree. The *pine* trees smelled wonderful. **pine** (pīn) *noun, plural* **pines**.

pine[2] To long intensely; yearn. The lonely boys *pine* for home. **pine** (pīn) *verb.*

pioneer 1. A person who is among the first to explore or settle a region. *Pioneers* settled the American West. **2.** A person who is among the first to develop an area of thought or research. The Wright brothers were *pioneers* in aviation. *Noun.* —To be among the first to explore for others. American scientists *pioneered* in sending human beings to the moon. *Verb.* **pi•o•neer** (pī′ə nîr′) *noun. plural* **pioneers**; *verb,* **pioneered, pioneering.**

at; āpe, fär, câre; end; mē, it, īce; pîerce; hot, ōld: sông, fôrk; oil; out; up; ūse; rüle; pu̇ll; tûrn; chin; sing; shop; thin; <u>th</u>is; hw in white; zh in treasure. The symbol ə stands for the unstressed vowel sound in about, taken, pencil, lemon, and circus.

Spelling Dictionary

playwright A person who writes plays. William Shakespeare was a very famous English *playwright*. **play•wright** (plā′rīt′) *noun, plural* **playwrights.**

pleasant **1.** Giving pleasure; enjoyable. The music she played was *pleasant* to hear. **2.** Easy to get along with. She is a very *pleasant* person. **pleas•ant** (plez′ənt) *adjective;* **pleasantly** *adverb.*

pleasure **1.** A feeling of enjoyment or happiness. Your piano playing gives me much *pleasure.* **2.** One's choice. What is your *pleasure* in this matter? **3.** Something that pleases. It's my *pleasure* to help you. **plea•sure** (plezh′ər) *noun, plural* **pleasures**.

plum **1.** A purple, round, juicy fruit. *Plums* are my favorite fruit. **2.** A dark bluish purple. **plum** (plum) *noun, plural* **plums**.

plural A word form used to show more than one person or thing. Underline all the *plurals* in the sentence. *Noun.*
—Concerning more than one person or thing. The word chicken should be *plural* in your sentence because you are talking about more than one. *Adjective.* **plu•ral** (plür′əl) *adjective, plural* **plurals**.

pocketbook A pocket-sized container for money and personal papers; purse. **pock•et book** (pok′it bùk) *noun, plural* **pocketbooks**.

polar **1.** Of or near the North or South Pole. Not many people live in the *polar* regions. **2.** Completely different. Andy and Misha are *polar* opposites in personality. *Adjective.* **po•lar** (pō′lər) *adjective.*

polish A smooth and shiny surface. The waxed floor had a bright *polish.* **2.** The act of polishing. He gave the floor a good *polish.* **3.** The substance used in polishing. Use plenty of shoe *polish* on those boots. *Noun.*
—**1.** To make smooth and shiny by rubbing. We waxed and *polished* the oak table. **2.** To remove errors from; to make perfect. Try to *polish* your last paragraph. *Verb.* **pol•ish** (pol′ish) *noun, plural* **polishes;** *verb.*

politics **1.** The work or study of government; the management of public affairs. He went into *politics* and ran for Congress. **2.** The activities of political leaders, candidates, and parties. Around election time, *politics* is always in the news. **3.** Opinions or beliefs about government. My parents' *politics* are conservative. **pol•i•tics** (pol′i tiks) *noun.*

pony A small breed of horse. At the circus, the clowns rode the *ponies* into the ring. **po•ny** (pō′nē) *noun, plural* **ponies**.

pony

population All the people who live in a region. What is the *population* of your city? **pop•u•la•tion** (pop′yə lā′shən) *noun, plural* **populations**.

port **1.** A place where ships can anchor safely. We were happy to get to the *port* after a long day of sailing. **2.** An opening in machinery for taking in or letting out fluids. There was a jam in the *port.* **port** (pôrt) *noun, plural* **ports**.

position **1.** The way something is placed or arranged. I put the vase in a *position* where we could all see it. **2.** Posture. The teacher was seated in a comfortable *position.* **3.** A way of looking at things. What is your *position* on this issue? *Noun.*
—To put something in correct position. The director wanted me to *position* myself so that the audience could hear what I was saying. *Verb.* **po•si•tion** (pə zish′ən) *noun, plural* **positions;** *verb.*

possible Able to be done. It is *possible* for us to travel faster than ever before. **pos•si•ble** (pos′ə bəl) *adjective.*

postage The cost fixed by law for sending a letter or package by mail. The letter I sent was returned to me because I forgot to put *postage* on it. **post•age** (pōs′tij) *noun.*

post office **1.** The postal service. My mother works for the *post office.* **2.** A branch of the post office department where mail is sorted. The line to send packages at the *post office* was too long. **post of•fice** (pōst ô′fis) *noun, plural* **post offices**.

Spelling Dictionary

powerful Having great strength or influence. She gave a *powerful* speech that really affected me. **pow•er•ful** (pou'ər fəl) *adjective*.

praise To say good things about. I heard the teacher *praise* Adam for his work. **praise** (prāz) *verb*.

pre- **1** Earlier or before; ahead of time. *Prehistoric* means before history was written down. *Prepaid* means paid for ahead of time. **pre-** (prē, pri) *prefix*.

predicting Telling beforehand. The weatherman is *predicting* rainfall tomorrow. **pre•dict•ing** (pri dikt'ing) *verb*, **predict, predicted.**

prefix A word or syllable added to the beginning of a word to change its meaning. The word dislike is made up of the *prefix* dis- and the word like. **pre•fix** (prē'fiks') *noun, plural* **prefixes**.

prehistoric Relating to the period before written history. Scientists have found remains of *prehistoric* humans. **pre•his•tor•ic** (prē'his tôr'ik) *adjective*.

prepaid Past tense of **prepay**. Paid for ahead of time. The store insisted the order be *prepaid*. **pre•paid** (prē pād') *verb*.

prepare To get or make ready. Let's *prepare* the food tonight. **pre•pare** (pri pâr') *verb*, **prepared, preparing.**

preschool A school attended before kindergarten. My little sister goes to *preschool. Noun.*
—Relating to a period in a child's life between the ages of 2 and 5. My youngest brother is still at the *preschool* age. *Adjective.* **pre•school** (prē'skül) *noun, plural* **preschools**.

preserve **1.** To keep from being lost, damaged, or decayed; protect. You can *preserve* the wood of the old table by waxing it. **2.** To fix food so that it won't spoil. Fruit can be *preserved* by drying. *Verb.*
—**1.** An area set aside for the protection of plants and animals. Rare birds and mammals breed in that nature *preserve*. **2. preserves.** Fruits that have been boiled with sugar and then put in glass jars for later use. We made some strawberry *preserves. Noun.* **pre•serve** (pri zûrv') *verb*, **preserved, preserving;** *noun, plural* **preserves.**

pressure **1.** Force caused by one thing pushing against another thing. The *pressure* of the driver's foot on the gas pedal made the car go faster. **2.** Strong influence or persuasion. Tad put *pressure* on Tad to join the team. **3.** A burden; strain. They went camping to get away from the *pressure* of city life. *Noun.*
—To urge strongly. The salesperson tried to *pressure* people into buying things they didn't need. *Verb.* **pres•sure** (presh'ər) *noun, plural* **pressures;** *verb,* **pressured, pressuring.**

pretest Test given beforehand to explore strengths and weaknesses. I was given a *pretest* before placement in the program. **pre•test** (prē'test') *noun, plural* **pretests**.

prevent To stop something before it happens. Bad weather can *prevent* a plane from landing. **pre•vent** (pri vent') *verb*.

preview An advance showing of a movie, play, or exhibit. Many famous stars came to the *preview* of the film. *Noun.*
—To see or show ahead of time. The critics will *preview* the movie. *Verb.* **pre•view** (prē'vū) *noun, plural* **previews;** *verb*.

produce Farm products, especially fruit and vegetables. I like to go to the farmer's market to buy fresh *produce. Noun.*
—**1.** To make; yield. The company *produces* automobiles. **2.** To cause. Overeating will *produce* a gain in weight. **3.** To show. Can you *produce* any evidence? **4.** To show to the public. Our class is going to *produce* a play. *Verb.* **pro•duce** (prod'üs', prōd'üs', prod'ūs', prōd'ūs' *for noun;* prə düs', prə dūs' *for verb*) *noun; verb*.

program **1.** A written announcement of something, such as a play or concert. As we

---

at; āpe, fär, câre; end; mē, it, īce; pîerce; hot, ōld: sông, fôrk; oil; out; up; ūse; rüle; pùll; tûrn; chin; sing; shop; thin; <u>th</u>is; hw in white; zh in treasure. The symbol ə stands for the unstressed vowel sound in about, taken, pencil, lemon, and circus.

Spelling Dictionary

entered the auditorium, we were handed a *program.* **2.** The actual performance. We enjoyed the entire *program.* **3.** A set of instructions for a computer. To understand what to do about the problem, I had to look at the *program. Noun.*
—**1.** To arrange a program of or for. **2.** To prepare a set of instructions for a computer. I'll *program* the computer to give us that information. *Verb.* **pro•gram** (prō′gram *or* prō′ grəm) *noun, plural* **programs;** *verb.*

project 1. A plan of activity to be done. He outlined his *project* for us. **2.** A piece of work assigned to someone. We worked many hours on our *project.* **3.** A group of houses or apartments operated as a unit. That is the new housing *project. Noun.*
—**1.** To throw forward. The rocket will *project* the space capsule into orbit. **2.** To cause to be seen on a surface. We can *project* these diagrams onto a screen. **3.** To stick out. The new dock will *project* far out into the water. *Verb.* **pro•ject** (proj′ekt′ *for noun,* prə jekt′ *for verb) noun, plural* **projects;** *verb.*

projection 1. The picture or other image that is projected onto a surface such as a screen. Turn off the lights so the class can see the *projection* clearly. **2.** A prediction based on certain given or known information. The network announced its *projection* of who would win the election. **pro•jec•tion** (prə jek′shən) *noun, plural* **projections.**

propose 1. To suggest something. I *propose* we go camping. **2.** To make an offer of marriage. He *proposed* to her in the restaurant. **pro•pose** (prə pōz′) *verb.*

protect To shield from harm. The mother held her baby close to *protect* her from the rain. **pro•tect** (prə tekt′) *verb.*

protest A declaration of an objection. The senator lodged a *protest* against the amendment. *Noun.*
—To object strongly. During the student riots, many *protested* the police action. *Verb.* **pro•test** (prō′test′ *for noun,* prə test′ *for verb) noun, plural* **protests;** *verb.*

protractor An instrument having a graduated arc for plotting or measuring angles. The math teacher showed us how to use a *protractor.* **pro•trac•tor** (prō trak′tər) *noun, plural* **protractors.**

prove 1. To test something by experiment. They asked the salesperson to *prove* that the soap would really get clothes cleaner. **2.** To show or demonstrate the truth. Shane will *prove* that he is a good runner in this race. **prove** (prüv) *verb,* **proved, proven, proving.**

provide 1. To give what is needed or wanted. We found an organization that will *provide* services for the elderly. **2** To state as a condition. The rules *provide* that members attend at least ten meetings. **pro•vide** (prə vīd′) *verb,* **provided, providing.**

prowl 1. To move about or wander stealthily. The burglar *prowled* about the house. **2.** To roam like a wild beast. The tiger *prowled* through the forest. **prowl** (proul) *verb.*

pudding A thick and sweet soft dessert that is cooked. Rice *pudding* is my favorite dessert. **pud•ding** (pùd′ing) *noun, plural* **puddings.**

puddle A small pool of water or other liquid that is not very deep. There were *puddles* in the road after the rain. **pud•dle** (pud′əl) *noun, plural* **puddles.**

pump A device for moving liquids or gases. The car drove up to the gasoline *pump. Noun.*
—To move with a pump. The farmer tried to *pump* water for his cattle. *Verb.* **pump** (pump) *noun, plural* **pumps;** *verb.*

pumpkin A large, round, yellow-orange vegetable that grows on a vine. Can you carve a face on the *pumpkin* for us? **pump•kin** (pump′kin, pum′kin) *noun, plural* **pumpkins.**

pumpkin

punch[1] 1. To hit a person or thing with the fist or part of the hand. I *punched* the elevator button for the eighth floor. **2.** To

Spelling Dictionary

herd or drive. The cowhands *punched* cattle in the fall. *Verb.*
—A blow with the fist or part of the hand. *Noun.* **punch** (punch) *verb; noun, plural* **punches.**

punch² A tool for making holes in or putting a design on a surface. One kind of *punch* can fix plain paper so that it will fit into a looseleaf notebook. *Noun.*
—To make holes in or press a design on with a punch. I *punched* another hole in the belt so I could tighten it. *Verb.* **punch** (punch) *noun, plural* **punches;** *verb.*

punch³ A drink made by mixing different fruit juices, sodas, or other ingredients. My mom made a huge bowl of *punch* for the party. **punch** (punch) *noun, plural* **punches.**

pupil¹ A young person in school. Martha was Mr. Jacob's best geography *pupil.* **pu•pil** (pū′pəl) *noun, plural* **pupils.**

pupil² The round opening in the iris of the eye that becomes smaller or larger as it adjusts to the amount of light that enters the eye. **pu•pil** (pū′pəl) *noun, plural* **pupils.**

purchase 1. The act of buying. I saved for the *purchase* of a new bike. **2.** That which is bought. We didn't have room to carry the *purchase* home. *Noun.*
—To buy. Where did you *purchase* that awful hat? *Verb.* **pur•chase** (pur′chəs) *noun, plural* **purchases;** *verb.*

purify To make pure or clean. The filter will *purify* the water. **pu•ri•fy** (pyur′ə fī) *verb.*

purpose The reason for doing something. What *purpose* did you have in mind? **pur•pose** (pur′pəs) *noun, plural* **purposes.**

purse 1. Any small bag or case for carrying money. **2.** A sum of money collected as a gift or prize. The winner of the horse race collected a large *purse. Noun.*
—To pucker. The actor *pursed* his lips to show anger. *Verb.* **purse** (purs) *noun, plural* **purses;** *verb.*

puzzle 1. A hard problem. We were given a *puzzle* to solve for extra credit in class. **2.** Something that puzzles. It is a *puzzle* to me how you got here so fast. *Noun.*
—To confuse the understanding of. This problem will *puzzle* you. *Verb.* **puz•zle** (puz′əl) *noun, plural* **puzzles;** *verb.*

quarterback The football player who leads the team when they are trying to score. A *quarterback* usually throws the passes. **quar•ter•back** (kwôr′tər bak′) *noun, plural* **quarterbacks.**

question 1. Something asked in order to find an answer. The tourists asked us a few *questions* about the history of our town. **2.** A matter to be talked over. Let's discuss the *question* of safety in the home. *Noun.*
—**1.** To ask in order to find an answer. The reporter *questioned* several bystanders. **2.** To express doubt about. I *question* her reason for leaving early. *Verb.* **ques•tion** (kwes′chən) *noun, plural* **questions;** *verb.*

quiz A short or informal test. *Noun.*
—To question. The teacher will *quiz* the class on last week's work. *Verb.* **quiz** (kwiz) *noun, plural* **quizzes;** *verb.*

racket¹ A loud or confusing noise. I could hardly hear what you were saying because of the *racket* in the bus. **rack•et** (rak′it) *noun, plural* **rackets.**

at; **āpe**, **fär**, **câre**; **end**; **mē**, **it**, **īce**; **pîerce**; **hot**, **ōld**: **sông**, **fôrk**; **oil**; **out**; **up**; **ūse**; **rüle**; **pùll**; **tûrn**; **chin**; **sing**; **shop**; **thin**; **this**; **hw** in **white**; **zh** in **treasure**. The symbol ə stands for the unstressed vowel sound in **about**, **taken**, **pencil**, **lemon**, and **circus**.

Spelling Dictionary

racket² A round or oval frame with a network of strings and a thin handle. Rackets are usually made of wood, metal, or some other material and are used to hit the ball in tennis and other games. **rack•et** (rak′it) *noun, plural* **rackets.**

radar A device used to find and track objects such as aircraft and automobiles. Radar uses reflected radio waves. **ra•dar** (rā′där) *noun.*

raise An increase in pay, price, or rent. I got a *raise* of ten dollars a week. *Noun.* —**1.** To lift or elevate. Can you *raise* the window? **2.** To increase in pay, price, or rent. The owner wants to *raise* the rent. **3.** To breed or grow. We *raise* wheat on our farm. **4.** To collect donations. We're trying to *raise* funds for the hospital. *Verb.* **raise** (rāz) *noun, plural* **raises;** *verb.*

raise

range 1. A series of things in a line, such as mountains. The Rockies are the largest mountain *range* in the United States. **2.** A cooking stove. **3.** Maximum distance. The missile has a *range* of fifteen miles at top speed. **4.** Variation between limits. There is a *range* in ticket prices from $7 to $20. *Noun.* —**1.** To set in proper order. The books on the shelf were *ranged* from A to Z. **2.** To roam freely. Cattle *ranged* over the prairie. **3.** To vary within limits. The temperature *ranged* from 75° to 85° during our vacation. *Verb.* **range** (rānj) *noun, plural* **ranges;** *verb,* **ranged, ranging.**

rare 1. Of meat, not cooked through. My father likes to eat his steaks *rare*. **2.** Not common. It was a *rare* performance. **rare** (râr) *adjective.*

ratio A comparison in number or quantity between two things. The ratio is the number or times the second thing can be divided into the first thing. If there are 12 apples and 6 pears, the ratio of apples to pears is 2 to 1. **ra•tio** (rā′shē ō′) *noun, plural* **ratios.**

re- 1. Again. *Reelect* means to elect again. **2.** Back. *Return* means to come back. **re-** (ri, rē) *prefix.*

reach 1. The act of reaching. With a *reach* of my arm I pulled the apple from the tree. **2.** The distance one is able to reach. That object is out of my *reach*. **3.** The ability to understand. The language is beyond my *reach*. *Noun.* —**1.** To stretch out or extend. We *reached* for the sky. **2.** To arrive at. We must *reach* home before dark. **3.** To achieve communication with. I can *reach* home by phone. *Verb.* **reach** (rēch) *noun, plural* **reaches;** *verb.*

rearrange To arrange again, especially in a different way. I *rearranged* my furniture. **re•ar•range** (rē′ə rānj′) *verb,* **rearranged, rearranging.**

reason 1. A cause or motive. I have no *reason* to doubt you. **2.** A statement that explains something; excuse. The student could give no *reason* for being late. **3.** The ability to think clearly. The sudden shock made me lose all *reason*. *Noun.* —**1.** To think or think about clearly. I was able to *reason* out the answer to the arithmetic problem. **2.** To try to change a person's mind. They are so stubborn that it is useless to *reason* with them. *Verb.* **rea•son** (rē′zən) *noun, plural* **reasons;** *verb.*

rebuild 1. To build again. After the tornado, we had to *rebuild* the barn. **2.** To make repairs to. The homeowner decided to *rebuild* his front porch. **re•build** (rē bild′) *verb,* **rebuilt, rebuilding.**

recall 1. A bringing back to mind. I don't have any *recall* of the accident. **2.** A taking back. Our petition for the *recall* of the senator failed again. *Noun.* —**1.** To ask or order to come back. The

company had to *recall* all of its recent cars.
2. To bring to mind or remember. Can you *recall* the date of your accident? **3.** To cancel. We need to *recall* the order. *Verb.* **re•call** (ri kôl′, rē′kôl′) *noun, plural* **recalls;** *verb.*

receipt 1. A written statement showing that a package, mail, or money has been received. The clerk in the store gave me a *receipt* for my purchase. **2. receipts.** The amount of money that has been received. The store's *receipts* for the week were over $1,000. **3.** A receiving or being received. We thanked them on *receipt* of their gift. **re•ceipt** (ri sēt′) *noun, plural* **receipts.**

receive 1. To take or get something given. I hope to *receive* a letter from John. **2.** To change incoming radio waves into sounds or pictures. The stormy weather made it difficult to *receive* a clear picture. **re•ceive** (ri sēv′) *verb.*

recent 1. Not long past. Our school paper covers all *recent* events of local interest. **2.** Done, made, or happening not long ago. The radio program reported the most *recent* election news. **re•cent** (rē′sənt) *adjective;* **recently** *adverb.*

record 1. The known facts about what someone has done. Her school *record* is outstanding. **2.** An official written account. The school keeps a *record* of each student's attendance. **3.** A thin, flat disc on which sounds are recorded to be played back on a phonograph. I will play for you my favorite *record.* **4.** The best yet done. She holds the *record* for the mile in track. *Noun.*
—**1.** To put down in writing. The secretary will *record* the business of our meeting. **2.** To put music, words, or sounds on a disc or tape. We can *record* the concert with this tape recorder. *Verb.* **re•cord** (rek′ərd *for noun,* ri kôrd′ *for verb*) *noun, plural* **records;** *verb,* **recorded, recording.**

recover 1. To get back. Have you been able to *recover* the lost papers? **2.** To make up for. He tried to *recover* the time he lost. **3.** To get well. She will fully *recover* from the accident. **4.** To bring back to a normal

condition or position. She slipped on the ice but was able to *recover* herself. **re•cov•er** (ri kuv′ər) *verb.*

refill A fresh supply of something. I need a *refill* for this pen. *Noun.*
—To fill again. Did you *refill* the tank? *Verb.* **re•fill** (rē′fil′*for noun,* rē fil′*for verb*) *noun, plural* **refills;** *verb.*

refugee A person who flees from a place to find safety or protection. The *refugees* left their homeland for another country. **ref•u•gee** (ref′yù jē′) *noun, plural* **refugees.**

refuse¹ Anything thrown away as useless or worthless; trash or rubbish. The street was littered with *refuse* after the parade. **ref•use** (ref′ūs′) *noun.*

refuse² 1. To say no to. She tried to *refuse* my offer of help. **2.** To decline to do. The horse might *refuse* to jump. **re•fuse** (ri fūz′) *verb.*

regular 1. Fixed by custom or rule. Our *regular* school day is from 8 A.M. to 3 P.M. **2.** Happening on a set schedule or at the same time. I make *regular* monthly visits to my doctor. **3.** According to habit or usual behavior. Sarah is a *regular* visitor at our house. **4.** Even in size, speed, or spacing. We relaxed when his breathing became *regular.* **reg•u•lar** (reg′yə lər) *adjective.*

rejoice To be glad. We'd *rejoice* at any news. **re•joice** (ri jois′) *verb,* **rejoiced, rejoicing.**

rely 1. To depend on. I *rely* on my neighbor. **2.** To trust. Can you *rely* on this truck? **re•ly** (ri lī′) *verb,* **relied, relying.**

remain 1. To stay in the same place. The young girl will *remain* with her parents. **2.** To continue unchanged. The weather *remains* foggy. **3.** To be a part not destroyed. All that *remained* of the shed after the storm was the foundation. **re•main** (ri mān′) *verb.*

at; āpe, fär, câre; end; mē, it, īce; pîerce; hot, ōld; sông, fôrk; oil; out; up; ūse; rüle; pùll; tûrn; chin; sing; shop; thin; **th**is; **hw** in white; **zh** in treasure. The symbol ə stands for the unstressed vowel sound in about, taken, pencil, lemon, and circus.

remainder 1. A remaining part. I gave my friend the *remainder* of my sandwich. **2.** The number found when one number is subtracted from another. If you subtract 3 from 10, the *remainder* is 7. **re•main•der** (ri mān ′dər) *noun, plural* **remainders.**

remark A short statement or comment. Her *remark* was uncalled for. *Noun.*
—**1.** To notice. Did you *remark* his strange manner? **2.** To comment. Can you *remark* on the event? *Verb.* **re•mark** (ri märk′) *noun, plural* **remarks**; *verb.*

remove 1. To take away. Please *remove* the cat. **2.** To get rid of. This new evidence should *remove* all doubt. **3.** To take off. Please *remove* your hat. **re•move** (ri müv′) *verb.*

rent Money paid for the use of something. The landlord collects my family's *rent. Noun.*
—**1.** To pay regularly for the use of something. I *rent* a storage unit to keep my extra belongings in. **2.** To lease for rent. Our landlord *rents* out ten apartments. *Verb.* **rent** (rent) *noun, plural* **rents**; *verb.*

repair 1. The process of repairing. The *repairs* cost a lot of money. **2.** Condition in terms of soundness. The roof is in good *repair. Noun.*
—To restore by replacing or fixing whatever is torn or broken. **re•pair** (ri pâr′) *noun, plural* **repairs**; *verb.*

repay To pay back. How can I ever *repay* all your kindness? **re•pay** (ri pā′) *verb,* **repaid.**

repeat 1. Something that is repeated. That television show is a *repeat* from last season. *Noun.*
—To say, do, or make again. She asked me to *repeat* what I had said. *Verb.* **re•peat** (ri pēt′) *noun, plural* **repeats**; *verb.*

reply To answer orally or in writing. She asked me to *reply* through the mail. **re•ply** (ri plī′) *verb.*

report An account or statement. The secretary wrote a *report* of the meeting. *Noun.*
—**1.** To make or give a report. Chuck will *report* to the class about his summer vacation. **2.** To tell the authorities. The boy saw smoke and *reported* it to the fire department. **3.** To present oneself. He will *report* to the principal's office on Monday. *Verb.* **re•port** (ri pôrt′) *noun, plural* **reports**; *verb.* **reportable** *adjective.*

represent 1. To show a likeness of. This play has done an accurate job of *representing* the actual person the story is based on. **2.** To be a sign or symbol of something. This new flag will *represent* our club. **3.** To act for another person or persons, as with elected officials. Two senators *represent* the citizens of each state. **re•pre•sent** (rep′ri zent′) *verb.*

republic 1. A form of government in which the authority belongs to the people. The people elect representatives to manage the government. A republic is usually headed by a president, rather than a royal ruler. **2.** A country that has such a form of government. The United States is a *republic.* **re•pub•lic** (ri pub′lik) *noun, plural* **republics.**

return 1. The act of coming back to a place. His *return* to his hometown will be exciting. **2.** *Plural.* A report of voting results. The candidate and his staff anxiously waited for the election *returns.* **3.** Something given or received in exchange. The longest line at the department store was the line for *returns. Noun.*
—**1.** To go back. Every year we *return* to the country for rest and relaxation. **2.** To take or put back. She *returned* the overdue book to the library. **3.** To send in response. Robert *returned* his RSVP to the bride. *Verb.*
—Used for returning. The airline passenger lost her *return* ticket while on vacation. *Adjective.* **re•turn** (ri turn′) *noun, plural* **returns**; *verb; adjective.*

reunion 1. The act of reuniting. The *reunion* of those two stars in another movie is sure to be exciting. **2.** A gathering of friends or relatives after separation. Will you attend your class *reunion?* **re•un•ion** (rē ūn′yən) *noun, plural* **reunions.**

review 1. A studying, going over, or examining again. There will be a *review* of the material before the test. **2.** A critical evaluation of a book, play, or movie. After reading the *review* I decided not to get the book. *Noun.*
—**1.** To look at again. Let's *review* the chapter. **2.** To study or go over again.

I *reviewed* my notes before the test. **3.** To examine. I'd like to *review* the plans for the banquet. **4.** To make an analysis of a book, play, or movie. Our assignment was to *review* the movie of the book we read. *Verb.* **re•view** (ri vū′) *noun, plural* **reviews**; *verb.*

rewrite To write in a different form or manner. The teacher told me to *rewrite* my paper because there were too many mistakes. **re•write** (rē rīt′) *verb.*

Rhode Island One of the northeastern states of the United States. The capital of Rhode Island is Providence. The abbreviation for Rhode Island is RI. **Rhode Is•land** (rōd ī′lənd) *noun.*

rise **1.** An upward movement. We could feel the *rise* of the airplane. **2.** The amount of an increase. There has been a $2.00 *rise* in price. **3.** A hill or piece of high ground. Our house is located on a *rise* overlooking the town. *Noun.*
—**1.** To get up from lying, kneeling, or sitting. The jury was asked to please *rise* when the judge entered the courtroom. **2.** To appear above the horizon. The sun should *rise* in an hour. **3.** To increase in quantity or number. Automobile production will *rise* this spring. **4.** To move upward. The curtain should *rise* in 15 minutes. *Verb.* **rise** (rīz) *noun, plural* **rises**; *verb,* **rose, risen, rising.**

roast A piece of meat cooked with little or no liquid. We had a *roast* of lamb for dinner. *Noun.*
—**1.** To cook with little or no moisture. My mother *roasted* the potatoes for dinner. **2.** To be hot. I'm *roasting* in this coat. *Verb.*
—Cooked by roasting. The *roast* beef was served medium rare. *Adjective.* **roast** (rōst) *noun, plural* **roasts**; *verb; adjective.*

rod **1.** A straight, thin stick or bar. The small flag was attached to a *rod* stuck in the ground. **2.** A pole used with a line and reel for fishing. Tom showed me his new fishing *rod.* **3.** A unit of length, about five meters or 5.5 yards. We measured the distance in *rods.* **rod** (rod) *noun, plural* **rods.**

roof **1.** The top part of a building. Mr. Brown's house has a slate *roof.* **2.** A place to live. The

shack was at least a *roof* over the wanderer's head. **3.** The upper part of the mouth. The peanut butter stuck to the *roof* of her mouth. **4.** Something that looks like a roof. The treetops formed a *roof* for the forest animals below. *Noun.*
—To cover with a roof. The beaver will *roof* his home with logs. *Verb.* **roof** (rüf, rùf) *noun, plural* **roofs**; *verb.*

rooster A male domestic chicken. The *rooster* woke the farmer at dawn. **roost•er** (rüs′tər) *noun, plural* **roosters.**

rural Of or having to do with the country or farming. My cousin lives in *rural* Pennsylvania. **ru•ral** (rùr′əl) *adjective.*

rooster

saddle **1.** A padded seat for a horseback rider; a seat for a bicycle or motorcycle. The cowboy uses a Western *saddle* on his horse. **2.** Something shaped like a saddle. **sad•dle** (sad′əl) *noun, plural* **saddles.**

sandal A shoe made of a sole fastened to the foot by straps. *Sandals* are my favorite shoes to wear in the summer. **san•dal** (san′dəl) *noun, plural* **sandles.**

Saturday The seventh day of the week. **Sat•ur•day** (sat′ər dē, sat′ər dā) *noun, plural* **Saturdays.**

saucer A small dish, usually used to set a cup upon. Give the cat a *saucer* of milk. **sau•cer** (sô′sər) *noun, plural* **saucers.**

at; āpe, fär, câre; end; mē, it, īce; pîerce; hot, ōld; sông, fôrk; oil; out; up; ūse; rüle; pùll; tûrn; chin; sing; shop; thin; this; hw in white; zh in treasure. The symbol ə stands for the unstressed vowel sound in about, taken, pencil, lemon, and circus.

Spelling Dictionary

scale¹ A machine for weighing people or things. I stepped on the *scale* to learn my weight. **scale** (skāl) *noun, plural* **scales**.

scale² One of the thin, flat plates that cover the body of fish, snakes, and lizards. *Noun.*
—To remove scales from a fish. Before cooking the fish we caught, my father helped me to *scale* it. *Verb* **scale** (skāl) *noun, plural* **scales**; *verb,* **scaled, scaling.**

scale³ 1. A series of regular marks made along a line at regular spaced points. The *scale* of my ruler is in inches. **2.** The size of a plan, map, or model compared with what it represents. The *scale* of that map is one inch for each 100 miles. **3.** In music, a series of tones going up or down. A *scale* is usually made up of eight notes. **scale** (skāl) *noun, plural* **scales**.

scar 1. A mark left after a wound has healed. The burn left a *scar* on my hand. **2.** A lasting effect after damage has been done. His experiences in the war left an emotional *scar. Noun.*
—To mark with a scar. Our cat *scarred* the door by scratching it. *Verb.* **scar** (skär) *noun, plural* **scars**; *verb.*

scent 1. An odor; smell. The *scent* of lilacs was in the air. **2.** A liquid with a pleasant smell; perfume. What *scent* is that you're wearing? **3.** The sense of smell. Bloodhounds are known for their keen *scent. Noun.*
—**1.** To sense by or as if by the sense of smell. **2.** To suspect. I *scent* trouble in the air. **3.** To perfume. We tried to *scent* the house with flowers. *Verb.* **scent** (sent) *noun, plural* **scents**; *verb.*

schedule 1. A written or printed list. I need to refer to the *schedule* to find where my classes will be held. **2.** A program. My *schedule* for tomorrow will be very busy. **3.** A list of times, events, or things to do. Check the bus *schedule* before you go. *Noun.*
—To plan; to place in a schedule. *Verb.* **sched•ule** (skej′ül) *noun, plural* **schedules**; *verb.*

scheme 1. A plan for doing something. Show me the *scheme* for the project. **2.** A

plot for doing something. We uncovered a *scheme* to rob the bank. **3.** A systematic arrangement. Tell me what the color *scheme* of your bedroom is. *Noun.*
—To plot; to form plans. We did some *scheming* to come up with this idea. *Verb.* **scheme** (skēm) *noun, plural* **schemes**; *verb,* **schemed, scheming.**

scholar 1. A person who has much knowledge. **2.** A person who attends school. **schol•ar** (skol′ər) *noun, plural* **scholars.**

science 1. Knowledge in which facts, laws, and causes are arrived at by testing and experimenting. In our *science* class, we made water evaporate. **2.** Organized knowledge in a specific area that is an object of study. My sister is interested in the *science* of politics. **sci•ence** (sī′əns) *noun, plural* **sciences.**

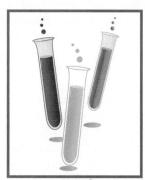

scientific

scientific Using the methods and principles of science. All of the students in our class had to plan and carry out a *scientific* experiment. *Adjective.* **sci•en•tif•ic** (sī′ən tif′ik) *adjective.*

scoreboard A large board that shows the score of a game or a contest. The *scoreboard* read: Hawks 24, Bulls 25. **score•board** (skôr′bôrd′) *noun, plural* **scoreboards.**

scramble 1. To climb or crawl hurriedly. The children *scrambled* down the rocks. **2.** To struggle for something. The runners *scrambled* for the lead. **3.** To mix together. We *scrambled* the pieces of the puzzle. **scram•ble** (skram′bəl) *verb.*

scrapbook A book used to keep pictures and clippings. My father keeps a *scrapbook* of photos and newspaper clippings about our family. **scrap•book** (skrap′bu̇k′) *noun, plural* **scrapbooks**.

scrape 1. The act or sound of scraping. We heard the *scrape* of sleds on the ground. **2.** A wound or injury made by scraping. He had a slight *scrape* on his elbow. *Noun.* —**1.** To remove by stroking with a sharp tool. We tried to *scrape* off the rust. **2.** To damage by rubbing against a rough surface. Did you *scrape* your fender? *Verb.* **scrape** (skrāp) *noun, plural* **scrapes**; *verb,* **scraped, scraping. —scrape by** to barely manage: We'll *scrape by* somehow.

screech 1. To make a shrill, harsh cry or sound. The monkeys *screeched* when the cage door opened. **screech** (skrēch) *verb.*

scribble To write hastily, and carelessly. Michael was rushing through his homework and just *scribbled* down the answers. **scrib•ble** (skrib′əl) *verb.*

scribe A person who writes down or copies letters, books, or other written materials. **scribe** (skrīb) *noun, plural* **scribes.**

script 1. Handwriting in which the letters are joined together. Our teacher taught us how to write *script.* **2.** The written text of a play. The director considered many *scripts* before choosing this one. **script** (skript) *noun, plural* **scripts.**

seal¹ 1. A flesh-eating mammal living in cold sea regions and having large, webbed flippers for swimming. We saw a *seal* swimming in the water. **seal** (sēl) *noun, plural* **seals.**

seal² 1. A design stamped onto paper or pressed into wax to show ownership or authenticity. This book has Sally's *seal* on it. **2.** A decorative stamp used to close a letter or package. I used a Christmas *seal* on the envelope. **3.** A thing that closes or fastens securely. I secured the *seal* on the case. —**1.** To mark with a seal. The diploma was stamped and *sealed* by the college. **2.** To close with a seal. Did you *seal* the letter yet? **seal** (sēl) *noun, plural* **seals**; *verb,* **sealed, sealing.**

Seattle A city in Washington. **Se•at•tle** (sē at′əl) *noun.*

secret Something kept hidden or unexplained. Let's share this *secret. Noun.* —**1.** Kept from general knowledge. You are not to disclose this *secret* information to anyone. **2.** Working with hidden methods. The *secret* agent was distressed by the news. *Adjective.* **se•cret** (sē′krət) *noun; adjective.*

security 1. Protection from harm or loss; safety. I ran to the *security* of the school during the storm. Having money in the bank gives me a feeling of *security.* **2.** Something that gives protection. A burglar alarm is *security* against thieves. **se•cu•ri•ty** (si kyu̇r′i tē) *noun, plural* **securities.**

selection 1. The act of choosing. I had to make a *selection* of a main dish from the menu. **2.** Someone or something that is chosen. It took some time to decide on our *selection* at the store. **3.** A collection of things to choose from. They have a wonderful *selection* of shoes. **se•lec•tion** (si lek′shən) *noun, plural* **selections**.

September The ninth month of the year. September has thirty days. **Sep•tem•ber** (sep tem′bər) *noun.*

settlement 1. An arrangement; a putting in order. We proposed a *settlement* of the dispute. **2.** A payment. *Settlement* of the bill was made in full. **3.** The settling of people in a new country. The *settlement* of the Irish in the United States brought many wonderful new customs. **4.** A group of buildings and the people living in them. The pioneers built many *settlements* in the West. **set•tle•ment** (set′əl mənt) *noun, plural* **settlements.**

severe 1. Very strict. The convicted criminals were given *severe* sentences by the judge. **2.** Dangerous; serious. Only people with *severe* illnesses are taken to the clinic.

at; āpe, fär, câre; end; mē, it, īce; pîerce; hot, ōld; sông, fôrk; oil; out; up; ūse; rüle; pu̇ll; tûrn; chin; sing; shop; thin; this; hw in white; zh in treasure. The symbol ə stands for the unstressed vowel sound in about, taken, pencil, lemon, and circus.

Spelling Dictionary

3. Violent or sharp. The ship was in a *severe* storm. **se•vere** (sə vîr′) *adjective*.

shake The act of shaking. The child scared the dog away with the *shake* of a stick. *Noun.* —**1.** To move irregularly to and fro. The house *shakes* when the trains go by. **2.** To vibrate as the result of a blow or shock. The earthquake began to *shake* the skyscrapers. *Verb.* **shake** (shāk) *noun, plural* **shakes**; *verb,* **shook, shaken, shaking.**

share A portion or part belonging to someone. She saved her *share* of the money. *Noun.* —**1.** To divide in parts. We agreed to *share* the sandwich. **2.** To use or experience something with others. It was a beautiful experience to *share* with others. *Verb.* **share** (shâr) *noun, plural* **shares**; *verb,* **shared, sharing.**

sharpen To make or become sharp. I am very careful when I *sharpen* the kitchen knife. **sharp•en** (shär′pən) *verb.*

shear 1. To trim; to cut off hair from. The ranger will *shear* his sheep in their pen. **2.** To cut or clip from someone or something. Please *shear* the hedge. **shear** (shîr) *verb,* **sheared, shorn, shearing.**

shears A cutting tool similar to large scissors. There are *shears* for cutting grass and cutting metal. **shears** (shîrz) *plural noun.*

she'd 1. Shortened form of "she had." *She'd* gone yesterday but the store was closed. **2.** Shortened form of "she would." *She'd* be here already if she left on time. **she'd** (shēd) *contraction.*

shine 1. Light or brightness. The *shine* from the lamp hurts my eyes. **2.** Liking; appreciation. My mother really took a *shine* to my boyfriend. **3.** A high polish on shoes. What a *shine* your shoes have! *Noun.* —**1.** To send out light. Move the light so it doesn't *shine* in your eyes. **2.** To be bright by reflecting light. These glasses really *shine.* **3.** To show unusual abilities. They all really *shine* in sports. **4.** To brighten by polishing. I need to *shine* my shoes. *Verb.* **shine** (shīn) *noun; verb,* **shone** or **shined, shining.**

shocking Causing horror, surprise, or disgust. We heard some *shocking* news. **shock•ing** (shok′ing) *adjective.*

shortage The lack of a needed amount. There's a *shortage* of desks in our classroom. **short•age** (shôrt′ij) *noun, plural* **shortages**.

shoulder 1. The part of the body where the arm or forelimb joins the body. I injured my *shoulder* playing football. **2.** Something that resembles a shoulder. The *shoulder* of the hill washed away in the heavy storm. **3.** The edge of a road. We nearly drove off the *shoulder. Noun.* —**1.** To push with the shoulder. I *shouldered* my way onto the train. **2.** To assume the responsibility for something. My friend tried to *shoulder* the blame for the accident. *Verb.* **shoul•der** (shōl′dər) *noun, plural* **shoulders**; *verb.*

shouldn't Shortened form of "should not." I *shouldn't* go because I have homework to do. **should•n't** (shùd′ənt) *contraction.*

should've Shortened form of "should have." You *should've* seen the look on the winner's face. **should'•ve** (shùd′əv) *contraction.*

shove 1. To push with a steady force. The mechanic *shoved* open the door to the garage. **2.** To push rudely or carelessly. Try not to *shove* ahead of someone in line. **shove** (shuv) *verb,* **shoved, shoving.**

shovel A scoop attached to a long handle, used for lifting loose material. We have a strong *shovel* to use for clearing the driveway of snow this winter. *Noun.* —To pick up and throw with a shovel. The worker *shoveled* dirt into the back of the truck. *Verb.* **shov•el** (shuv′əl) *noun, plural* **shovels**; *verb.*

shower 1. A brief rainfall. The forecast is for *showers* today. **2.** A party for a particular occasion given by friends who bring gifts. We had a good time at Sally's wedding *shower.* **3.** A bath in which water pours down on a person from an overhead nozzle. *Noun.* —**1.** To rain or fall as in a shower. It *showered* all day, so I stayed home. **2.** To

Spelling Dictionary

bathe by standing under a nozzle spraying water. **3.** To give lavishly. Everyone will *shower* them with praise. *Verb.* **show•er** (shou′ər) *noun, plural* **showers**; *verb.*

shut **1.** To close or be closed. The door *shut* behind me. **2.** To keep within limits. We were *shut* inside by the violent storm. **shut** (shut) *verb,* **shutting.**

silk A fine, glossy, strong fiber spun by silkworms that can be woven into cloth. My mother has a beautiful scarf made out of *silk.* **silk** (silk) *noun, plural* **silks.**

single **1.** A separate, individual person or thing. The roses are sold as *singles* at this flower store. **2.** A hit in baseball that lets a batter get only to first base. She hit a *single* at the game today. *Noun.*
—**1.** To select from a group. Why do you want to *single* me out? **2.** To make a one-base hit in baseball. I *singled* my first game at bat. *Verb.*
—**1.** Not married. My older cousin is *single.* **2.** Only one. I'd like only a *single* piece. *Adjective.* **sin•gle** (sing′gəl) *noun, plural* **singles**; *verb,* **singled, singling**; *adjective.*

sink **1.** To go down or cause to go down partly or completely below a surface. The canoe could *sink* if it has a hole in it. **2.** To become less. Our voices *sank* to a whisper. **3.** To fall into a certain state. I *sank* into a deep sleep as soon as I got into bed. **4.** To dig. We *sunk* a well in the yard. **5.** To go or cause to go through or into deeply. *Sink* your teeth into this, it's great! *Verb.*
—A basin of metal, porcelain, or other material that is used to hold water for washing. A sink has faucets to turn water on and off and a drain to take water away. *Noun.* **sink** (singk) *verb,* **sank** *or* **sunk, sunk** *or* **sunken, sinking**; *noun, plural* **sinks.**

siren A device that makes a loud, shrill sound. It is used as a signal or warning. Ambulances and police cars have *sirens.* **si•ren** (sī′rən) *noun, plural* **sirens.**

site **1.** The location of a structure or a set of structures. The workers took a break at the *site* they were working on. **2.** The place of

something. The boys rode their bikes to see the *site* of the accident. **3.** *Computers: Web site.* A location on a computer network where information can be found. Ted found the *Web site* for his city's weather information. **site** (sīt) *noun, plural* **sites.**

skeleton **1.** A framework that supports and protects the body of an animal. Birds, fish, and humans have *skeletons* made up of bones or cartilage. **2.** Any framework or structure used as a support. The workers built the steel *skeleton* of the building first. **skel•e•ton** (skel′i tən) *noun, plural* **skeletons.**

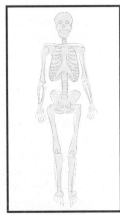

skeleton

sketch **1.** A rough first drawing. The artist made several *sketches* of the model before starting the painting. **2.** An outline or plan. We met to agree on a rough *sketch* of our arrangements. **3.** A short play or story. The drama students rehearsed the new *sketch* for us. *Noun.*
—**1.** To draw roughly. I *sketched* an old barn for my class. **2.** To draw or paint sketches. I want to learn to *sketch.* *Verb.* **sketch** (skech) *noun, plural* **sketches**; *verb.*

smear **1.** A spot made by something sticky, oily, or dirty. There was a *smear* of dirt on my cat's fur. **2.** Something harmful and usually false said about something or someone. They almost ruined his political career with that *smear.* **3.** A small amount of a substance smeared on a surface. It was hard to see the *smear* on the wall from far away. *Noun.*
—**1.** To stain with something sticky, oily, or dirty. The baby tried to *smear* its

at; āpe, fär, câre; end; mē, it, īce; pîerce; hot, ōld: sông, fôrk; oil; out; up; ūse; rüle; pùll; tûrn; chin; sing; shop; thin; this; hw in white; zh in treasure. The symbol ə stands for the unstressed vowel sound in about, taken, pencil, lemon, and circus.

Spelling Dictionary

clothes with jam. **2.** To rub or spread something onto something else. I love to *smear* a piece of bread with peanut butter. **3.** To harm or spoil. Someone tried to *smear* my reputation by telling lies about me. *Verb.* **smear** (smîr) *noun, plural* **smears**; *verb.*

soak 1. To become wet clear through. We were *soaked* by the sudden thunderstorm. **2.** To absorb something. The sponge *soaked* up the spilled juice. **3.** To become absorbed. I gave the words of the poem time to *soak* into my mind. **soak** (sōk) *verb.*

solar 1. Having to do with or coming from the sun. Next week there will be a *solar* eclipse. **2.** Using or powered by the energy of the sun. This *solar* car uses sunshine for energy. **so•lar** (sō′lər) *adjective.*

somebody 1. Some person. We have been looking for *somebody* to care for our cats while we are out of town. **2.** A person of importance. She thinks she's *somebody* because she has a big house. *Pronoun.* **some•bod•y** (sum′bod′ē) *pronoun, plural* **somebodies**.

somewhere In or to some place not known or named. I know I left my keys *somewhere* in the kitchen. **some•where** (sum′hwâr *or* sum′wâr) *adverb.*

sonar An instrument that sends out radio waves to discover and locate objects under the water. The *sonar* detected a submerged submarine that was lost since 1978. **so•nar** (sō′när) *noun, plural* **sonars**.

soothe To quiet, calm, or ease. The nurse *soothed* the crying child by singing a lullaby. The lotion *soothed* my sunburn. **soothe** (sü͟th) *verb,* **soothed, soothing.**

sort 1. Type; category. What *sort* of shoes did you buy? **2.** Quality. These tools are of an inferior *sort*. **3.** Person. He's not a bad *sort*. *Noun.*
—To arrange by kind. I'll *sort* the clothes. *Verb.* **sort** (sôrt) *noun, plural* **sorts**; *verb.*

sought Past tense of **seek**. **1.** Went to look for. She *sought* a better school for her children. **2.** Tried. I *sought* to improve my income. **sought** (sôt) *verb.*

sour To become sour. The milk *soured* because it wasn't kept cold. *Verb.*
—**1.** Having a sharp, acid taste. My friend really likes *sour* candy. **2.** Having an acid taste because of fermentation. The milk was *sour*. **3.** Unpleasant or irritable. She was in a *sour* mood this afternoon. *Adjective.* **sour** (sour, *or* sou′ər) *verb; adjective.*

source 1. A place or thing from which something comes. My father was a great *source* of strength to me. **2.** The beginning of something. The *source* of the pollution was the chemical plant. **3.** A book, magazine, or person that supplies information. The encyclopedia was the main *source* for my report. **4.** The start of a river or stream. The *source* of the Amazon River is deep in the Andes Mountains. **source** (sôrs) *noun, plural* **sources**.

south 1. The direction toward the South Pole. *South* is directly opposite north. **2.** *Capitalized*: The southern part of a country. Someday I'd like to live in the *South*. *Noun.*
—Referring to the direction toward the South Pole. The *south* side of the garage gets the most sun. *Adjective.*
—To or toward the south. We decided to drive *south*. *Adverb.* **south** (south) *noun; adjective; adverb.*

South Carolina One of the southeastern states of the United States. The capital is Columbia. The abbreviation for South Carolina is SC. **South Car•o•li•na** (south kar′ə lī′nə) *noun.*

South Dakota One of the midwestern states of the United States. The capital of South Dakota is Pierre. The abbreviation for South Dakota is SD. **South Da•ko•ta** (south də kōt′ə) *noun.*

southeast 1. The direction midway between south and east. **2.** *Capitalized*: The southeastern part of a country. There were many storms in the *Southeast* yesterday. *Noun.*
—Referring to the direction midway between south and east. My mother's

house is in the *southeast* part of town. *Adjective.*
—To or toward the southeast. If you walk *southeast*, you'll get to the lake. *Adverb.* **south•east** (south ēst′) *noun; adjective; adverb.*

southwest **1.** The direction midway between south and west. **2.** *Capitalized*: The southwestern part of a country. There are many deserts in the *Southwest. Noun.*
—Referring to the direction midway between south and west. The school is in the *southwest* part of town. *Adjective.*
—To or toward the southwest. We followed the road *southwest* for ten miles. *Adverb.* **south•west** (south west′) *noun; adjective; adverb.*

special Different from others in a certain way; not ordinary; unusual. The sports fan had a *special* interest in hockey. **spe•cial** (spesh′əl) *adjective.*

specimen A single person or thing that shows what the whole group is like; sample. I collect **specimens** of different kinds of butterflies. **spec•i•men** (spes′ə mən) *noun, plural* **specimens.**

speech **1.** The ability to use spoken words to express ideas, thoughts, and feelings. Humans are among the few animals that have *speech.* **2.** A public talk. She gave a clear and sensible *speech.* **3.** Manner of speaking. Their *speech* was a giveaway that they were from New York. **speech** (spēch) *noun, plural* **speeches.**

spider A small, eight-legged animal with no wings and a two-part body. Most *spiders* spin webs to catch insects for food. **spi•der** (spī′dər) *noun, plural* **spiders.**

spider

split **1.** The act of splitting. **2.** A break or crack. There is a *split* in the seam. *Noun.*

—**1.** To divide lengthwise. *Split* the wood into sticks. **2.** To divide into parts or shares. We'll *split* the money among the three winners. *Verb.* **split** (split) **splitting** *verb.*

spoon A tool used for eating and cooking. I eat soup with a large *spoon. Noun.*
—To take up with or as if with a spoon. Let me *spoon* up more soup. *Verb.* **spoon** (spün) *noun, plural* **spoons;** *verb.*

sprang Past tense of **spring.** **1.** Leaped. She *sprang* from her seat. **2.** Flew back as if by elastic force. The door suddenly *sprang* open. **3.** Grew or came forth. Plants *sprang* from seeds planted in early spring. **sprang** (sprang) *verb.*

spray A mist of fine liquid drops. I felt a *spray* as I walked by the sprinklers. *Noun.*
—To squirt fine drops of liquid. He will *spray* paint on one side of the house. *Verb.* **spray** (sprā) *noun, plural* **sprays;** *verb.*

sprint To run or race at full speed. The winner *sprinted* across the finish line. **sprint** (sprint) *verb.*

spy A person who watches others secretly. A person is sometimes hired as a spy by a government to discover secret information about another government. *Noun.*
—**1.** To watch others secretly; act as a *spy.* The submarine was sent to *spy* on enemy ships. **2.** To catch sight of; spot. I *spied* my friend coming over the hill. *Verb.* **spy** (spī) *noun, plural* **spies;** *verb,* **spied, spying.**

squeeze The act of squeezing. Mom gave me a *squeeze* when I won the award. *Noun.*
—**1.** To press hard. He *squeezed* my hand when he shook it. **2.** To hug. Let me *squeeze* you. **3.** To force by pressing. *Squeeze* the juice from ten oranges. **4.** To crowd. Ten of us tried to *squeeze* into the small car. *Verb.* **squeeze** (skwēz) *noun, plural* **squeezes;** *verb,* **squeezed, squeezing.**

at; āpe, fär, câre; end; mē, it, īce; pîerce; hot, ōld: sông, fôrk; oil; out; up; ūse; rüle; pùll; tûrn; chin; sing; shop; thin; this; hw in white; zh in treasure. The symbol ə stands for the unstressed vowel sound in about, taken, pencil, lemon, and circus.

Spelling Dictionary

stable¹ 1. A building in which horses are kept. It is my chore to clean the *stables*. **2.** A group of racehorses belonging to one owner. This particular *stable* is well taken care of. *Noun.*
—To keep in a stable. The horses are *stabled* here. *Verb.* **sta•ble** (stā′bəl) *noun, plural* **stables**; *verb* **stabled, stabling.**

stable² 1. Secure; not likely to get worse. People say that America has a *stable* economy. **2.** Not likely to change in character. She is a very *stable* person. *Adjective.* **sta•ble** (stā′bəl) *adjective,* **stabler, stablest.**

stage 1. A platform built especially for speaking or presenting plays. **2.** Any level of a river above zero point, as with a flood stage. Fortunately, the river by our house is past the flood *stage*. **3.** A degree of advancement or growth. That dog still seems to be at the puppy *stage. Noun.*
—To exhibit something or present a play on a stage. Our school will *stage* two plays this year. *Verb.* **stage** (stāj) *noun, plural* **stages**; *verb.*

statehood The status or condition of being a state. Pennsylvania is going into its third century of *statehood*. **state•hood** (stāt′hüd) *noun.*

statement 1. The act of stating. She made her *statement* loud and clear. **2.** Something stated. The police took a *statement* from the witness about the robbery. **3.** A brief record of a financial account. Your monthly bank *statement* shows a balance of $526. **state•ment** (stāt′mənt) *noun, plural* **statements.**

station 1. A regular stopping place along a route; a building at such a place. Take a taxi from the train *station* to my house. **2.** A building or place used for a special purpose. My cousin works at a gas *station*. **3.** A regular post. Go to your *station* when the bell rings. *Noun.*
—**1.** To assign to a post. *Station* some of your people around the building. *Verb.* **sta•tion** (stā′shən) *noun, plural* **stations**; *verb,* **stationed, stationing.**

stew A dish made of pieces of meat or fish and vegetables cooked together in a liquid. We had beef *stew* for dinner. *Noun.*
—To cook food slowly in a liquid. The chef let the prunes *stew* on the stove. *Verb.* **stew** (stü *or* stū) *noun, plural* **stews**; *verb,* **stewed, stewing.**

stir 1. Movement; commotion. We were startled by a *stir* in the bushes. **2.** A burst of activity or excitement. The television broadcast caused a great *stir*. **3.** The act of stirring. This cake batter needs a good *stir. Noun.*
—**1.** To cause a small movement. The wind *stirred* the leaves. **2.** To disturb the quiet. The commotion outside *stirred* the napping children. **3.** To mix in a circular movement. *Stir* the flour and water together. **4.** To rouse to action. The stories *stirred* my desire to travel. *Verb.* **stir** (stûr) *noun, plural* **stirs**; *verb,* **stirred, stirring.**

stir

stitch 1. One complete movement of a threaded needle in sewing or surgery. The *stitches* were perfectly spaced. **2.** A loop of thread made by a stitch. Several *stitches* on the new dress had come loose. *Noun.*
—**1.** To make stitches in. The doctor will *stitch* up your wound. **2.** To make, fasten, or mend with stitches; sew. I *stitched* up the tear in my shirt. *Verb.* **stitch** (stich) *noun, plural* **stitches**; *verb.*

St. Louis A city in east Missouri on the Mississippi River. **St. Lou•is** (sānt′lü′is) *noun.*

stock 1. Things for sale or use. We just increased our *stock* of toys. **2.** Farm animals. The farm and all its *stock* were lost in the fire. **3.** Shares in a company. Our *stocks* have increased in value. **4.** Liquid in which meat, fish, or vegetables has been cooked, used as a base for soup. My favorite soup recipe calls for chicken *stock. Noun.*
—**1.** To supply. We bought canned foods to *stock* our cupboard. **2.** To keep for use on a

Spelling Dictionary

regular basis. We always *stock* popcorn at our house. **3.** To supply with farm animals. My uncle spent thousands of dollars to *stock* his farm. *Verb.*
—**1.** Regularly kept on hand. This dress is a *stock* item. **2.** Commonly used; ordinary. He always has a *stock* answer for everything. *Adjective.* **stock** (stok) *noun, plural* **stocks;** *verb; adjective.*

straight 1. Free from curves and bends; linear. I use a ruler to draw a *straight* line. **2.** Honest. You can get a *straight* answer from her. *Adjective.* **straight** (strāt) *adjective.*

straighten To make straight-often used with *up* or *out.* Joe *straightened* up his room at last. **straight•en** (strāt′ən) *verb.*

strain A bodily injury caused by too much effort. The athlete has a severe *strain* in his neck.
—To draw tight; stretch. The large dog *strained* at the leash. **2.** To injure by overuse, misuse, or excessive pressure. The baseball player *strained* his back when he swung at the ball. **3.** To pass through a strainer. We always *strain* the fresh orange juice we make. **strain** (strān) *noun, plural* **strains;** *verb,* **strained, straining.**

strategy 1. The science of planning and directing troops and ships during a war. **2.** A careful plan. The recent graduate's *strategy* was to practice her interviewing skills. **strat•e•gy** (strat′i jē) *noun, plural* **strategies.**

strawberry The small, juicy red fruit of a short plant that has white flowers and long, thin runners. **straw•ber•ry** (strô′ber′ē, strô′bə rē) *noun, plural* **strawberries.**

stray A person or animal that roams. The cat we found in the alley is a *stray. Noun.*
—**1.** To roam; wander. The kitten *strayed* from the yard. **2.** To go wrong by taking a wrong course. Her love of sports caused her to *stray* from her studies. *Verb.*
—**1.** Wandering or lost. A *stray* cat fell asleep on our doorstep. **2.** Found here and there; scattered. Let me remove these few *stray* hairs. *Adjective.* **stray** (strā) *noun, plural* **strays;** *verb; adjective.*

strength 1. The state of being strong. I lift weights to develop my *strength.* **2.** The degree of concentration or intensity. The *strength* of this medicine makes it very effective. **3.** Force measured in numbers. The army attacked at full *strength.* **4.** Support. Our cause has enough *strength* to defeat this bill. **strength** (strength or strengkth) *noun, plural* **strengths; strengthen** *verb.*

stripe A long, narrow section that differs in color or texture from its background. Her dress was decorated with a pink *stripe.* **2.** Braid on the sleeve that shows military rank. The sergeant's uniform had three *stripes.*
—To make stripes on. The city crew will *stripe* the crosswalks tomorrow. *Verb.* **stripe** (strīp) *noun, plural* **stripes;** *verb.*

struggle 1. To make a great effort. The children *struggled* through the heavy snow. **2.** To fight; battle. The soldiers *struggled* bravely with the enemy. *Verb.*
—**1.** A great effort. It was a *struggle* to learn French. **2.** A fight, battle, or war. The *struggle* resulted in a victory for the team. *Noun.* **strug•gle** (strug′əl) *verb,* **struggled, struggling;** *noun, plural* **struggles.**

subject 1. Something thought about and discussed. The *subject* of his paper was UFOs. **2.** A course or field that is studied. Science is my favorite *subject* in school. **3.** A person or thing that experienced something. This mouse is the *subject* of our experiment. **4.** In grammar, a word or group of words that performs the action of the verb. In the sentence "Astronauts get a lot of training," "Astronauts" is the subject. *Noun.*
—**1.** To bring under one's power or influence. Hitler tried to *subject* all of Europe to his rule. **2.** To cause to experience something. The coach will *subject* you to many tests before accepting you on the team. *Verb.*

at; āpe, fär, câre; end; mē, it, īce; pîerce; hot, ōld: sông, fôrk; oil; out; up; ūse; rüle; pu̇ll; tûrn; chin; sing; shop; thin; **th**is; **hw** in **wh**ite; **zh** in treasure. The symbol ə stands for the unstressed vowel sound in about, taken, pencil, lemon, and circus.

Spelling Dictionary

—**1.** Obedient to some power or influence. I am *subject* to my parents' wishes. **2.** Likely to have or receive. I am *subject* to allergies. **3.** Depending on. I'll leave tomorrow, *subject* to your approval. *Adjective.* **sub•ject** (sub'jikt *for noun,* səb jekt' *for verb,* sub'jikt *for adjective*) *noun, plural* **subjects**; *verb,* **subjected, subjecting**; *adjective.*

suggestion 1. The act of suggesting. We went to that movie because of your *suggestion.* **2.** Something suggested; an idea or proposal. Buying a lock for my bicycle was my friend's *suggestion.* **3.** A small amount. There was just a *suggestion* of ginger in that dish. **4.** The process by which one thought prompts another. The teacher used *suggestion* to spark our memories. **sug•ges•tion** (sə jes'chən, səg jes'chən) *noun, plural* **suggestions.**

suitcase A rigid traveling bag. I packed my own *suitcase* for our trip. **suit•case** (süt'kās) *noun, plural* **suitcases.**

sunshine The light rays of the sun. My room gets plenty of *sunshine.* **sun•shine** (sun'shīn') *noun.*

sunshine

supply To provide with something needed or wanted. Rain *supplies* water. *Verb.*
—A quantity of something that is needed or ready to use. We have brought the *supplies* for our camping trip. *Noun.* **sup•ply** (sə plī') *verb,* **supplied, supplying**; *noun, plural* **supplies.**

suppose 1. To take as possible. *Suppose* it rains tomorrow. **2.** To believe. I *suppose* the Cardinals will win the World Series. **sup•pose** (sə pōz') *verb,* **supposed, supposing, supposedly**; *adverb;* **supposable**; *adjective.*

sure 1. Steady; firm. You should have a *sure* grip on the bat when you swing it. **2.** Certain to be; dependable. Our team is a *sure* winner. **3.** Without doubt; certain. We were *sure* of his honesty. **4.** Certain to

happen. The poorly planned project was *sure* to fail. *Adjective.* **sure** (shür) *adjective.*

surely 1. Without doubt; certainly. I will *surely* be there. **2.** Really. I *surely* hope it doesn't rain today. **sure•ly** (shür'lē) *adverb.*

surgeon A doctor who performs surgery. My brother is studying to be a brain *surgeon.* **sur•geon** (sûr'jən) *noun, plural* **surgeons.**

surprise 1. A coming upon someone without warning. We caught them by *surprise.* **2.** Something that surprises. We had a *surprise* for everyone. **3.** The feeling caused by something happening suddenly. The audience was taken by *surprise* when the actress fainted. *Noun.*
—**1.** To come upon suddenly. One morning we *surprised* two deer in our back yard. **2.** To cause to feel sudden wonder or amazement. You *surprised* us with all the gifts you brought. *Verb.* **sur•prise** (sər prīz') *noun, plural* **surprises**; *verb.*

sweater A knitted or crocheted garment worn on the upper part of the body. The weather is still not cold enough to wear a *sweater.* **sweat•er** (swet'ər) *noun, plural* **sweaters.**

sweep 1. The act of clearing away. The cat batted the ball with a *sweep* of its paw. **2.** A steady, driving motion. The *sweep* of the waves ate away the foundations of the homes. **3.** A stretch. A wide *sweep* of forest lay before us. **4.** A complete victory. Winning all five games gave us a *sweep* of the tournament. *Noun.*
—**1.** To remove from a surface with a broom; to brush away. Please *sweep* the floor. **2.** To drive or carry along with great force. The high waters might *sweep* away our homes. **3.** To move swiftly. The sailor's eyes *swept* the horizon. *Verb.* **sweep** (swēp) *noun, plural* **sweeps**; *verb* **swept.**

sword A hand weapon with a long, pointed blade set in a hilt. **sword** (sôrd) *noun, plural* **swords.**

syllable A word or part of a word pronounced with a single, uninterrupted sounding of the voice. The word "important" has three *syllables.* **syl•la•ble** (sil'ə bəl) *noun, plural* **syllables.**

Spelling Dictionary

symbol Something that represents something else. The dove is a *symbol* of peace. **sym•bol** (sim′bəl) *noun, plural* **symbols.**

system **1.** A group of things that form a whole. Our state has a good *system* of roads. **2.** A group of laws, beliefs, or facts. In school, we study different *systems* of government. **3.** An orderly method. You have a good *system* for studying. **sys•tem** (sis′təm) *noun, plural* **systems.**

tardy **1.** Sluggish; slow. We were *tardy* in planning this event. **2.** Not prompt; late. The Lances are always *tardy* to meetings. **tar•dy** (tär′dē) *adjective,* **tardier, tardiest**.

target **1.** A point to shoot at. We threw darts at the *target*. **2.** A person or thing that is gossiped about or laughed at. The losing team was an easy *target* for cruel jokes. **3.** Something to be accomplished. Our *target* for the fund-raising project is a thousand dollars. **tar•get** (tär′gət) *noun, plural* **targets**.

tease **1.** The act or state of being teased. I hope your remarks are just a *tease*. **2.** A person who teases. A *tease* in the class keeps kidding me about my hair. *Noun.*
—To pester constantly. Jimmy loves to *tease* his sister. *Verb.* **tease** (tēz) *noun, plural* **teases;** *verb.*

teaspoon **1.** A small spoon that is used to eat soft foods and to stir liquids. **2.** A unit of measure in cooking equal to one third of a tablespoon. Put one *teaspoon* of vanilla in the cake batter. **tea•spoon** (tē′spün′) *noun, plural* **teaspoons.**

telegraph An electrical system used to send messages by code over wires. The message came from Alaska by *telegraph.* **tel•e•graph** (tel′ə graf′) *noun, plural* **telegraphs.**

temple¹ A building that is used for religious worship. In Greece, we saw the ruins of the ancient *temples.* **tem•ple** (tem′pəl) *noun, plural* **temples.**

temple² The flattened part on either side of the forehead. The *temple* is above the cheek and in front of the ear. **tem•ple** (tem′pəl) *noun, plural* **temples.**

tendon A strong cord or band of tissue that attaches a muscle to a bone or other part of the body. **ten•don** (ten′dən) *noun, plural* **tendons.**

Tennessee One of the south central states of the United States. The capital of Tennessee is Nashville. The abbreviation for Tennessee is TN. **Ten•nes•see** (ten′ə sē′) *noun.*

term **1.** A word or phrase used in connection with a special subject. "Serve" is a *term* used in tennis. **2.** The length of time that something lasts; duration. His presidential *term* will soon be over. **3.** One of the periods into which the school year is divided. *Noun.*
—To name or call. I'd *term* him a genius. *Verb.* **term** (tûrm) *noun, plural* **terms;** *verb.*

terrible **1.** Causing terror; fearsome, awful. The hurricane was a *terrible* disaster. **2.** Great in degree; awesome. The tornado made a *terrible* mess of the small town. **ter•ri•ble** (ter′ə bəl) *adjective.*

terror **1.** Extreme fear; horror. That movie about monsters filled me with *terror.* **2.** Someone or something that causes intense fear or worry. That vicious dog is a *terror* to the neighborhood. **ter•ror** (ter′ər) *noun, plural* **terrors**.

Texas One of the southwestern states of the United States. The capital of Texas is Austin. The abbreviation for Texas is TX. **Tex•as** (tek′səs) *noun.*

textbook A book used in the study of a subject. For the course the student purchased three *textbooks.* **text•book** (tekst′bùk′) *noun, plural* **textbooks**.

Thanksgiving The fourth Thursday in November, observed as a legal holiday in the United

at; āpe, fär, câre; end; mē, it, īce; pîerce; hot, ōld: sông, fôrk; oil; out; up; ūse; rüle; pùll; tûrn; chin; sing; shop; thin; **this**; hw in white; zh in treasure. The symbol ə stands for the unstressed vowel sound in about, taken, pencil, lemon, and circus.

Spelling Dictionary

States for public thanksgiving. On *Thanksgiving* many families eat a traditional meal that includes a turkey. **Thanks•giv•ing** (thangks′giv′ing) *noun, plural* **Thanksgivings.**

that'll Shortened form of "that will." *That'll* teach him to not play with his food. **that•'ll** (that′əl) *contraction.*

theme 1. A subject of discourse or artistic representation. The *theme* of the movie was difficult to understand. 2. A written composition. The teacher assigned the English class a *theme* to be completed by Friday. **theme** (thēm) *noun, plural* **themes. thematic** *adjective.*

there's 1. Shortened form of "there is." *There's* no time to get your book. 2. Shortened form of "there has." *There's* been no rain since July. **there's** (thârz) *contraction.*

they'd 1. Shortened form of "they had." *They'd* waited for hours. 2. Shortened form of "they would." *They'd* have done it but they thought you did it already. **they'd** (thād) *contraction.*

they'll 1. Shortened form of "they will." *They'll* be here in ten minutes. 2. Shortened form of "they shall." *They'll* reap a good crop. **they'll** (thāl) *contraction.*

they're Shortened form of "they are." *They're* identical twins. **they're** (thâr) *contraction.*

they've Shortened form of "they have." *They've* never been in a place like this before. **they've** (thāv) *contraction.*

thorough 1. Leaving nothing out; complete. The doctor gave me a *thorough* examination. 2. Careful. She is very *thorough* in her work. **thor•ough** (thûr′ō) *adjective.*

thoughtful 1. Lost in thought. The reader looked up with a *thoughtful* expression. 2. Considerate of others. Sally is a kind, *thoughtful* hostess. **thought•ful** (thôt′fəl) *noun,* **thoughtfulness; thoughtfully** *adverb.*

thread 1. A thin cord used in sewing. She went out of her way to find silver *thread* for the dress she was making. 2. Something that is like a thread. *Threads* of icing dripped from the cake. 3. The main idea of a story or speech. We had trouble following the *thread* of her story. *Noun.*
—1. To pass a thread through the eye of a needle. Please *thread* this needle for me. 2. To pass through carefully. We must *thread* our way between the rows of glass figures. *Verb.* **thread** (thred) *noun, plural* **threads;** *verb.*

thread

threaten 1. To make threats; intimidate, bully. 2. To give a warning. The dark clouds *threaten* stormy weather. 3. To menace. Water pollution *threatens* people as well as wildlife. **threat•en** (thret′ən) *verb.*

throne 1. The chair on which a person of high rank sits during ceremonies. 2. The power of a king or queen. The young prince came to the *throne* after the death of his mother, the queen. **throne** (thrōn) *noun, plural* **thrones.**

throughout 1. All the way through. There was a smell of smoke *throughout* the house. 2. During the whole time. The boys ate the popcorn *throughout* the movie. *Preposition.*
—1. In every part of; everywhere. The flaw in the computer program was corrected *throughout.* 2. From beginning to end; completely. The home was cleaned *throughout. Adverb.* **through•out** (thrü out′) *preposition; adverb.*

thrown Past participle of **throw.** 1. Sent through the air with force. The ball was *thrown.* 2. Brought to the ground. I was *thrown* from my horse. 3. Put in a condition or position suddenly. The fire alarm has *thrown* the crowd into a panic. **thrown** (thrōn) *verb.*

Thursday The fifth day of the week. **Thurs•day** (thurz′dē, thurz′dā) *noun, plural* **Thursdays**.

Word History

Thursday comes from the Old English word meaning "Thor's day." Thor was the pagan English god of thunder.

tiger 1. A large mammal of the cat family having a coat striped with black. The Bengal *tiger* arrived at the zoo. **2.** Any of several large wildcats. *Tigers* are my favorite animals. **ti•ger** (tī′gər) *noun, plural* **tigers**.

tire[1] A rubber cushion filled with air that fits around the rim of a wheel. We had to fill the rear left *tire* on our car with air today. **tire** (tīr) *noun, plural* **tires**.

tire[2] **1.** To become or make weary. I *tire* easily when I am sick. **2.** To lose interest. I *tired* of the dull TV show. **tire** (tīr) *verb*.

tissue 1. A group of cells in a plant or animal that are similar in form and in function. The bark that protects a tree is a kind of plant *tissue*. **2.** A soft, thin paper. I sneezed into the *tissue* that was given me. **tis•sue** (tish′ü) *noun, plural* **tissues.**

tomorrow The day after today. If today is Monday, then *tomorrow* is Tuesday. *Noun.*
—On the day after today. We are going on a trip *tomorrow. Adverb.* **to•mor•row** (tə mor′ō or tə môr′ō) *noun, plural* **tomorrows;** *adverb.*

Topeka The capital city of Kansas, in the northeast section of the state. **To•pe•ka** (tə pē′kə) *noun.*

toss 1. To throw lightly. Robert *tossed* the ball to his brother Michael. **2.** To lift quickly. The diners watched the waiter *toss* the Caesar salad. **3.** To throw about restlessly. The small boat was *tossed* about on the bay. **toss** (tôs) *verb;* **toss** *noun, plural* **tosses.**

touchdown 1. A score made in football by carrying the ball across the other team's goal line. A *touchdown* counts six points. **2.** The act or moment of landing an aircraft or spacecraft. The shuttle made a *touchdown*

on the moon. **touch•down** (tuch′doun′) *noun, plural* **touchdowns.**

tour 1. A short trip or walk around, usually ending at the point of beginning. We did a quick *tour* of the building. **2.** A period of military or other activity in a certain place. His *tour* of duty took him to Germany. *Noun.*
—To travel as a tourist. They *toured* the country. *Verb.* **tour** (tùr) *noun, plural* **tours;** *verb.*

tourism The activity or practice of touring. I went to Jamaica to study the effects of *tourism* on the country. **tour•ism** (tùr′iz əm) *noun.*

tourist A person who travels for pleasure. The *tourists* visited the Houses of Parliament. **tour•ist** (tùr′ist) *noun, plural* **tourists.**

toward Also **towards 1.** In the direction of. Laura was walking *toward* her brother when he fell off his bike. **2.** Facing. Turn the chair *toward* the window so you can read better. **3.** In regard to. The patient has a wonderful attitude *toward* life. **to•ward** (tə wôrd′ or tôrd) *preposition.*

tray An open, shallow vessel with a flat bottom and a raised rim, used for holding, carrying, or exhibiting things. The waitress carried the dinners on a round *tray.* **tray** (trā) *noun, plural* **trays.**

treasure 1. Stored-up wealth, especially in the form of jewels or precious metals. **2.** Something of great value. This dog is a *treasure* to me. *Noun.*
—To hold as precious; cherish. I *treasure* my time alone. *Verb.* **trea•sure** (trezh′ər) *noun, plural* **treasures;** *verb,* **treasured, treasuring.**

treatment 1. The act or manner of handling. His *treatment* of animals is very gentle. **2.** A technique or substance used in treating.

at; āpe, fär, câre; end; mē, it, īce; pîerce; hot, ōld: sông, fôrk; oil; out; up; ūse; rüle; pùll; tûrn; chin; sing; shop; thin; **th**is; hw in white; zh in treasure. The symbol ə stands for the unstressed vowel sound in about, taken, pencil, lemon, and circus.

Spelling Dictionary

This beauty *treatment* is very expensive. **treat•ment** (trēt′mənt) *noun, plural* **treatments**.

trim **1.** Good condition or order; fitness. My cat is healthy and in good *trim*. **2.** Something that decorates or ornaments. The *trim* on your jacket has faded. **3.** Woodwork around doors and windows. *Noun.*
—**1.** To make neat by cutting away. My favorite chore is *trimming* the hedges. **2.** To decorate. They *trimmed* the gym with red and white balloons. *Verb.*
—Neat and orderly in line or structure. She wore a *trim* uniform. *Adjective.* **trim** (trim) *noun, plural* **trims;** *verb,* **trimmed, trimming;** *adjective,* **trimmer, trimmest, trimly** *adverb.*

triumph **1.** A special victory. The winning of the game was a *triumph* for all of us. **2.** A great success. The discovery of a polio vaccine was a medical *triumph*. **3.** The joy resulting from victory or success. The winning runner shouted in *triumph*. *Noun.*
—**1.** To achieve a victory. Our team *triumphed* over the other team. **2.** To celebrate a victory or success. We *triumphed* over the election results. *Verb.* **tri•umph** (trī′umf) *noun, plural* **triumphs;** *verb.*

trophy **1.** A prize awarded to a winner. She proudly displayed her soccer *trophy* on the shelf. **2.** Something taken as a reminder or proof of victory. I took the ball as a *trophy* to remind me of the great game. **tro•phy** (trō′fē) *noun, plural* **trophies**.

trousers A piece of clothing that reaches from the waist to the ankles and covers each leg separately; pants. I just bought a pair of purple *trousers* to wear to the party. **trou•sers** (trou′zerz) *noun.*

trousers

truly **1.** In a real, genuine, or honest way; sincerely. I can speak quite *truly* about my behavior. **2.** Really; honestly. The Rocky Mountains were *truly* a beautiful sight. **tru•ly** (trü′lē) *adverb.*

trust **1.** To believe to be true, honest, or reliable. I *trust* my best friend. **2.** To feel sure; hope or expect confidently. I *trust* that you will enjoy this show. *Verb.*
—**1.** A belief that someone or something is true, honest, or reliable; confidence. I have complete *trust* in you. **2.** The care or keeping of someone or something. The neighbor's dog was left in my *trust* for one week. *Noun.* **trust** (trust) *verb,* **trusted, trusting;** *noun, plural* **trusts**.

tunnel An enclosed passage, especially one underground. The train goes through a *tunnel* under the river. *Noun.*
—To make, use, or form a tunnel. The dog *tunneled* under the fence and got loose. *Verb.* **tun•nel** (tun′əl) *noun, plural* **tunnels;** *verb.*

turquoise **1.** A sky-blue or greenish blue mineral valued as a gem. *Turquoise* is often used in jewelry made by the Navajo people. **2.** A sky-blue or greenish blue color. *Noun.*
—Sky-blue or greenish blue. We were in awe of the *turquoise* sky. *Adjective.* **tur•quoise** (tûr′kwoiz or tûr′koiz) *noun,* **turquoises;** *adjective.*

twenty-five The number following twenty-four; 25. *Noun.*
—One more than twenty-four. There are *twenty-five* jars on the shelf. *Adjective.* **twen•ty-five** (twen′tē fīv′) *noun, plural; adjective.*

twin One of two persons or animals born together. Many *twins* look exactly alike. *Noun.*
—**1.** Being one of two siblings born together. I have a *twin* sister. **2.** Made up of two similar or related parts. Look at the *twin* mountain peaks. *Adjective.* **twin** (twin) *noun, plural* **twins;** *adjective.*

type **1.** A class or group having characteristics in common. We have more than one *type* of radio. **2.** Example, kind. This is a modern *type* of kitchen. **3.** A piece of metal or wood having a raised letter or symbol on its upper surface for printing purposes. *Type* is coated

with ink and pressed onto paper in printing.
4. Printed or typewritten letters. Read the
bold *type* first. *Noun.*
—**1.** To write with a typewriter. I like to
type letters to my friends. **2.** To find out the
type of; classify. We can *type* your blood
immediately. *Verb.* **type** (tīp) *noun, plural*
types; *verb,* **typed, typing.**

ugly Not pleasant, especially to the sight. The
scene of the accident was an *ugly* sight.
ug•ly (ug′lē) *adjective.*

un- Not or opposite of; in-, im-, non-, dis-.
Unexpected means not expected. *Prefix.*
un- (un) *prefix.*

understood Past tense and past participle of
understand. 1. Grasped the meaning of.
I *understood* what she was saying. **2.** Knew
well. I *understood* the child's needs. *Verb.*
—**1.** Fully known. The success of this
woman's life was *understood* by everyone at
the celebration. **2.** Taken as a fact. It's
understood that the class is to be seated
when the bell rings. **3.** Agreed upon;
assumed. There was an *understood*
agreement that Carmen waited for Leah
after school. *Adjective.* **un•der•stood**
(un′dər stὸd′) *verb; adjective.*

unfair Marked by injustice or deception. The
attorney requested a new hearing because
the first judge was *unfair.* **un•fair** (un′fâr′)
adjective; **unfairly** *adverb;* **unfairness**
noun.

United States A North American country made
up of 50 states and the District of Columbia.
U•ni•ted States (ū nīt′əd stāts′) *noun.*

unknown Something that remains to be
discovered. The location of the planet was an
unknown until just a few years ago. *Noun.*
—Having an unidentified value; unfamiliar.
There was an *unknown* number of jelly
beans in the jar. *Adjective.* **un•known**
(un nōn′) *noun, plural* **unknowns**;
adjective.

upset 1. A throwing into confusion or
disorder. The crowd was in a state of
upset after the fire. **2.** A minor physical
disorder. Tea may be good for stomach *upset.*
3. An unexpected defeat. We were all
surprised by the *upset* of the team. *Noun.*
—**1.** To overturn. I *upset* the vase of
flowers when I bumped into the table.
2. To disturb emotionally. His yelling *upset*
the young animal. **3.** To make ill. The
food *upset* my stomach. **4.** To defeat
unexpectedly. Our team *upset* the
champions. *Verb.* **up•set** (up′set′*for
noun,* up set′*for verb*) *noun, plural*
upsets; *verb.*

useful 1. Able to be put to good use. A
pocketknife can be very *useful* on a
camping trip. **2.** Valuable. The computer
was a *useful* invention. **use•ful** (ūs′fəl)
adjective, **usefully** *adverb,* **usefulness**
noun.

usual Expected or normal. We took the
usual route. **usu•al** (ū′zhü əl)
adjective.

usually Normally; regularly. I *usually* eat a
banana in the morning. **usu•al•ly**
(ū′zhü əl ē) *adverb.*

Utah One of the western states of the United
States. The capital of Utah is Salt Lake City.
The abbreviation for Utah is UT. **U•tah**
(ū′tô, ū′tä) *noun.*

vacation 1. A period of rest or relaxation from
school or work. I am looking forward to
my summer *vacation.* **2.** Time spent in travel
or rest. She took a one-week *vacation* to rest
from the tiring project. **va•ca•tion**
(vā kā′shən) *noun, plural* **vacations**.

at; āpe, fär, câre; end; mē, it, īce; pîerce; hot,
ōld: sông, fôrk; oil; out; up; ūse; rüle; pûll; tûrn;
chin; sing; shop; thin; **this**; hw in white; zh in
treasure. The symbol ə stands for the unstressed
vowel sound in about, taken, pencil, lemon,
and circus.

Spelling Dictionary

Valentine's Day The day, February 14, named in honor of Saint Valentine, an early Christian saint. People often send valentines to special friends to mark the day.

Valentine's Day

variable 1. Likely to change. The weather is *variable* at this time of the year. **2.** Able to be changed. This wrench has *variable* jaws for different jobs. *Adjective.*
—Something that changes or is likely to change. The temperature is a *variable* at this time of the year. *Noun.* **var•i•a•ble** (vâr′ē ə bəl) *adjective; noun, plural* **variables.**

vault 1. A place for storage and safekeeping. Put your valuables in the *vault.* **2.** An arched roof or ceiling. The *vault* of the tunnel curved up into darkness. **3.** A place for burial. *Noun.*
—To jump over, using the hands or a pole. The athlete set a new record in the *vault.* *Verb.* **vault** (vôlt) *noun, plural* **vaults; vaulter;** *verb.* **vaultlike** *adjective.*

Vermont One of the northeastern states of the United States. The capital of Vermont is Montpelier. The abbreviation for Vermont is VT. **Ver•mont** (vər mont′) *noun.*

verse 1. Words that are written in a particular rhythmic pattern and often in rhyme; poetry. The *verse* evoked a feeling of sadness in the group. **2.** Section of a poem or song; stanza. The choir sang the first *verse* with enthusiasm. **3.** A short part of a chapter in the Bible. We examined the *verse* to try to understand its meaning. **verse** (vûrs) *noun, plural* **verses.**

vice president An official who ranks in power just below the president and who takes the place of the president when necessary. The workers liked the *vice president* as much as they liked the president of their company. **vice pres•i•dent** (vīs′prez′i dənt) *noun, plural* **vice presidents.**

viceroy A person appointed to rule a country as the deputy of the sovereign. The country was ruled by a *viceroy* because the king was only seven years old. **vice•roy** (vīs′roi) *noun, plural* **viceroys.**

Virginia One of the southeastern states of the United States. The capital of Virginia is Richmond. The abbreviation for Virginia is VA. **Vir•gin•ia** (vər jin′yə) *noun.*

virus 1. Tiny particles of living matter that can cause illness. **2.** An illness caused by a virus. **3.** *Computers.* A program that can change or destroy computer files. A *virus* got into the computer and erased several files. **vi•rus** (vī′rəs) *noun, plural* **viruses.**

visit A brief stay for friendly, business, or official purposes. We paid a *visit* to our old friend yesterday. *Noun.*
—**1.** To go or come to see. I *visited* my grandparents last weekend. **2.** To socialize. The party guests *visited* with each other before dinner was served. *Verb.* **vis•it** (viz′it) *noun, plural* **visits; visitor;** *verb.*

volleyball 1. A game in which two teams stand on either side of a high net and hit a ball back and forth with their hands. In the game of *volleyball* each side tries not to let the ball touch the ground. **2.** The ball that is used. Someone hit the *volleyball* over into the water, so we had to get it. **vol•ley•ball** (vol′ē bôl′) *noun, plural* **volleyballs.**

volunteer 1. A person who offers to help or does something by choice and often without pay. The teacher asked for a *volunteer* for being the head of the decorating committee. **2.** A person who makes a voluntary decision to join the armed forces. The captain lined up the *volunteers* and marched them off to the barracks. *Noun.*
—**1.** To offer to help or do something of one's own free will. My friend *volunteered* to coach the basketball team. **2.** To give or offer readily. I *volunteered* an answer to the question. *Verb.*
—having to do with or serving as a volunteer. My cousin is a *volunteer* firefighter in our town. *Adjective.* **vol•un•teer** (vol′ən tîr′) *noun, plural* **volunteers;** *verb,* **volunteered, volunteering;** *adjective.*

Spelling Dictionary

© McGraw-Hill School Division

voyage A long trip by land, sea, or air. We enjoyed our *voyage. Noun.*
—To travel a long distance by land, sea, or air. The explorers *voyaged* into the new territory. *Verb.* **voy•age** (voi′ij) *noun, plural* **voyages; voyager;** *verb,* **voyaged, voyaging.**

waist The part of a human body between the bottom of the ribs and the hips. The seamstress measured my *waist* to know how much to alter my pants. **waist** (wāst) *noun, plural* **waists.**

wallpaper Decorated paper for putting on the walls of a room. The *wallpaper* in my room is peeling off. **wall•pa•per** (wôl′pā′pər) *noun, plural* **wallpapers.**

Washington One of the Pacific states of the United States. The capital of Washington is Olympia. The abbreviation for Washington is WA. **Wash•ing•ton** (wôsh′ing tən, or wosh′ing tən) *noun.*

waste 1. Something thrown away as worthless after it is used. They dumped the *waste* in the dumpsite outside. 2. Barren land. Some people call the desert a *waste.* 3. The act of wasting. It's a *waste* of time trying to mend that sock. *Noun.*
—1. To wear away a little at a time. The homeless kitten was *wasting* away from lack of food when we found it. 2. To use or spend carelessly. He *wasted* the money left to him on worthless objects. *Verb.* **waste** (wāst) *noun, plural* **wastes;** *verb.*

weak Not having physical strength. The young boy was too *weak* to lift the large box. **weak** (wēk) *adjective.*

wear 1. To carry or have on the body. We *wear* warm clothes in the winter. 2. To have or show. She *wears* her hair long. 3. To damage or reduce by long use or exposure. The ocean *wore* the rocks until they were smooth and slippery. 4. To cause or make by rubbing or scraping. You'll *wear* holes in your socks. *Verb.*
—1. The act of wearing or the state of being worn. This suit has had five years of *wear.* 2. Clothing. This store sells children's *wear.* 3. Damage caused by age or use. The old farmhouse showed signs of *wear. Noun.* **wear** (wâr) *verb,* **wore, worn, wearing;** *noun.*

we'd 1. Shortened form of "we had." *We'd* all enjoyed our party. 2. Shortened form of "we would." *We'd* have bought you one, too, but we didn't have enough money. **we'd** (wēd) *contraction.*

Wednesday The fourth day of the week. **Wednes•day** (wenz′dē, wenz′dā) *noun, plural* **Wednesdays.**

week A period of seven days. A *week* is usually thought of as starting with Sunday. **week** (wēk) *noun, plural* **weeks.**

west 1. The direction in which the sun appears to set. At dusk it is sometimes hard to look toward the *west* because it is so bright. 2. *Capitalized:* The western part of a country. My family is moving from New York to the *West. Noun.*
—Referring to the direction in which the sun appears to set. The *west* side of our apartment is the coldest. *Adjective.*
—To or toward the west. Our house faces *west. Adverb.* **west** (west) *noun; adjective; adverb.*

West Virginia One of the southeastern states of the United States. The capital of West Virginia is Charleston. The abbreviation for West Virginia is WV. **West Vir•gin•ia** (west vər jin′yə) *noun.*

we've Shortened form of "we have." *We've* nothing to eat, so let's go shopping. **we•'ve** (wēv) *contraction.*

wharf A structure built on a shore to be used as a landing place for boats and ships. The

at; āpe, fär, câre; end; mē, it, īce; pîerce; hot, ōld: sông, fôrk; oil; out; up; ūse; rüle; pu̇ll; tûrn; chin; sing; shop; thin; <u>th</u>is; hw in white; zh in treasure. The symbol ə stands for the unstressed vowel sound in about, taken, pencil, lemon, and circus.

Spelling Dictionary

fishermen keep their boats at the *wharf* near my house. **wharf** (hwôrf) *noun, plural* **wharves**.

what'd **1.** Shortened form of "what did." *What'd* you do before you came here? **2.** Shortened form of "what would." *What'd* be a good reason for me to stay? **what•'d** (hwot'id *or* wut'id) *contraction.*

whatever **1.** Anything that. I'll do *whatever* I can. **2.** No matter what. *Whatever* happens, I'll be there. *Pronoun.*
—**1.** Any that. Take *whatever* supplies you need. **2.** No matter what. *Whatever* day you pick will be fine. *Adjective.* **what•ev•er** (hwət ev'ər *or* wət ev'ər) *pronoun; adjective.*

what'll **1.** Shortened form of "what will." *What'll* help you get better grades? **2.** Shortened form of "what shall." *What'll* I do without you? **what•'ll** (hwot'əl *or* wut'əl) *contraction.*

wheelchair A chair specially mounted on wheels for use by people who are sick or unable to walk. I am good at moving my *wheelchair* from place to place. **wheel•chair** (hwēl'châr'or wēl'châr) *noun, plural* **wheelchairs**.

wheelchair

wherever Where in the world. *Wherever* did you get that dress? *Adverb.*
—At, in, or to whatever place. He makes friends *wherever* he goes. *Conjunction.* **wher•ev•er** (hwâr ev'ər *or* wâr ev'ər) *adverb; conjunction.*

whine A plaintive cry. The sick baby let out a *whine* when I picked her up. *Noun.*
—To make a cry or sound of complaint or distress. The dog will *whine* if it is left alone. *Verb.* **whine** (hwīn, wīn) *noun, plural* **whines**; *verb,* **whined, whining.**

whirl **1.** To turn or cause to turn quickly in a circle. The blades of a fan *whirl.* **2.** To move or turn around suddenly or quickly. The

guards *whirled* when they heard the noise. *Verb.*
—**1.** A quick turn in a circle; whirling movement. We watched the skaters make graceful leaps and *whirls* on the ice. **2.** A confused or dizzy condition. My head was in a *whirl* after I was hit by the ball. *Noun.* **whirl** (hwûrl or wûrl) *verb,* **whirled, whirling;** *noun, plural* **whirls.**

whisper Something said very softly. There were *whispers* in the audience when the famous actor made his entrance. *Noun.*
—To speak very softly. In the library you are expected to *whisper. Verb.* **whis•per** (hwis'pər, wis'pər) *noun, plural* **whispers;** *verb,* **whispered, whispering.**

whittle To cut small bits or pieces from wood or soap with a knife. We *whittled* the wood into interesting shapes. **whit•tle** (hwit'əl *or* wit'əl) *verb,* **whittled, whittling.**

who'd **1.** Shortened form of "who would." *Who'd* be here tomorrow? **2.** Shortened form of "who had." I knew someone *who'd* climbed that mountain. **who'd** (hüd) *contraction.*

who'll **1.** Shortened form of "who will" or "who shall." *Who'll* bake the cake? **who•'ll** (hül) *contraction.*

who's **1.** Shortened form of "who is." *Who's* the one who did this? **2.** Shortened form of "who has." *Who's* been eating my porridge? **who's** (hüz) *contraction.*

whose Of whom; of which. *Whose* is this? *Pronoun.*
—Relating to whom or to which. Do you know *whose* shoes these are? *Adjective.* **whose** (hüz) *pronoun; adjective.*

Wisconsin One of the north central states of the United States. The capital of Wisconsin is Madison. The abbreviation for Wisconsin is WI. **Wis•con•sin** (wis kon'sin) *noun.*

woman An adult female person. My mother is a very strong *woman.* **wom•an** (wùm'ən) *noun, plural* **women.**

wonderful Very good; fine. We had a *wonderful* time on vacation. **won•der•ful** (wun'dər fəl) *adjective.*

Spelling Dictionary

wooden 1. Made of wood. The *wooden* floor was recently polished. **2.** Stiff; awkward. The startling sound forced the animal into a *wooden* posture. **wood•en** (wǔd′ən) *adjective,* **woodenly,** *adverb;* **woodenness** *noun.*

worn Past participle of **wear. 1.** Put on, like clothing. I have *worn* this coat for three years. **2.** Shown, as with a smile. She's *worn* a smile on her face all morning. **3.** Damaged by use or wear. The blanket is *worn* with age. **4.** Tired. The team was *worn* out by the long game. **worn** (wôrn) *verb.*

wouldn't Shortened form of "would not." I *wouldn't* go there again. **would•n't** (wǔd′ənt) *contraction.*

would've Shortened form of "would have." If I had known you were ready, I *would've* come sooner. **would•'ve** (wǔd′əv) *contraction.*

wound[1] **1.** An injury to the body, especially one in which the skin is torn or broken. I washed the *wound* right away to keep it from getting infected. **2.** An injury to one's feelings or reputation. That newspaper article inflicted a lasting *wound* to his reputation. *Noun.* —**1.** To injure by breaking the skin. She *wounded* herself with the knife by mistake. **2.** To injure one's feelings or reputation. She did not intend to *wound* him by being honest. *Verb.* **wound** (wünd) *noun, plural* **wounds;** *verb.*

wound[2] Past tense and past participle of **wind. 1.** Moved first in one direction and then another. The stream *wound* through the trees. **2.** Folded or wrapped around something. He *wound* his arms around her in greeting. **3.** Rolled into a ball. They *wound* the string into a ball. **4.** Made a machine to operate by turning a spring. They *wound* up the toy with a key. **wound** (wound) *verb.*

wreck 1. Remains cast up on land after a shipwreck. We could see the *wreck* from far away as we were walking to it. **2.** Broken remains of something wrecked. They towed the *wreck* to the junkyard. *Noun.* —To damage or dismantle, as a building or an automobile. The construction workers *wrecked* the old building. *Verb.* **wreck** (rek) *noun, plural* **wrecks;** *verb.*

wrench 1. A violent twist or pull. With one quick *wrench,* the door sprang open. **2.** A tool for holding and turning nuts and bolts. I need a *wrench* to fix my bicycle. *Noun.* —**1.** To twist or pull violently. She *wrenched* the trunk open. **2.** To injure by twisting. He *wrenched* his ankle, but it's healing well. **3.** To snatch with force. One dog tried to *wrench* a bone away from the other. *Verb.* **wrench** (rench) *noun, plural* **wrenches;** *verb.*

wring 1. To twist in order to remove liquid. *Wring* out your wet clothes before hanging them up. **2.** To get by force or persuasion. I hope to *wring* the truth out of him. **wring** (ring) *verb,* **wrung, wringing.**

wrinkle 1. A fold in skin or cloth. He ironed the *wrinkles* out of his shirt. **2.** A special method. They showed the others their special *wrinkle* for this situation. *Noun.* —To develop or cause to develop a fold in skin or cloth. Some people *wrinkle* their foreheads when they frown. *Verb.* **wrin•kle** (ring′kəl) *noun, plural* **wrinkles;** *verb.*

wrist The joint or the area of the joint between the hand and the arm. Jamie sprained his *wrist* when he fell off the swing. **wrist** (rist) *noun, plural* **wrists.**

writer A person who writes, often to earn a living; author. Maria wants to become a professional *writer.* **writ•er** (rīt′ər) *noun, plural* **writers.**

written Past participle of **write. 1.** Marked with a pen or pencil. She had *written* all over the book. **2.** Expressed in writing. The author had *written* a beautiful poem about nature. **3.** Composed. This music was *written* by a famous composer. **4.** Communicated by letter. Many letters were *written* before we

at; āpe, fär, câre; end; mē, it, īce; pîerce; hot, ōld: sông, fôrk; oil; out; up; ūse; rüle; pu̇ll; tûrn; chin; sing; shop; thin; <u>th</u>is; hw in white; zh in treasure. The symbol ə stands for the unstressed vowel sound in about, taken, pencil, lemon, and circus.

Spelling Dictionary

finally got to see each other. **writ•ten** (rit′ən) *verb*.

Wyoming One of the western states of the United States. The capital of Wyoming is Cheyenne. The abbreviation for Wyoming is WY. **Wy•o•ming** (wī ō′ming) *noun*.

-y Also **-ey 1.** Full of. **2.** Like. **3.** Inclined to. **4.** Rather. *Adjective suffix.*
—**1.** Condition or quality. **2.** Place of activity. **3.** Group. **4.** Instance of a certain action. *Noun suffix.* **-y** (ē) *adjective suffix; noun suffix, plural* **-ies.**

yet 1. At the present time; now. I'm not *yet* old enough to drive a car. **2.** Up to the present time; so far. They have never *yet* been late for a meeting. **3.** Continuously up to this or that time; still. The farmers went to the fields early and are working *yet.* **4.** At some future time; eventually. The mystery will be solved *yet.* **5.** In addition. There are three days *yet* to go until our vacation. *Adverb.*
—Nevertheless; however; but. I thought I knew the way, *yet* I soon got lost. *Conjunction.* **yet** (yet) *adverb; conjunction.*

you'd 1. Shortened form of "you would." *You'd* have done the same thing if you were there.

2. Shortened form of "you had." *You'd* been gone for hours! **you'd** (ūd) *contraction.*

you'll Shortened form of "you will" or "you shall." *You'll* be really tall someday. **you'll** (ūl) *contraction.*

yours 1. The one or ones belonging to you. This book is *yours.* **2.** At your service. I am *yours* to instruct. **3.** A closing for a letter, just before the signature. The letter was signed, "*Yours* truly, Irene." **yours** (yùrz *or* yôrz) *pronoun.*

you've Shortened form of "you have." *You've* a nice place here. **you've** (ūv *or* yùv) *contraction.*

zipper A sliding fastener for clothing. I couldn't close my jacket because the *zipper* is broken. *Noun.*
—To fasten or close with a zipper. I tried to *zipper* my jacket shut. *Verb.* **zip•per** (zip′ər) *noun, plural* **zippers**; *verb.*

zipper

Spelling Dictionary

Handwriting Models

A B C D E F G H I

J K L M N O P Q R

S T U V W X Y Z

a b c d e f g h i j

k l m n o p q r s

t u v w x y z

Handwriting Models

Credits

PHOTO CREDITS

3, Yellow Dog Prods./The Image Bank; **7,** Richard T. Nowitz/Photo Researchers, Inc.; **11,** Lawrence Migdale; **15,** Pat and Tom Leeson/Photo Researchers, Inc.; **19,** Guy Gillette/Photo Researchers, Inc.; **29,** Comstock; **33,** Peter Beck/The Stock Market; **37,** Ira Block/The Image Bank; **41,** James Marshall/The Stock Market; **43,** Andrea Pistolesi/The Image Bank; **45,** William Roy/The Stock Market; **55,** Henley & Savage/ The Stock Market; **59,** P. Johansky/FPG International; **63,** David W. Hamilton/The Image Bank; **67,** S.R. Maglione/Photo Researchers; **69,** Hans Reinhard/Bruce Coleman, Inc.; **71,** Joseph Van Os/The Image Bank; **81,** David Woods/The Stock Market; **85,** Douglas T. Mesney/The Stock Market; **89,** Paul Steel/The Stock Market; **93,** Peter Beck/The Stock Market; **95,** Joseph Marzullo/Retna; **97,** Thomas Del Brase/The Stock Market; **107,** Scala/Art Resource; **111,** Richard Shock/The Gamma Liaison Network; **115,** David W. Hamilton; **119,** Walter Bibikow/The Image Bank; **121,** Ben Simmons/The Stock Market; **123,** Larry Busacca/Retna Ltd.; **125,** Tom Tracy/FPG International; **133,** Joseph Van Os/The Image Bank; **137,** Marvin E. Newman/The Image Bank; **141,** David W. Hamilton/The Image Bank; **145,** Harald Sund/The Image Bank; **149,** Viviane Moos/The Stock Market; **151,** Henley & Savage/The Stock Market; **217,** NASA; **218,** Romilly Lockyer/The Image Bank; **224,** Jeff Spielman/The Image Bank; **229,** Grant V. Faint/The Image Bank; **237,** Gerard Vandystadt/Photo Researchers, Inc.; **238,** Patti Murray/Animals Animals/Earth Scenes; **241,** Tom Brakefield/The Stock Market; **245,** G.R. Hibgee/Photo Researchers, Inc.; **252,** Zefa Lenz/The Stock Market; **255,** Joseph Nettis/Photo Researchers, Inc.; **265,** John Mitchell/Photo Researchers, Inc.; **268,** Grant V. Faint/The Image Bank; **276,** Frank Siteman/Monkmeyer Press Photos

COVER PHOTO
Stephen Ogilvy

ART CREDITS
Harry Campbell, Annie Gusman, Dan Potash